# BUILDING CONSTRUCTION ESTIMATING

# McGraw-Hill Series in Construction Engineering and Project Management

## Consulting Editor
*Raymond E. Levitt, Stanford University*

**Barrie and Paulson:** *Professional Construction Management: Including CM, Design-Construct, and General Contracting*
**Callahan, Quackenbush, and Rowings:** *Construction Project Scheduling*
**Hinze:** *Construction Contracts*
**Jervis and Levin:** *Construction Law: Principles and Practice*
**Koerner:** *Construction and Geotechnical Methods in Foundation Engineering*
**Oberlender:** *Project Management for Engineering and Construction*
**Oglesby, Parker, and Howell:** *Productivity Improvement in Construction*
**Peurifoy and Ledbetter:** *Construction Planning, Equipment, and Methods*
**Peurifoy and Oberlender:** *Estimating Construction Costs*
**Schuette and Liska:** *Building Construction Estimating*
**Shuttleworth:** *Mechanical and Electrical Systems for Construction*
**Stevens:** *Techniques for Construction Network Scheduling*

Also Available from McGraw-Hill

## Schaum's Outline Series in Civil Engineering

Most outlines include basic theory, definitions and hundreds of example problems solved in step-by-step detail, and supplementary problems with answers.

Related titles on the current list include:

*Descriptive Geometry*
*Dynamic Structural Analysis*
*Engineering Economics*
*Engineering Mechanics*
*Fluid Dynamics*
*Fluid Mechanics & Hydraulics*
*Introductory Surveying*
*Mathematical Handbook of Formulas & Tables*
*Mechanical Vibrations*
*Reinforced Concrete Design*
*Statics & Mechanics of Materials*
*Strength of Materials*
*Structural Steel Design, (LRFD Method)*
*Theoretical Mechanics*

## Schaum's Solved Problems Books

Each title in this series is a complete and expert source of solved problems with solutions worked out in step-by-step detail.

Related titles on the current list include:

*3000 Solved Problems in Calculus*
*2500 Solved Problems in Differential Equations*
*2500 Solved Problems in Fluid Mechanics & Hydraulics*
*3000 Solved Problems in Linear Algebra*
*2000 Solved Problems in Numerical Analysis*
*700 Solved Problems in Vector Mechanics for Engineers: Dynamics*
*800 Solved Problems in Vector Mechanics for Engineers: Statics*

Available at most college bookstores, or for a complete list of titles and prices, write to:
Schaum Division
McGraw-Hill, Inc.
Princeton Road, S-1
Hightstown, NJ 08520

# BUILDING CONSTRUCTION ESTIMATING

## Stephen D. Schuette
*Purdue University*

## Roger W. Liska
*Clemson University*

**McGraw-Hill, Inc.**

New York   St. Louis   San Francisco   Auckland   Bogotá   Caracas
Lisbon   London   Madrid   Mexico City   Milan   Montreal
New Delhi   San Juan   Singapore   Sydney   Tokyo   Toronto

This book was set in Times Roman by Publication Services.
The editors were B. J. Clark and John M. Morriss;
the production supervisor was Kathryn Porzio.
The cover was designed by Rafael Hernandez.
Project supervision was done by Publication Services.
R. R. Donnelley & Sons Company was printer and binder.

**BUILDING CONSTRUCTION ESTIMATING**

This book is printed on acid-free paper.

2 3 4 5 6 7 8 9 0    DOC    DOC    9 0 9 8 7 6 5

P/N 037907-6
PART OF
ISBN 0-07-911816-X

**Library of Congress Cataloging-in-Publication Data**

Schuette, Stephen D.
   Building construction estimating / Stephen D. Schuette, Roger W.
Liska.
      p.       cm.
   Includes index.
   ISBN 0-07-911816-X
   1. Building—Estimates.    I. Liska, Roger W.    II. Title.
TH435.S38      1994
692'.5—dc20
                        93-46813

# ABOUT THE AUTHORS

**Stephen D. Schuette** is head and professor of the Department of Building Construction and Contracting at Purdue University. He holds bachelor of science and master of science degrees from Bradley University. Professor Schuette has over 25 years of experience in the construction industry and affiliations with academic institutions. For eight years he was in charge of the estimating department for a midwestern general contractor and has served on the faculty of Auburn University, Clemson University, and Purdue University. He is listed in *Who's Who in Finance and Industry* and has served on several boards of construction professional organizations.

**Roger W. Liska** is head and professor of the Department of Construction Science and Management at Clemson University. Dr. Liska holds a B.S. in Civil Engineering from Michigan Technological University, an M.S. in Civil Engineering from Wayne State University, and a doctorate in Educational Administration from the University of Georgia. He has over 25 years of experience in construction and construction education and has served on the faculty of the College of Dupage, Auburn University, University of Maryland, and Clemson University. He is the author of many publications and journal articles and has participated in various research and service activities for the construction industry. Dr. Liska is the recipient of both the John Trimmer Award of Excellence in Education from the Associated Builders and Contractors and the W. A. Klinger Construction Education Award from the American Institute of Constructors.

# CONTENTS

Preface                                                                        xv

**1  Overview of the Construction Estimating Process**          1
   The Estimator                                                             2
   Types of Construction                                                  3
   Types of Contracts                                                      4
   Bidding Documents for a Stipulated Sum Contract            6
      Working Drawings                                                    6
      Specifications (Project Manual)                                 7
   The Construction Company                                          18
   Qualifications of the Construction Firm                          20
   Types of Estimates                                                     20
      Feasibility Estimates                                              20
      Conceptual Estimates                                            21
      System Estimate (Elemental Estimates or Parametric Estimates)   23
   Risks in Estimating                                                    27
   Sources of Estimating Information                               29
   Ethics in the Estimating Process                                 32
   Cost to Perform an Estimate                                      32
   Student Exercises                                                     33

**2  Computers in Construction Estimating**                    35
   Impact on the Estimating Process                               36
   Estimating and the Spreadsheet                                 36
      Design of the Spreadsheet                                     37
   Computer Disk                                                          39
   Dedicated Construction Estimating Software                39
   Student Exercise                                                      43

**ix**

**3  Overview of the Detailed Estimate**                                45

Purpose of the Detailed Estimate                                        45
Organization of the Detailed Estimate                                   46
Major Phases of Developing the Detailed Estimate                        46
Defining the Work Items                                                 47
Documentation of the Estimate                                           49
Steps in the Development of a Detailed Estimate                         50
    Acquisition of the Contract Documents           50
    Review of Documents and Project Facts            50
    Attending the Prebid Meeting                     58
    Deciding Whether to Develop a Bid                58
    Bidding Strategy Considerations                  58
    Solicitation of Prices from Material Suppliers and Subcontractors   59
    Developing the Construction Method, Planning, and Scheduling   59
    Bonding and Insurance Requirements and Costs     62
    Preparing a Specification Takeoff                62
    Developing a Material Quantity Takeoff           64
    Order and Consistency of Material Quantity Takeoff   66
    Unit of Measure                                  67
    Measuring Calculations                           68
Pricing Studies                                                         76
Pricing the Quantity Takeoff                                            76
Subcontractor System Estimate and Analysis                             76
Forms Used to Develop a Detailed Estimate                               77
Addendum Considerations                                                 81
Finalizing the Bid                                                      82
Delivery of the Bid                                                     82
Attending the Bid Opening                                               83
Over-the-Budget Negotiations                                            83
Assessment of the Bidding Process                                       85
Transfer of Estimate to Project Management and Accounting               86
Student Exercises                                                       86

**4  Developing the Cost for a Detailed Estimate**                      87

Material Pricing                                                        88
    Quantity Discounts                               89
    Time                                             89
    Delivery                                         89
    Handling                                         91
    Storage                                          91
    Terms of Payments and Discounts                  91
    The Buyer and Supplier                           91
    Allowance                                        92
    Taxes                                            92
    Government Regulations                           92
    Owner Supplied Material                          93
    Material Pricing Checklist                       93
Labor Pricing                                                           93
    Quantity Takeoff Considerations                  93
    Wage Rates                                       93
    Productivity                                     94

Worker Hours per Unit and Crew Hours per Unit    95
Unit Price    96
Total Worker Hours, Crew Hours, or Total Price    96
Equipment Cost    97
   Heavy Construction Equipment    97
   Examples of Earthwork-Related Activities    100
   Small Equipment for a Specific Task    103
   Job Overhead Tools    104
Subcontractor Pricing    105
   Subcontractor System Estimate    105
   Subcontractor Capability    106
   Subcontractor Bid Analysis    106
   Receipt of Subcontractor and Material Supply Bids    106
Other Costs    108
   General Overhead    108
   Job Overhead    111
   Contingencies    113
   Profit    113
   Calculations of Other Costs    113
   Alternates    113
Student Exercises    116

**5   Earthwork**    119
Taking Off Excavation Work    120
   Sitework Takeoff    121
   Building Excavation Quantity Takeoff    131
Backfilling    136
Excess or Borrow    138
Underslab Requirements    139
Other Earthwork-Related Activities    139
   Grading    139
   Trenching    140
   Rock Excavation    140
   Filling and Compacting Soil    140
Pricing Excavation Work    141
Student Exercises    145

**6   Concrete**    147
Taking Off Formwork    148
   Job-Built Forms    150
   Prebuilt Forms    150
Pricing of Formwork    150
   Formwork Material Cost    150
   Formwork Labor Cost    155
   Formwork Equipment Cost    156
Takeoff of Reinforcing Steel and Other Embedments    156
Pricing Reinforcing Steel    163
   Reinforcing Material Cost    163
   Reinforcing Labor Cost    163
   Reinforcing Equipment Cost    163

|  |  |  |
|---|---|---|
| Taking Off Concrete | | 163 |
| Pricing Concrete | | 165 |
| Concrete Material Cost | | 165 |
| Concrete Labor Cost | | 165 |
| Concrete Equipment Cost | | 166 |
| Taking Off Finishing, Curing, and Protecting Concrete | | 169 |
| Pricing Finishing, Curing, and Protecting Concrete | | 170 |
| Taking Off Precast Concrete | | 170 |
| Pricing Precast Concrete Members | | 173 |
| Estimating Other Division 3 Items | | 173 |
| Student Exercises | | 174 |

**7 Masonry** — 177

| Wall Types and Bond Patterns | 178 |
|---|---|
| Takeoff of Brick and Concrete Block | 179 |
| Square Foot Method | 182 |
| Coursing Method | 183 |
| Taking Off Accessories and Mortar | 185 |
| Ties, Anchors, and Inserts Takeoff | 185 |
| Horizontal Masonry Reinforcing Takeoff | 185 |
| Deformed Bar Reinforcing Takeoff | 188 |
| Taking Off Grout | 188 |
| Control Joint Takeoff | 189 |
| Flashing Takeoff | 189 |
| Lintels, Sills, and Copings Takeoff | 190 |
| Mortar Takeoff | 191 |
| Sample Panels | 191 |
| Insulation Takeoff | 191 |
| Cleaning Takeoff | 193 |
| Labor Requirements | 193 |
| Material Cost | 198 |
| Climate Considerations | 198 |
| Tools and Equipment Costs | 198 |
| Subcontractors | 199 |
| Taking Off and Pricing Masonry Work | 199 |
| Masonry Reminder List | 202 |
| Student Exercises | 204 |

**8 Metals** — 205

| Taking Off Structural Steel Items | 206 |
|---|---|
| Structural Steel Members | 206 |
| Steel Plates and Rods | 208 |
| Connections | 211 |
| Taking Off Steel Joists, Decking, Light-Gauge Metal, and Miscellaneous Items | 217 |
| Pricing of Structural Steel | 222 |
| Material | 223 |
| Labor | 223 |
| Equipment | 225 |
| Summary of Pricing Structural Steel | 225 |
| Student Exercises | 229 |

**9** Carpentry — 231

Taking Off Rough Carpentry — 234
   Floor and Ceiling Framing — 235
   Subflooring, Sheathing, and Decking — 236
   Wall Framing — 237
   Roof Framing — 239
   Fasteners — 241
Finish Carpentry Takeoff — 242
   Exterior Finish Carpentry — 242
   Interior Finish Carpentry — 245
   Fasteners — 245
Pricing Rough and Finish Carpentry Work — 246
   Material Cost — 246
   Labor Cost — 248
   Equipment/Tools Cost — 248
Estimating Other Division Six Items — 248
Student Exercises — 254

**10** Miscellaneous and Specialty Work — 255

Thermal and Moisture Protection — 256
   Taking Off Insulation — 257
   Taking Off Roof Shingles and Tiles — 258
   Taking Off Built-Up, Single-Ply, and Sheet Roofing — 260
   Taking Off Flashing — 261
   Taking Off Roof Trim and Other Components — 261
   Taking Off Sealants and Caulking — 261
Windows and Doors — 262
Finishes — 264
   Taking Off Drywall, Lath, and Plaster — 265
   Taking Off Tile and Terrazzo — 266
   Taking Off Carpeting — 266
   Taking Off Painting and Wall Coverings — 266
Specialties, Equipment, Furnishings, Special Construction,
   and Conveying Systems — 269
Material Pricing — 269
Labor and Equipment Pricing — 272
Student Exercises — 272

**11** Plumbing, Mechanical, and Electrical — 275

Mechanical and Plumbing — 276
   Taking Off Plumbing Work — 276
   Taking Off Mechanical Work — 281
Electrical — 281
   Taking Off Electrical Work — 283
Pricing Plumbing, Mechanical, and Electrical Work — 287
Student Exercises — 287

**12** Transfer of the Estimate to the Construction Process — 289

Transfer to Purchasing — 289
   Transfer to Accounting — 291

Transfer to Project Management 292
    Development of the Construction Schedule 292
    Development of a Schedule of Values 293
    Data Entry Explanation and Help Notes for VALUE.WQ.1
      (VALUE.WK1) 294
    Explanation of How VALUE.WQ1 (VALUE.WK1) Works 297
    Projected Cost Estimates 299
    Progress Estimate 299
    Change Order Estimate 299
Student Exercises 302

## Appendixes 303
    A  The American Institute of Architects Document A201 303
    B  The American Institute of Architects Document A101 329
## Bibliography 339
## Index 343

# PREFACE

The major objective of this book is to provide specific details on how a general building contractor derives the cost of a project before it begins and how the estimate fits into the total construction process. This involves determining labor productivity and wages, selecting equipment and assigning productivity rates and costs, acquiring specialty contractor prices, and assigning overhead costs and profit.

The construction estimating profession requires a thorough knowledge of construction materials and construction methodologies. There is no attempt to present, in this book, all of the construction materials or methods of construction.

There are many types of contractual methods in the building construction process, and the contractual method selected can affect the estimating process. This book is presented from the point of view of a general contractor working on a competitively bid stipulated-sum (lump-sum) contract. However, other contract methods and the effects they have on the estimating process are discussed in Chapter 1.

The principles of estimating for the specialty trades are discussed from the reference of a general building contractor and how the subcontractor's bid will affect the total project cost. It should be noted, however, that specialty construction firms use essentially the same principles as the general contractor when determining the cost of their work. There will be, however, some minor differences in terminology and the strategies of competition during the estimating process.

One of the unique features of this text is the introduction and utilization of computers in the estimating process. Any new technology must be utilized in an effective and efficient manner. One must first understand the basics; in the case of estimating, being able to perform the activity manually is essential. This book is organized such that the reader will first learn to perform many of the estimating activities manually, then develop a computer spreadsheet.

With the use of spreadsheets the authors have given the student the opportunity to go beyond the manual calculations and develop new and more proficient solutions to estimating problems. It is assumed that the student has a basic working knowledge of spreadsheets. Many spreadsheet templates have been provided on a disk in the Quattro Pro and Lotus 123 formats. The templates will be used in exercises in the text, and they will serve as a basis for the development of additional templates.

Chapter 1 introduces the reader to the various types of estimates and provides an overview of the estimating process. Chapter 2 presents some specific information about the disks provided with this book. Chapter 3 presents the fundamentals of the detailed estimating process and the steps required. Chapter 4 discusses the various facets of pricing, including how to price material, labor, equipment, subcontractor work, overhead, and profit.

Chapters 5 through 11 present information on specific items typically found in a general contractor's estimate. Each of these chapters includes general information and quantity takeoff and pricing details for the specific items covered. By presenting the quantity takeoff and pricing information together in one chapter, the reader will attain a better understanding of the total estimating process. Finally, Chapter 12 presents how the estimate is used after the bid has been submitted and the project is being constructed.

In summary, this text provides the reader with a thorough understanding of the requirements of the estimating process and the role of the estimate in the execution of the total construction process.

## ACKNOWLEDGMENTS

Without the patience, support, and help of many people, this book would not have been possible. We would like to thank Debbie Blessé, graduate student, Reta Hancock, Administrative Assistant, Kirk Bingenheimer, Assistant Professor in the Department of Construction Science and Management, Clemson University, and Carmine Hensley, Purdue University, for their help in conducting research and developing illustrations and figures. We are grateful to Mark Federle, Iowa State University and Bob McCollough, Purdue University for reviewing drafts of the written material.

We would also like to thank all the companies who granted permission to allow their materials to be included in this book.

Finally, but most importantly, we thank our wives, Ann and Judy, for their patience and encouragement, which has been the catalyst needed to bring this book to reality.

*Stephen D. Schuette*
*Roger W. Liska*

# BUILDING CONSTRUCTION ESTIMATING

# CHAPTER

# 1

# OVERVIEW
# OF THE
# CONSTRUCTION
# ESTIMATING
# PROCESS

Estimating is the fundamental process of the construction industry that answers the question "How much is the project expected to cost?" The financial commitment to a construction project is very large, and inaccurate project estimates can have a detrimental effect on all parties. The estimating process for construction is different from that used for many manufactured goods. The price of manufactured goods is often determined from cost data collected as the product is being made. However, because buildings take a relatively long time to construct and financial commitments have to be made before construction, they usually have to be priced before they are built. In addition, unlike manufactured goods, the exact same building project is seldom undertaken more than once.

In addition, the estimate will serve as the basis for developing the job costing system and the construction schedule. The job costing system compares the actual cost of a project to specific line items of the estimate. This data will tell which items need more cost control during the construction process. Also, the duration of the various activities in a construction schedule will be derived from the estimate.

The essence of an estimate consists of forecasting future events in the construction process and then placing a dollar value on those events. The estimator starts by studying the drawings and specifications, then accurately lists the required quantities of materials, and finally prices the estimated quantities. However, many additional factors can affect the future events of construction: labor productivity, material availability, financial markets, weather, constructability issues, equipment

1

availability, contract types, ethics, quality issues, control systems, management ability, and so on. For these reasons it is important that the estimator have a good understanding of the total construction process.

## THE ESTIMATOR

During the design process the architect takes three-dimensional thoughts and puts them into two-dimensional drawings. The estimator must then take the two-dimensional drawings and turn them into a three-dimensional building. The transfer of the drawings to a building is difficult because the effective estimator must not only quantify what is shown on the drawings and specifications but also anticipate all construction activities. For example, the drawings may show that the frame of a building is structural steel, but they will not indicate that a crane and a crew of iron workers will be required to unload the steel when it is delivered to the job site. The drawings and specifications do not spell out the construction methods and all processes necessary to complete the project; they simply state the final expected results of the construction process. For this reason the estimator has a much greater responsibility than simply listing the quantities of materials necessary to construct a building and then applying a factor for calculating the cost. The estimator must analyze all the factors of the project to make informed decisions.

The following are the most important qualifications of a successful estimator.

1. Ability to read and interpret drawings and specifications
2. Good communication skills
3. Knowledge of basic mathematics
4. Patience and ability to do careful, thorough work
5. Good understanding of field operations and procedures
6. Ability to visualize the three-dimensional project from looking at the drawings
7. Ability to identify risks and then neutralize them as much as possible
8. Ability to anticipate all the construction steps in building the project
9. Good organizational ability, to communicate the estimate in a logical and clear presentation
10. Ability to produce or help produce a construction schedule
11. Good understanding of labor productivity and equipment performance
12. Understanding and ability to use the construction company's job costing systems
13. Ability to recognize when the construction company's standards for estimating costs do not apply to a particular line item in the estimate
14. Understanding of the contractual relationships
15. Creativity and ability to think of alternative construction methods
16. Ability to develop a strategy for being successful in the bidding and negotiating phase of the project

**17.** Ability to meet deadlines and still remain calm

**18.** A solid code of ethics

## TYPES OF CONSTRUCTION

Construction is often classified according to a functional description. Construction companies will usually specialize in one of the following categories; they will, however, often build projects in more than one.

**1.** *Residential construction.* Residential construction can consist of single or multifamily housing.

**2.** *Commercial construction.* Projects such as banks, retail facilities, schools, office buildings, and buildings for recreational purposes are included in this category.

**3.** *Institutional construction.* Hospitals and correctional facilities are examples of institutional construction.

**4.** *Industrial construction.* Construction of manufacturing or processing plants such as steel mills, paper mills, petrochemical refineries, electrical plants, and nuclear power generating stations is considered industrial construction. Many times these "megaprojects" are undertaken by companies that both design and construct the project.

**5.** *Heavy and highway construction.* Included in this work is the construction of bridges, roads, sewage and water treatment plants, and railroads.

Projects may also be classified by the type of funding they receive. Construction projects are funded with either public or private money. In general, projects funded by federal, state, city, or local governments must be competitively bid. The bidding procedures are prescribed by various procurement statutes, and the public authority does not have the right to modify or waive these procedures. If all the bidding procedures have been carefully followed and the firm with the low bid is capable of performing the work, the lowest lump-sum bidder is awarded the contract.

The procedures for privately funded projects are normally conducted by rules and regulations established by the owner, with the advice and assistance of a designer (architect and/or engineer) or construction manager. Projects that are competitively bid with private or public funding require that the drawings and specifications be completed before the detailed estimating procedure begins. Projects with private funding sources, however, do not have to be competitively bid. This allows the construction firm and owner to negotiate for the construction of the project. The negotiations can be based on such factors as cost, schedule, construction method, quality, safety, and past reputation. In addition, the drawings and specifications do not have to be completed before the project is actually under construction. Negotiated projects provide the opportunity to develop alternative types of construction contracts; some governmental agencies are considering adopting some of these.

## TYPES OF CONTRACTS

The type of contract will affect the estimating procedures. The estimator should always understand the type of contract that will be signed before beginning the estimating process. Some contracts require that more attention be given to the details of the project, whereas others may require more attention to preliminary estimates. In addition, the risk associated with the contract will have to be considered when developing an estimate. Figure 1.1 shows how the risk to the construction firm may vary with the different types of contracts.

The most common contract is the *stipulated sum contract,* also known as a lump-sum agreement. This type of contract provides the owner advance knowledge of the construction costs, which can be changed only with the appropriate approvals. Determining the construction company that will perform the work under this type of contract is usually accomplished by the competitive bid process. The estimator needs to study the possible construction methods and develop a detailed material takeoff. All costs must be identified before the contract is signed. With this type of contract, the accounting process is simple. It is flexible with regard to alternative designs, and changes on the project are relatively easy. However, the total process of design and construction may take longer. In this case the construction documents must be complete before the bidding process begins, and it is important that the construction firms bidding the project understand accurately and completely the work required on the project.

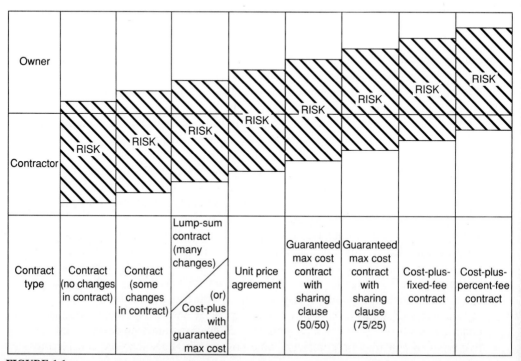

**FIGURE 1.1**
Degree of risk for owner and contractor.

The *cost-plus fee agreements* shift much of the risk from the construction firm to the project owner. The construction firm will be reimbursed for the actual cost plus an additional amount for overhead and profit. Under this type of agreement, extensive cost accounting is required and the total cost to the owner will not be known before construction begins. Calculating the amount for overhead and profit can be done in several ways. A fixed sum, a percentage added to the cost, a sliding-scale fee, or a fixed fee with a bonus or penalty can be used to determine the amount for overhead and profit. It is very important that the contract define what is reimbursable as a cost and what is included in the overhead and profit. For example, is the salary for the construction superintendent considered a reimbursable cost or is it a part of the fee? The selection of construction firms for projects with cost-plus agreements are not determined by total estimated price. There may be an estimating function before the contract is signed, but it will not usually determine what firm will do the project. Marketing, schedule, construction method, quality assurance program, safety program, past reputation, and fee requirements all help to determine the selection of the construction firm.

A *cost plus a fee with a guaranteed maximum cost* is in many ways the same as any cost-plus agreement except for one important distinction: the construction firm will guarantee the maximum cost. Obviously, with this type of agreement a detailed estimate will need to be done before the contract is signed. The execution of the contract will proceed the same as a cost-plus contract, but if the maximum guaranteed cost is exceeded, no additional payments will be made to the construction firm.

Many roads, dams, and utility projects are constructed under a *unit price agreement*. The quantities of materials are given to the construction firms for the purposes of estimating a unit cost. All bidders will base their estimates on the quantities listed and will bid a unit price for each item (price per cubic yard, square foot, ton, etc.). Payments are then made on the basis of how many units were actually installed. However, this means that neither the owner nor the construction firm will know the exact cost of the project before construction begins. During the bidding process the unit price agreement allows the estimator to spend more time on developing the most economical approach to the construction process.

The *design-build contract* combines the construction and design processes. The selected firm will provide the design services and may guarantee the price, or it may construct the project on a cost-plus basis. The estimator needs to provide cost estimates at several different steps during the design process. These estimates are conceptual in nature because the drawings and specifications have not been completed. The estimator will have to make many assumptions and then convey those assumptions to the designers.

Like the design-build firm, a firm that specializes in *construction management contracts* will have to determine the cost of building before the design is completed. The construction management firm will advise the architect on constructability issues during design, develop cost estimates during design, establish contract packages, develop construction schedules, and manage the various contracts during the construction process.

Figure 1.2 shows the contractual relationships of the stipulated sum contract, design-build contract, and a construction management project.

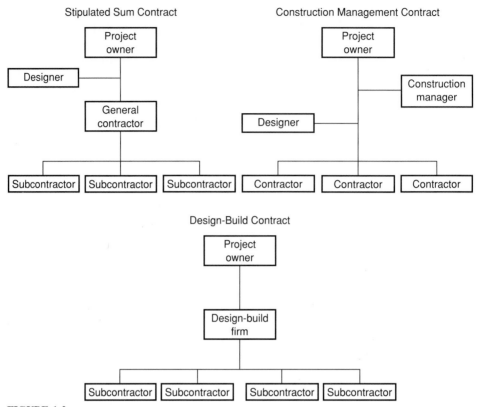

**FIGURE 1.2**
Relationships for various types of contract agreement.

## BIDDING DOCUMENTS FOR
## A STIPULATED SUM CONTRACT

The bidding and contract documents of a stipulated sum contract convey to the estimator the requirements of the proposed project. Most of the contract documents are contained in the working drawings and the bound volume of specifications (project manual). It is important for the estimator to study all the documents during the preparation of the bid.

The documents are available to the prime contractors from the architect/engineer. It is common practice for a deposit to be charged for the documents; the deposit is refunded when the documents are returned. General contractors will often receive several sets of the documents and then make them available to the subcontractors and material suppliers. The documents can also be reviewed at local plan rooms.

### Working Drawings

The working drawings convey the size and shape of the building and location of building elements; they also delineate how materials fit together. The estimator develops the quantity takeoff for the estimate from the working drawings.

## Specifications (Project Manual)

Whereas the working drawings address the quantity of work to be performed, the specifications generally address the quality issues. The project manual is a bound volume of written instructions concerning the project requirements. The volume is usually arranged in the Uniform Construction Index format. This is more commonly known as the Construction Specification Institute (CSI) or 16-division format (see Fig. 1.3). Divisions 2 through 16 are known as the technical parts of the specifications. These divisions include the required materials and the expected results. Each division is usually further subdivided into the following sections:

1. Scope of work
2. Quality of materials
3. Workmanship in terms of fabrication and erection

The *scope of work* defines the items to be furnished and installed, with additional information about shop drawings, samples, testing, and storage requirements. The *quality of materials* is defined in terms of meeting a performance standard, known as a performance specification, or by listing several acceptable brands. If several brands are listed, the phrase "or equal" is often included. It is common practice to require that any brand used as an "or equal" must have approval prior to the bid opening; approved brands would be listed in an addendum. It is important that the estimator comply with these material specification requirements and ensure that all subcontractors comply. The last subdivision of the various technical divisions covers *workmanship*. It defines the acceptable quality of fabrication and installation. In addition to the technical sections, the bound volume of specifications also includes the following.

**ADVERTISEMENT FOR BIDS OR INVITATION TO BID.** Projects funded with public money must be publicly advertised to conform to regulations. The advertisement generally describes the nature of the work, when the bids are due, where the bids are to be received, start and completion dates of the work, and bonding requirements. Figure 1.4 is an example of an advertisement for bid. Projects funded with private money may publicly advertise the project, send out invitations to only selected construction firms, or negotiate with only one firm.

**INSTRUCTIONS TO BIDDERS.** The instructions to the bidders provide information about the bidding procedures. This document should be checked thoroughly. It states the time and place for receiving proposals, whether the bids will be publicly opened and read aloud, commencement and completion dates of the work, bond and security requirements, and rights of the owner to accept or reject any and all bids (see Fig 1.5).

**GENERAL CONDITIONS.** This part of the document defines the responsibilities, rights, and relations of all parties to the construction contract. The estimator must be aware of the contents of the general conditions document because several of

### Div. 1 - General requirements

| | |
|---|---|
| 01010 | Summary of work |
| 01020 | Allowances |
| 01025 | Measurement and payment |
| 01030 | Alternates/alternatives |
| 01040 | Coordination |
| 01050 | Field engineering |
| 01060 | Regulatory requirements |
| 01070 | Abbreviations and symbols |
| 01080 | Identification systems |
| 01090 | Reference standards |
| 01100 | Special project procedures |
| 01200 | Project meetings |
| 01300 | Submittals |
| 01400 | Quality control |
| 01500 | Construction facilities and temporary controls |
| 01600 | Material and equipment |
| 01650 | Starting of system/commissioning |
| 01700 | Contract closeout |
| 01800 | Maintenance |

### Div. 2 - Sitework

| | |
|---|---|
| 02010 | Subsurface investigation |
| 02050 | Demolition |
| 02100 | Site preparation |
| 02140 | Dewatering |
| 02150 | Shoring and underpinning |
| 02160 | Excavation support systems |
| 02170 | Cofferdams |
| 02200 | Earthwork |
| 02300 | Tunneling |
| 02350 | Piles and caissons |
| 02450 | Railroad work |
| 02480 | Marine work |
| 02500 | Paving and surfacing |
| 02600 | Piped utility materials |
| 02660 | Water distribution |
| 02700 | Sewage and drainage |
| 02760 | Restoration of underground pipelines |
| 02770 | Ponds and reservoirs |
| 02780 | Power and communications |
| 20800 | Site improvements |
| 02900 | Landscaping |

### Div. 3 - Concrete

| | |
|---|---|
| 03100 | Concrete formwork |
| 03200 | Concrete reinforcement |
| 03250 | Concrete accessories |
| 03300 | Cast-in-place concrete |
| 03370 | Concrete curing |
| 03400 | Precast concrete |
| 03500 | Cementitious decks |
| 03600 | Grout |
| 03700 | Concrete restoration and cleaning |
| 03800 | Mass concrete |

### Div. 4 - Masonry

| | |
|---|---|
| 04100 | Mortar |
| 04150 | Masonry accessories |
| 04200 | Unit masonry |
| 04400 | Stone |
| 04500 | Masonry restoration and cleaning |
| 04550 | Refractories |
| 04600 | Corrosion resistant masonry |

### Div. 5 - Metals

| | |
|---|---|
| 05010 | Metal materials |
| 05030 | Metal finishes |
| 05050 | Metal fastening |
| 05100 | Structural metal framing |
| 05200 | Metal joist |
| 05300 | Metal decking |
| 05400 | Cold-formed metal framing |
| 05500 | Metal fabrications |
| 05580 | Sheet metal fabrications |
| 05700 | Ornamental metal |
| 05800 | Expansion control |
| 05900 | Hydraulic structures |

### Div. 6 - Wood and plastics

| | |
|---|---|
| 06050 | Fasteners and adhesives |
| 06100 | Rough carpentry |
| 06130 | Heavy timber construction |
| 06150 | Wood-metal systems |
| 06170 | Prefabricated structural wood |
| 06200 | Finish carpentry |
| 06300 | Wood treatment |
| 06400 | Architectural woodwork |
| 06500 | Prefabricated structural plastics |
| 06600 | Plastic fabrications |

### Div. 7 - Thermal and moisture protection

| | |
|---|---|
| 07100 | Waterproofing |
| 07150 | Dampproofing |
| 07190 | Vapor and air retarders |
| 07200 | Insulation |
| 07250 | Fireproofing |
| 07300 | Shingles and roofing tiles |
| 07400 | Preformed roofing and cladding/siding |
| 07500 | Membrane roofing |
| 07570 | Traffic topping |
| 07600 | Flashing and sheet metal |
| 07700 | Roof specialties and accessories |
| 07800 | Skylights |
| 07900 | Joint sealers |

### Div. 8 - Doors and windows

| | |
|---|---|
| 08100 | Metal doors and frames |
| 08200 | Wood and plastic doors |
| 08250 | Door opening assemblies |

**FIGURE 1.3**
CSI format.

## Div. 8 - Doors and windows (continued)

| | |
|---|---|
| 08400 | Entrances and storefronts |
| 08500 | Metal windows |
| 08600 | Wood and plastic windows |
| 08650 | Special windows |
| 08700 | Hardware |
| 08800 | Glazing |
| 08900 | Glazed curtain walls |

## Div. 9 - Finishes

| | |
|---|---|
| 09100 | Metal support systems |
| 09200 | Lath and plaster |
| 09230 | Aggregate coatings |
| 09250 | Gypsum board |
| 09300 | Tile |
| 09400 | Terrazzo |
| 09500 | Acoustical treatment |
| 09540 | Special surfaces |
| 09550 | Wood flooring |
| 09600 | Stone flooring |
| 09630 | Unit masonry flooring |
| 09650 | Resilient flooring |
| 09680 | Carpeting |
| 09700 | Special flooring |
| 09780 | Floor treatment |
| 09800 | Special coatings |
| 09900 | Painting |
| 09950 | Wall coverings |

## Div. 10 - Specialties

| | |
|---|---|
| 10100 | Chalkboards and tackboards |
| 10150 | Compartments and cubicles |
| 10200 | Louvers and vents |
| 10240 | Grilles and screens |
| 10250 | Service wall systems |
| 10260 | Wall and corner guards |
| 10270 | Access flooring |
| 10280 | Specialty modules |
| 10290 | Pest control |
| 10300 | Fireplaces and stoves |
| 10340 | Prefabricated exterior specialties |
| 10350 | Flagpoles |
| 10400 | Identifying devices |
| 10450 | Pedestrian control devices |
| 10500 | Lockers |
| 10520 | Fire protection specialties |
| 10530 | Protective covers |
| 10550 | Postal specialties |
| 10600 | Partitions |
| 10650 | Operable partitions |
| 10670 | Storage shelving |
| 10700 | Exterior sun control devices |
| 10750 | Telephone specialties |
| 10800 | Toilet and bath accessories |
| 10880 | Scales |
| 10900 | Wardrobe and closet specialties |

## Div. 11 - Equipment

| | |
|---|---|
| 11010 | Maintenance equipment |
| 11020 | Security and vault equipment |
| 11030 | Teller and service equipment |
| 11040 | Ecclesiastical equipment |
| 11050 | Library equipment |
| 11060 | Theater and stage equipment |
| 11070 | Instrumental equipment |
| 11080 | Registration equipment |
| 11090 | Checkroom equipment |
| 11100 | Mercantile equipment |
| 11110 | Commercial laundry and dry cleaning equipment |
| 11120 | Vending equipment |
| 11130 | Audio-visual equipment |
| 11140 | Service station equipment |
| 11150 | Parking control equipment |
| 11160 | Loading dock equipment |
| 11170 | Solid waste handling equipment |
| 11190 | Detention equipment |
| 11200 | Water supply and treatment equipment |
| 11280 | Hydraulic gates and valves |
| 11300 | Fluid waste treatment and disposal equipment |
| 11400 | Food service equipment |
| 11450 | Residential equipment |
| 11460 | Unit kitchens |
| 11470 | Darkroom equipment |
| 11480 | Athletic, recreational, and therapeutic equipment |
| 11500 | Industrial and process equipment |
| 11600 | Laboratory equipment |
| 11650 | Planetarium equipment |
| 11660 | Observatory equipment |
| 11700 | Medical equipment |
| 11780 | Mortuary equipment |
| 11850 | Navigation equipment |

## Div. 12 - Furnishings

| | |
|---|---|
| 12050 | Fabrics |
| 12100 | Artwork |
| 12300 | Manufactured casework |
| 12500 | Window treatment |
| 12600 | Furniture and accessories |
| 12670 | Rugs and mats |
| 12700 | Multiple seating |
| 12800 | Interior plants and planters |

## Div. 13 - Special construction

| | |
|---|---|
| 13010 | Air supported structures |
| 13020 | Integrated assemblies |
| 13030 | Special purpose rooms |
| 13080 | Sound, vibration, and seismic control |
| 13090 | Radiation protection |
| 13100 | Nuclear reactors |
| 13120 | Pre-engineered structures |

**FIGURE 1.3** (*continued*)

**Div. 13 - Special construction (continued)**

| | |
|---|---|
| 13150 | Pools |
| 13160 | Ice rinks |
| 13170 | Kennels and animal shelters |
| 13180 | Site contructed incinerators |
| 13200 | Liquid and gas storage tanks |
| 13220 | Filter underdrains and media |
| 13230 | Digestion tank covers and appurtenances |
| 13240 | Oxygenation systems |
| 13260 | Sludge conditioning systems |
| 13300 | Utility control systems |
| 13400 | Industrial and process control systems |
| 13500 | Recording instrumentation |
| 13550 | Transportation control instrumentation |
| 13600 | Solar energy systems |
| 13700 | Wind energy systems |
| 13800 | Building automation systems |
| 13900 | Fire suppression and supervisory systems |

**Div. 14 - Conveying systems**

| | |
|---|---|
| 14100 | Dumbwaiters |
| 14200 | Elevators |
| 14300 | Moving stairs and walks |
| 14400 | Lifts |
| 14500 | Material handling systems |
| 14600 | Hoists and cranes |
| 14700 | Turntables |
| 14800 | Scaffolding |
| 14900 | Transportation systems |

**Div. 15 - Mechanical**

| | |
|---|---|
| 15050 | Basic mechanical materials and methods |
| 15250 | Mechanical insulation |
| 15300 | Fire protection |
| 15400 | Plumbing |
| 15500 | Heating, ventilating, and air conditioning (HVAC) |
| 15550 | Heat generation |
| 15650 | Refrigeration |
| 15750 | Heat transfer |
| 15850 | Air handling |
| 15880 | Air distribution |
| 15950 | Controls |
| 15990 | Testing, adjusting, and balancing |

**Div. 16 - Electrical**

| | |
|---|---|
| 16050 | Basic electrical materials and methods |
| 16200 | Power generation |
| 16300 | High voltage distribution (above 600-volt) |
| 16400 | Service and distribution (600-volt and below) |
| 16500 | Lighting |
| 16600 | Special systems |
| 16700 | Communications |
| 16850 | Electrical resistance heating |
| 16900 | Controls |
| 16950 | Testing |

**FIGURE 1.3** *(continued)*

---

### ADVERTISEMENT FOR BIDS

   Sealed bids for the construction of a Municipal Airport Terminal Building at Any City, Texas, will be received by the City at the City Manager's Office until 5:00 P.M. (E.S.T.), Monday, June 1, 19--, and then publicly opened and read aloud.  Bids submitted after closing time will be returned unopened.  No oral or telephoned proposals or modifications will be considered.

   Plans, specifications, and contract documents will be available May 25, 19--, and may be examined without charge in the City Manager's Office and in Plan Services in Dallas, Austin, El Paso, and Beaumont, Texas;  Pittsburgh, Pennsylvania;  Detroit, Michigan; and Washington, D.C.  General Contractors may procure five sets from the Architect-Engineer upon a deposit of $100.00 per set as a guarantee for the safe return of the plans and specifications within 10 days after receipt of bids.  Others may procure sets for the cost of production.

   A cashier's check, certified check, or acceptable bidder's bond payable to Any City in an amount not less than 5% of the largest possible total for the bid submitted including the consideration of the additive alternatives must accompany each bid as a guarantee that, if awarded the contract, the bidder will promptly enter into a contract and execute such bonds as may be required.

   The Architect-Engineer's estimate cost is $5,700,000.

   Full compliance with applicable Federal, State, and Municipal Wage Laws is required and not less than the rates of wages legally prescribed or set forth in the Contract, whichever is higher, shall be paid.

   Proposals shall be submitted on the forms prescribed and the Owner reserves the right, as its interests may require, to reject any and all proposals; waive any formalities or technicalities.  No bidder may withdraw his proposal after the hour set for the opening thereof, or before award of contract, unless said award is delayed for a period exceeding thirty (30) days.

Any City, TEXAS

By John Doe, City Manager

May 24, 19--

**FIGURE 1.4**
Advertisement for bid.

the items will be expenses to the construction firm. Most architectural firms use a standardized document such as the AIA (American Institute of Architects) Form 201 as the general conditions. A copy of AIA 201 is included in Appendix A.

**SUPPLEMENTARY GENERAL CONDITIONS OR SPECIAL CONDITIONS.** The standardized general conditions often need to be amended for each particular project. This is accomplished with the supplementary general conditions, which generally address issues that pertain to the particular project, such as tempo-rary offices, temporary utilities, soil conditions, signs, surveys, pumping, and allowances.

# INSTRUCTION TO BIDDERS

1. CONTRACT DOCUMENTS. The Notice to Bidders, the Instructions to Bidders, the General Conditions, the Supplementary Conditions, the Drawings and Specifications, the Contractor's Proposal Form, and the Agreement as finally negotiated compose

Copies of these documents can be obtained from the office of Jim Smith, Architect Engineers, 123 South St., Peoria, Illinois, upon deposit of $100.00 for each set thereof, said deposit being refundable upon return of the documents in good order within 10 days after the bidding date.

2. PRINTED FORM FOR PROPOSAL. All proposals must be made upon the Contractor's Proposal Form attached hereto and should give the amounts bid for the work, both in words and in figures, and must be signed and acknowledged by the Contractor. In order to ensure consideration, the Proposal should be enclosed in a sealed envelope marked "Proposal for Municipal Airport Terminal Building to be opened at 3:30 P.M. (C.S.T.), May 19, 19--," showing the return address of the sender and addressed to John Doe, City Manager, Peoria, Illinois.

If the proposal is made by a partnership, it shall contain the names of each partner and shall be signed in the firm name, followed by the signature of the person authorized to sign. If the proposal is made by a corporation, it shall be signed by the name of the corporation, followed by the written signature of the officer signing, and the printed or typewritten designation of the office he holds in the corporation, together with the corporation seal. All blank spaces in the proposal form shall be properly filled in.

3. ALTERNATES. Each bidder shall submit with his proposal, on forms provided, alternate proposals stating the differences in price (additions or deductions) from the base bid for substituting, omitting, or changing the materials or construction from that shown on the drawings and as specified in a manner as described in the Division "Alternate Proposals" of these specifications.

The difference in price shall include all omissions, additions, and adjustments of all trades as may be necessary because of each change, substitution, or omission as described.

4. PAYMENT OF EMPLOYEES. For work done in the State of Illinois, the payment of employees of the Contractor and any and all subcontractors shall comply with the current minimum wage scale as is published by the Labor Commission of the State of Illinois, a copy of which is made a part of the Supplementary Conditions.

The Contractor and each of his subcontractors shall pay each of their employees engaged in work on the project under this contract in full, less deductions made mandatory by law, and not less often than once each week. All forms required by local authorities, the State of Illinois, and the United States Government, shall be properly submitted.

5. TELEGRAPHIC MODIFICATION. Any bidder may modify his bid by telegraphic communication at any time prior to the scheduled closing time for receipt of bids provided such telegraphic communication is received by the City Manager prior to said closing time, and provided further that the City Manager is satisfied that a written confirmation of such telegraphic modification over the signature of the bidder was mailed prior to said closing time. If such written confirmation is not received within two (2) days from said closing time, no consideration will be given to the said telegraphic modification.

**FIGURE 1.5**
Instructions to bidders.

6. DELIVERY OF PROPOSALS. It is the bidder's responsibility to deliver his proposal at the proper time to the proper place. The mere fact that a proposal was dispatched will not be considered. The bidder must have the proposal actually delivered. Any proposal received after the scheduled closing time will be returned unopened to the bidder.

7. OPENING OF PROPOSALS. At 3:30 P.M. (C.S.T.), May 19, 19--, in the Office of the City Manager, City Hall, Peoria, Illinois, each and every proposal (except those which have been withdrawn in accordance with Item 10, "Withdrawal of Proposals,") received prior to the scheduled closing time for receipt of proposals, will be publicly opened and read aloud, irrespective of any irregularities or informalities in such proposals.

8. ALTERATIONS IN PROPOSAL. Except as otherwise provided herein, proposals which are incomplete or which are conditioned in any way or which contain erasures not authenticated as provided herein or items not called for in the proposal or which may have been altered or are not in conformity with the law, may be rejected as informal.

The proposal form invites bids on definite plans and specifications. Only the amounts and information asked on the proposal form furnished will be considered as the bid. Each bidder shall bid upon the work exactly as specified and as provided in the proposal.

9. ERASURES. The proposal submitted must not contain erasures, interlineations, or other corrections unless each such correction is suitably authenticated by affixing in the margin immediately opposite the correction the surname or surnames of the person or persons signing the bid.

10. WITHDRAWAL OF PROPOSALS. At any time prior to the scheduled closing time for receipt of proposals, any bidder may withdraw his proposal, either personally or by telegraphic or written request. If withdrawal is made personally, proper receipt shall be given therefor.

After the scheduled closing time for the receipt of proposals and before award of contract, no bidder will be permitted to withdraw his proposal unless said award is delayed for a period exceeding thirty (30) days. Negligence on the part of the bidder in preparing his bid confers no rights for the withdrawal of the proposal after it has been opened.

11. DETERMINATION OF LOW BID. In making award of contract, the owner reserves the right to take into consideration the plant facilities of the bidders and the bidder's ability to complete the contract within the time specified in the proposal. The owner also reserves the right to evaluate factors that in his opinion would affect the final total cost.

12. REJECTION OF PROPOSALS. The owner reserves the right to reject any or all proposals. Without limiting the generality of the foregoing, any proposal which is incomplete, obscure, or irregular may be rejected; any proposal which omits a bid for any one or more items in the price sheet may be rejected; any proposal in which unit prices are omitted or in which unit prices are obviously unbalanced may be rejected; any proposal accompanied by an insufficient or irregular certified check, cashier's check, or bid bond may be rejected.

13. PROPOSAL AND PERFORMANCE GUARANTEES. A certified check, cashier's check, or bid bond for an amount equal to at least five per cent (5%) of the total amount bid shall accompany each proposal as evidence of good faith and as a guarantee that if awarded the Contract, the bidder will execute the Contract and give bond as required. The successful bidder's check or bid bond will be retained until he has

FIGURE 1.5 (continued)

entered into a satisfactory contract and furnished required contract bonds. The owner reserves the right to hold the certified checks, cashier's checks, or bid bonds of the three lowest bidders, until the successful bidder has entered into a contract and furnished the required contract bonds.

14. ACCEPTANCE OF PROPOSALS. Within thirty (30) days after receipt of the proposals the owner will act upon them. The acceptance of a proposal will be a Notice of Acceptance in writing signed by a duly authorized representative of the owner and no other act of the owner shall constitute the acceptance of a proposal. The acceptance of a proposal shall bind the successful bidder to execute the Contract. The rights and obligations provided for in the Contract shall become effective and binding upon the parties only upon its formal execution.

15. TIME FOR EXECUTING CONTRACT AND PROVIDING CONTRACT BOND. Any contractor whose proposal shall be accepted will be required to execute the Contract and furnish contract bonds as required within ten (10) days after notice that the Contract has been awarded to him. Failure or neglect to do so shall constitute a breach of the agreement effected by the acceptance of the proposal.

16. PRICES. In the event of a discrepancy between the prices quoted in words and those quoted in figures in the proposal, the words shall control. The prices are to include the furnishing of all materials, plant, equipment, tools, and all other facilities, and the performance of all labor and services necessary or proper for the completion of the work except as may be otherwise expressly provided in the Contract Documents.

17. EXAMINATION OF DRAWINGS. Bidders shall thoroughly examine and be familiar with the drawings and specifications. The failure or omission of any bidder to receive or examine any form, instrument, addendum, or other document shall in no way relieve any bidder from obligation with respect to his proposal or to the Contract. The submission of a bid shall be taken as prima facie evidence of compliance with this Section.

18. INTERPRETATIONS. No oral interpretations will be made to any bidder as to the meaning of the drawings and specifications or other contract documents. Every request for such and interpretation shall be made in writing and addressed and forwarded to the owner's authorized representative (Architect-Engineer) five (5) or more days before the date fixed for opening of proposals. Every interpretation made to a bidder will be in the form of an addendum to the Contract Documents which, if issued, will be sent as promptly as is practicable to all persons to whom the drawings and specifications have been issued. All such addenda shall become part of the Contract Documents.

19. POSTPONEMENT OF DATE FOR OPENING PROPOSALS. The owner reserves the right to postpone the date of presentation and opening of proposals and will give telegraphic notice of any such postponement to each interested party.

**FIGURE 1.5** *(continued)*

**ADDENDA.** Before the bids are submitted, changes, modifications, revisions, corrections, and clarifications to the contract may be made by the architect. The changes must be in the form of one or more written addenda. The estimator should not make any changes to the estimate based on verbal instructions. All construction firms that are submitting a bid to the owner must acknowledge the receipt of the addenda on the bid form. It is suggested that a call be made to the architect on the day of the bid to confirm the number of addenda that have been issued. It is equally important that all subcontractors and material suppliers acknowledge to the general contractor receipt of the addenda during the bidding process.

**ASSOCIATED DOCUMENTS.** There are many associated documents that may not be bound in the specifications but are referred to in them. It is common practice for the architect to make reference to a standard that may be a part of a publication by ASTM (American Society for Testing and Materials), ACI (American Concrete Institute), SJI (Steel Joist Institute), or other organizations. It is the responsibility of the estimator to obtain and understand those standards and make sure that any cost ramifications are reflected in the estimate.

**BID FORM OR PROPOSAL FORM.** Most architects require that a standardized bid form be used. By using a standardized bid form, the owner can evaluate all bids on the same basis. The proposal form stipulates the price for which the construction firm agrees to perform the work, the price for any alternates, any unit prices, and acknowledgment of those addenda that have been reviewed. In addition, some bid forms require the construction firm to indicate the expected construction time and the names of subcontractors. The bid form must be filled out completely and accurately, with the required number of copies delivered to the right place on time, or the bid may be rejected. Figure 1.6 is an example of a bid form.

**BID BOND.** The proposal form is only an offer from the contractor to perform the work; theoretically, the contractor could withdraw it. However, the owner usually requires that the contractor provide a bond or certified check in the amount of 5 percent or 10 percent of the bid to ensure that the construction firm will proceed with signing a contract and supplying the other necessary bonds. If the construction firm fails to proceed without justification, the bond or check is forfeited to the owner. The courts may rule that the firm is not subject to the conditions of the bid bond if, for example, it can be proven that the construction firm made a gross mathematical error. However, errors in judgment for such things as labor productivity, construction method, and process are not grounds for withdrawing a bid. The ramifications of withdrawing a bid go beyond the forfeiture of a bid bond for the construction firm. If a bond is forfeited the surety company has the right to collect for the damages from the construction company, and it will be difficult for the construction company to obtain bonding for future projects.

The bid bond is provided by the surety company for free or for a minimum charge to approved construction companies. If a surety company does provide a

# PROPOSAL FOR
# LUMP-SUM CONTRACT

Peoria, Illinois
(Place)

May 19,19--
(Date)

PROPOSAL of ___John Doe Construction Company___ a corporation organized and existing under the laws of the State of Illinois, a partnership consisting of

_____

an individual doing business as _____

TO: The City of Peoria, Illinois
PROJECT: Municipal Airport Terminal Building
For the City of Peoria, Illinois

Sir/Madam:

The Undersigned, in compliance with your Invitation for Bids for the General Construction of the above-described project, having examined the drawings and specifications with related contract documents carefully, with all addenda thereto, and the site of the work, and being familiar with all of the conditions surrounding the construction of the proposed project, hereby proposes to furnish all plant, labor, equipment, appliances, supplies, and materials and to perform all work for the construction of the project as required by and in strict accordance with the contract documents, specifications, schedules, and drawings with all addenda issued by the Architect-Engineer, at the prices stated below.

The Undersigned hereby acknowledges receipt of the following Addenda:
Addendum No.1 dated April 28, 19--.
Addendum No.2 dated May 6, 19--.

BASE PROPOSAL: For all work described in the detailed specifications and shown on the contract drawings for the building, I (or We) agree to perform all the work for the sum of
Four million, six hundred sixty-eight thousand, eight hundred sixty-one and no/100 ($4,668,861.00) dollars. (Amount shall be shown in both written form and figures. In case of discrepancy between the written amount and the figures, the written amount will govern.)
The above-stated compensation covers all expenses incurred in performing the work, including premium for contract bonds, required under the contract documents, of which this proposal is a part.

**FIGURE 1.6**
Bid form.

**16**

ALTERNATE NO. 1: QUARRY TILE IN PLACE OF TERRAZZO: If the substitutions specified under this alternate are made, you may (~~deduct from~~) (add to) the base proposal the sum of Nine thousand, seven hundred fourteen and no/100 ($9,714.00) dollars.

ALTERNATE NO. 2: CHANGE STRUCTURAL GLAZED TILE TO BRICK IN CONCOURSE: If the substitutions specified under this alternate are made, you may (deduct from) (~~add to~~) the base proposal the sum of Four thousand, two hundred eighty and no/100 ($4,280.00) dollars.

ALTERNATE NO. 3: OMIT KITCHEN EQUIPMENT: If the substitutions specified under this alternate are made, you may (deduct from) (~~add to~~) the base proposal the sum of Sixty-six thousand, seven hundred twenty-three and no/100 ($66,723.00) dollars.

BID SECURITY: Attached cashier's check (certified check) (Bid Bond) payable without condition, in the sum of 5% of maximum possible bid amount ($_____) dollars (equal to 5% of the largest possible combination) is to become the property of the City of Peoria, Illinois, in the event the Contract and contract bonds are not executed within the time set forth hereinafter, as liquidated damages for the delay and additional work caused thereby.

CONTRACT SECURITY: The Undersigned hereby agrees, if awarded the contract, to furnish the contract bonds, as specified, with the   Dalton Accident and Indemnity Company  Surety Company of  Dalton, Virginia.

  Upon receipt of notice of the acceptance of this bid, the Undersigned hereby agrees that he will execute and deliver the formal written Contract in the form prescribed, in accordance with the bid as accepted and that he will give contract bonds, all within ten days after the prescribed forms are presented to him for signature.

  If awarded the Contract, the Undersigned proposes to commence work within 10 calendar days after receipt of notice to proceed and to fully complete all of the work under his Contract, ready for occupancy, within 380 calendar days thereafter.

Repectfully submitted,


John Doe Construction Company

*By C V Patterson*

Vice-President

(Title)

10818 Anderson Drive

Peoria, Illinois

(Business Address)

(309) 123-4567

(Telephone Number)

SEAL:
(If bid is by a Corporation)

**FIGURE 1.6** *(continued)*

bid bond they will have to provide additional bonds as required by the contract documents if the project proceeds with construction. The surety company will then charge for the additional bonds.

The surety company makes a thorough investigation of the construction company before any bid bonds are issued. If the construction company is approved, the surety company sets a limit on the amount of bonding that they will provide. The limits are based on the total amount of work under construction by the company and the total estimated on a single project. For example, a company could have a total work under construction limit of $20,000,000 and a $5,000,000 limit on a single project. If either of these limits are exceeded the surety company will not provide a bond.

**LABOR AND MATERIAL PAYMENT BOND.** The payment bond guarantees the payment of the construction firm's bills for labor and material. If the construction firm does not pay for labor and material supplied to the project, liens can be filed on the property. Claims must be filed within 90 days after the last day the claimant performed any work on the project or supplied materials to it. The laws vary from state to state concerning the time period and other details.

**PERFORMANCE BOND.** This bond guarantees to the owner that the construction firm will perform all work in accordance with the contract documents. It protects the owner against default on the part of the construction firm for up to the face amount of the bond. The face amount for both the performance and payment bonds is usually 100 percent of the contract amount. Depending on the size of the project, the cost of the performance and labor and material payment bonds is usually on a sliding scale in the range of 1 percent of the contract amount.

**INSURANCE.** Insurance policies are required for a specified loss or liability. The specifications will require various types of insurance. It is beyond the scope of this book to describe each type. The specifications should be reviewed thoroughly to make sure costs for insurance required on the project being bid are included. The cost of the various types of insurance that the construction company wishes to carry beyond that required by a set of specifications should also be included in the overhead expenses of the bid.

**FORM OF AGREEMENT.** A copy of the agreement form should be included in the specifications. The exact type of agreement may vary. However, all should contain certain provisions, and the construction firm (and their lawyers) must check each item carefully before signing the agreement. A copy of the AIA 101 Stipulated Form of Agreement is in Appendix B.

## THE CONSTRUCTION COMPANY

The construction company should develop a written plan to define its goals and objectives. The plan will identify the company's strengths and weaknesses and develop a strategy for achieving its goals. Within the strategic plan, the type of work performed, legal organization, and functional organization are developed.

The construction company will usually perform most of its work in one of the classifications discussed earlier in this chapter. However, some construction companies may perform work in other categories. The estimating function depends on the type of work performed by the company. Units of measure in the quantity takeoff, pricing, and construction methods vary and need to be studied by the estimator.

The functional organization of the company depends on the type of construction work performed, available assets, and other elements of the strategic plan. The estimating function will have to be identified whether the company is a general contractor, specialty contractor, design-build firm, or construction management firm. Figure 1.7 shows an organization chart with estimating as a separate department for a general contractor. This is the most common organizational method, and with this organization the company is ensured of an ongoing effort to obtain work in the bid market. Figure 1.8 shows an organization chart with the estimating function as one of the duties of the project manager in a general contracting firm. This type of organization requires the project manager to be skilled in both the project management and estimating functions.

The transfer of the successful bid to project management, purchasing, field operations, and other departments of the construction company can affect the functional organization of the company. An estimating system that can easily be followed by others describing the quantities of materials, productivity rates of labor and equipment, subcontractor evaluations, assumptions by the estimator, and method of construction is a must for a smooth transition.

The legal organization of a company has little bearing on the estimating process. However, most construction companies are organized as legal corporations. There are tax and liability advantages with this type of organization. However,

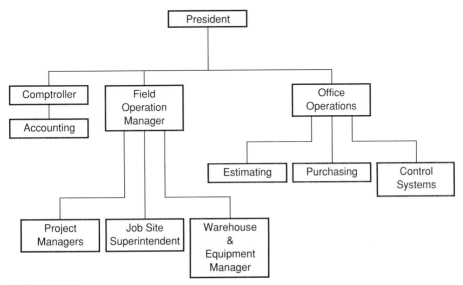

**FIGURE 1.7**
Organization chart with estimating as a separate department.

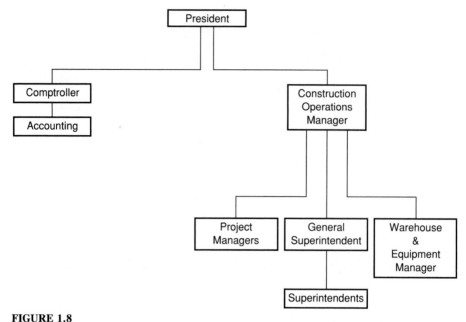

**FIGURE 1.8**
Organization chart with the estimating function as one of the duties of the project manager.

surety companies and financial institutions often require that principal stockholders be held liable for any claims.

## QUALIFICATIONS OF THE CONSTRUCTION FIRM

Some states require that construction firms be licensed. The licensing process varies from state to state. Some states simply require that a fee be paid; others may require a fee, successful completion of an examination, and approval of the financial condition of the company. Some states have no requirements.

Whether the state requires a license or not, almost all projects require some type of qualification process. For states that do not have a licensing process, a qualification process is usually set up for publicly funded projects. On privately funded projects, the owner will usually prequalify contractors based on specific criteria such as financial condition of the company, past experience, and safety record.

## TYPES OF ESTIMATES

Estimates are performed throughout the construction process. The success or failure of a project depends on the accuracy of several major estimates. Figure 1.9 shows the various types of estimates and their relationship to the total building process.

### Feasibility Estimates

The purpose of the feasibility estimate is to determine whether or not the project should be built. The project must be a sound economic investment for a private owner; in the case of public funds, it must satisfy the needs of society with fiscal

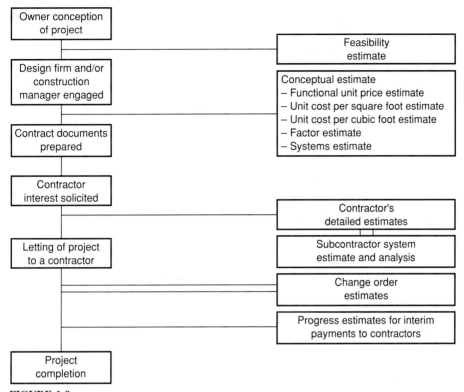

**FIGURE 1.9**
Types of estimates.

responsibility. The cost of the construction is only one part of a feasibility estimate. Before the process can begin the owner will also need to consider the following costs: land, design, tax depreciation, investment tax credit, capital gains, annual maintenance and repairs, and financing. Some of these costs occur only once; others occur over a period of years. All of the costs then have to be compared to the expected gross income on an annual basis. The net income (and thus the net return on the investment) can be estimated. The owner can then make a decision based on the economics of the process. A person responsible for a feasibility estimate not only has to have the skills required to make a complete and reliable estimate but must also be knowledgeable of the expected life of construction materials, accounting principles, current related tax laws, and an awareness of design.

## Conceptual Estimates

Typically, several iterations of the building design will be needed before a final decision is made. Each iteration is accompanied by a cost estimate, called a *conceptual estimate*. The estimator must conceptualize the completed building before it is fully designed. The estimate may have to be revised several times throughout the design process as the aesthetics and materials are determined. With each estimate the reliability of the expected cost increases, because more decisions have been made about the design.

Design-build and construction management depend heavily on conceptual estimates. These projects are usually built on a fast track or phased construction process. If the conceptual estimate fails to provide reliable information, the owner may start the project only to find that there is not enough capital to complete it as originally designed.

A person who does a conceptual estimate must have all of the qualities and skills of a detailed estimator plus the ability to anticipate design decisions and communicate those assumptions made during the conceptual estimating process. The estimator must be able to think and see holistically and then perceive the details of the project. The conceptual estimator understands the details of a building, but they are not the essence of the conceptual estimate—the concept is more important at this stage of the design and construction process.

The pricing data of the conceptual estimate will come from the details of similar projects, summarized into work packages, and then applied to the project being estimated. A reliable cost data bank will have to be developed for the conceptual estimating process. Adjustments for economic conditions and geographical locations must be made. It is also important to clearly define the elements of the data bank so there will be no misunderstandings on what information is included.

There are several different types of conceptual estimates. Some estimates require less detail than others. These estimates are usually performed at the beginning of the design process. The amount of time and effort spent on these preliminary estimates will vary with the amount of detail required. The time that is spent on a $3,000,000 project may progress from one hour for the first estimate to over 150 hours for the final detailed estimate. The following is a discussion of the various types of conceptual estimates.

**FUNCTIONAL UNIT PRICE ESTIMATE.** The functional unit price estimate uses the function of the facility as the basis for establishing cost. Some typical formats are:

| | |
|---|---|
| Schools | Cost per pupil |
| Parking garages | Cost per parking space |
| Hospitals | Cost per bed |
| Generating station | Cost per kilowatt of output |

For example, a school is expected to have 1500 students. The total cost would be:

$$1500 \times \$8000 = \$12,000,000$$

This method requires the estimator to have a historical data bank on the overall cost of similar projects. In the above example it was determined that similar past school projects cost $8000 per student. This type of conceptual estimate is the broadest based, requires the least amount of time, and is the least accurate.

**UNIT COST PER SQUARE FOOT ESTIMATE.** This is the most common type of conceptual estimate and is reliable for only the early stages of the planning and design process. The cost per square foot of a particular building type is multiplied by the total expected square footage of the proposed building. For example, the estimate for a proposed apartment building with 15,000 square feet (sf) is

$$15,000 \times \$60/sf = \$800,000$$

The $60/sf is determined from previously built similar projects. This method relies on the historical cost per square foot of similar projects. The data can be obtained from projects that have been built by the company or published cost data books. Naturally, more reliable information would come from buildings that the company actually built.

**UNIT COST PER CUBIC FOOT ESTIMATE.** The cost per cubic foot estimate is similar to the cost per square foot estimate and can be used for buildings where volume is important, such as warehouses. However, this method is only reliable for buildings that are virtually identical.

**FACTOR ESTIMATING.** Conceptual estimating by a factor can be used for similar types of projects. This method is most valid for projects that have a similar major component, such as the boiler in a power generation plant. The predominant cost component will serve as the base factor of 1.00. All other components of the project will be a function of the predominant component. Figure 1.10 is an example of a factored estimate. The equipment is the predominant component of the project, and all other items are calculated as percentages of the equipment cost. The percentage factors shown in Fig. 1.10 are calculated from previous projects completed by the construction company. Factor estimating can be fairly reliable if accurate data is kept from previous projects and if the previous projects are consistent with the project being estimated.

## System Estimate (Elemental Estimates or Parametric Estimates)

The system estimate is also known as an elemental or parametric estimate. This method has the potential of being the most accurate of all the conceptual estimating methods. However, it does require that the estimator perform some basic quantity takeoff.

With the systems approach, the project is first divided into functional systems. The construction company will need to define what is included in each system. However, the systems are usually all-encompassing. For example, the exterior wall system could be defined as exterior face brick, sheathing, steel studs, insulation, interior gypsum board, taping, and interior painting. All of the individual components form one unit of measure. In this example the unit of measure is the area in square feet of exterior wall. The pricing is accomplished by multiplying the square feet of wall by a unit price that includes all the elements of the system. For example, 15,000 square feet of brick veneer wall system × $10.75 per square foot will cost $161,250. The $10.75 is the sum of all the unit prices of the elements that make up the system, as shown below.

| Type of work | Factor | Projected cost |
|---|---|---|
| General conditions | 0.09 | $54,000 |
| Excavation | 0.07 | 42,000 |
| Framing system | 0.22 | 132,000 |
| Equipment | 1.00 | 600,000 |
| Equipment installation | 0.18 | 108,000 |
| Process piping | 0.70 | 420,000 |
| Instrumentation costs | 0.20 | 120,000 |
| Finish material | 0.15 | 90,000 |
| Electrical | 0.10 | 60,000 |
| Plumbing | 0.18 | 108,000 |
| Mechanical | 0.44 | 264,000 |
| **Total project cost** | | $1,998,000 |

**FIGURE 1.10**
Factored estimate.

| Brick | $ 3.50 |
|---|---|
| Sheathing | 1.00 |
| Steel studs | 2.50 |
| Insulation | 1.50 |
| Interior gypsum | 1.00 |
| Finish | 0.75 |
| Paint | 0.50 |
| Total | $10.75 |

The unit pricing may be determined by summing all of the unit prices of the elements of the system, as shown above, or by multiplying the system takeoff unit by a factor from the company historical data bank. For example,

Price for HVAC = 12,000 sf of floor space × $5.50 = $66,000

The $5.50 figure is the cost per square foot of floor space for similar heating systems of projects that the company has previously built. The price may have to be adjusted for different economic and project conditions and geographic locations.

Some organizations have made an attempt to generally organize the format of a systems estimate. Figure 1.11 is a summary of some suggested general formats. Under each general heading a series of subheadings would have to be developed. For example, under exterior enclosure, Fig. 1.11 shows the systems that might be found.

Means

1. Substructure
2. Superstructure
3. Exterior enclosure
4. Interior construction
5. Conveying systems
6. Plumbing systems
7. HVAC systems
8. Electrical systems
9. Fixed equipment
10. Special foundations
11. Site construction
12. General contingencies
13. Related costs

Canadian Institute
of Quantity Surveyors

1. Substructure
2. Structure
3. Exterior cladding
4. Interior partitions and doors
5. Vertical movement
6. Interior finishes
7. Fittings and equipment
8. Services
9. Site development
10. Overhead and profit
11. Contingencies

Engineering News-Record

1. Site work
2. Foundations
3. Floor systems
4. Interior columns
5. Roof systems
6. Exterior wall
7. Exterior glazed openings
8. Interior wall systems
9. Doors
10. Specialities
11. Equipment
12. Conveying systems
13. Plumbing
14. HVAC
15. Electrical systems
16. Special electrical
17. Markup

**FIGURE 1.11**
Formats for system estimates.

By using the computer the systems approach to conceptual estimating has the potential of being very reliable. For systems similar to the exterior wall example, the computer will be able to use the same data that would be used in the detailed method of estimating to develop a system unit price.

**DETAILED ESTIMATES.** The most common estimate for a general contractor is the detailed estimate, and it is the subject of most of this book. This is the type of estimate that an estimator would develop for a competitive bid. The first step of a detailed estimate is a thorough quantity takeoff. It should be based on a complete set of project documents consisting of drawings and specifications.

After the takeoff is complete the estimator must assemble the costs of material, labor, equipment, subcontracting, and the other costs of overhead and profit. The construction firm's cost of building a project is somewhat fixed, since it is a function of the drawings and specifications. However, the construction firm has a great deal of flexibility in construction methodology, labor productivity, material price negotiations, equipment usage, subcontractor analysis and negotiations, and overhead and profit costs. The successful general contractor optimizes these elements without making errors.

In addition to the purpose of project acquisition the detailed estimate will serve as the basis for the job costing and control system. Each line item of the detailed estimate will receive a cost code. All labor, materials, equipment, and other costs will be charged against the respective codes. In this way project management can monitor the cost and progress of the project. The job costing system will then serve as a basis of the historical cost data bank of the company, which in turn is used for other project acquisitions.

**SUBCONTRACTOR SYSTEM ESTIMATE.** Typically, a general contractor does not do a detailed takeoff for all 16 divisions. Most general contractors rely on subcontractors for greater than 60% of the actual work. The subcontractors will, however, do a detailed takeoff for their scope of work. For areas that a general contractor expects to subcontract, a "subcontractor system estimate" should be performed by the general contractor. This estimate is similar to a system estimate, but it is general in nature and is applied to specific construction specialities. For each subcontracted component the quantity of a key element is taken off and all other elements are listed. This gives the estimator an understanding of the scope of work of the subcontractor. A unit price for the key element is then applied to derive the approximate subcontractor bid. An example of a subcontractor analysis estimate is shown below.

### Roofing and Sheet metal

Roofing                     50 squares
   Single ply
Gravel stop
2″ roof insulation
Roof drains
Cant strip
Curbs for mech. equip
Curbs for roof hatch

$$50 \text{ squares} \times \$250 \text{ per sq} = \$12,500$$

The general contractor expects to receive a bid for the roofing in the above example, but in case one is not received before the bid is due by the general contractor the $12,500 could be plugged into the bid to cover the cost of roofing. Needless to say, there is a considerable amount of risk that the general contractor is assuming. However, the general contractor usually will not have to do this because several bids for the roofing and sheet metal will normally be received.

In the previous roofing estimating example no quantities for items other than the squares of roofing has been calculated. The quantities for the other items can also be calculated if the estimator has enough time, but at a minimum the components should be listed.

It is recommended that the general contractor always perform a subcontractor system estimate because, in addition to the safety of having a number that could be used on the day of the bid, the estimator has gained a good understanding of what the scope of work of the subcontractors should be. Chapter 4 contains additional discussion on subcontractor system estimates.

**CHANGE ORDER ESTIMATES.** During the actual construction process changes will be necessary. The changes may be due to owner needs, errors and omissions in the contract documents, or changed job site conditions such as rock excavation. Additional information about this can be found in Chapter 12.

**PROGRESS ESTIMATES.** During construction the project manager will need to make progress estimates. The progress estimate has two purposes:

**1.** It serves as a basis for the pay request.
**2.** It confirms the projected profit and loss on the project.

Chapter 12 has additional information on the progress estimate.

## RISKS IN ESTIMATING

The environment that surrounds the construction cost estimate is very risky. The estimator does not have control of the circumstances that follow the estimating process. However, the estimator should try to identify as many of those risk areas as possible. Risk can be decreased by making as few assumptions as possible, doing the estimate in a methodical fashion, and making logical decisions. The risk can be divided into risks associated with the project and risks associated with the process of estimating.

The identification of all the risks or uncertainties that are associated with a particular project can be difficult. However, this is one of the responsibilities of the estimator. The following are some of the ways to identify uncertainties associated with the project.

**1.** Study all documents associated with the project thoroughly, including those that are referenced in the contract documents.
**2.** Make a site visitation before the bid.
**3.** Develop a construction schedule before the bid.
**4.** Investigate the financial capabilities of the owners and their ethical business relations.
**5.** Identify responsible subcontractors and material suppliers that can meet the demands of the project.
**6.** Attend the prebid meetings.

7. Be certain the resources are available to build the project.
8. Develop a fact sheet about the project.
9. Develop a strategy for getting the project.
10. Investigate the reputation of the architect and the architect's ethical working relationships with construction firms.
11. Identify clauses in the specifications that are open-ended or would transfer risk to the construction firm.
12. Identify clauses in the supplementary or special conditions of the specifications that transfer additional risk to the construction firm.
13. Identify governmental permit and other requirements.
14. Identify environmental hazards associated with the project.
15. Identify any adverse public reaction to the project.
16. Identify the availability of local labor and whether or not unions are involved.
17. Review the historical weather patterns for the area.
18. Identify disposal sites.
19. Review the soil report for unusual soil conditions on the site.
20. Review the project and construction methods for unsafe conditions.
21. Review the proposed construction method to identify activities that will have small quantities of materials and thus lower the expected production rate of labor.
22. An analysis should be done for each area that is subcontracted to ensure that all items in the scope of work are included.

Risks associated with the estimating process are often attributed to faulty estimating procedures. The following are some of the ways to identify risks associated with the estimating process.

1. Develop a procedure for checking for mathematical errors.
2. Review for illegible handwriting.
3. Review the labor production, material, and equipment standards of the historical data bank to identify items that are not clear on what is included in the standard.
4. Review the system for distribution of drawings and specifications to subcontractors and material suppliers. Only complete sets should be made available.
5. Review the system for receiving and distributing addenda.
6. Review the estimating sheets for unnecessary calculations.
7. Review procedures for rounding off numbers.
8. Avoid scaling drawings.
9. Review the procedure for adding waste.
10. Review checklists and update as necessary to include areas that are not evident from the project documents such as transportation costs, equipment requirements, and storage costs.

11. Make sure that items are taken off from the correct drawings (i.e., structural items should be taken off from the structural set of drawings).

12. Review procedures for receiving bids from subcontractors and material suppliers (see Chapter 4 for more information on this topic).

13. Review the consistency of detail in the estimate.

14. Avoid the use of percentages.

15. Review the system for carrying the bid to the bid receiving station.

16. Review the standardized forms used in the estimating process to eliminate any procedural problems, and create standardized forms where none exist.

17. Review in detail all systems associated with estimating by computer. Estimating by computer can have additional risks associated with the estimating process. It is important for the company to provide training in the estimating software. The estimator should thoroughly understand all aspects of the software before a computerized estimate is submitted.

After the identification of the risks, the estimator should try to eliminate or reduce them. The estimator can eliminate some risks by using subcontractors that are more capable of handling them. Risk reduction can be accomplished by taking action to correct any of the weaknesses that have been identified within the project or estimating procedures.

## SOURCES OF ESTIMATING INFORMATION

The best sources of information for estimating costs is a company's own past experience. This is why an accurate job cost system should be maintained. Information about the actual quantity of materials installed, the actual number of labor or work hours, and the actual equipment hours required to perform each task is invaluable information to the estimating and project control process. It is important that accurate field information be received to develop the estimating information data bank. Figure 1.12 is a diagram that illustrates the information-gathering process for the estimating department.

The job cost system serves as the foundation for organizing all of the information used in the estimating process. This system should be designed with

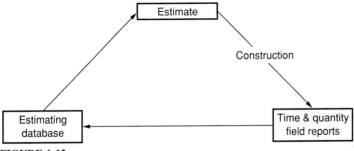

**FIGURE 1.12**
Gathering information.

| | | | |
|---|---|---|---|
| 031.00 | Formwork | | |
| | 031.10 | Formwork material and accessories | |
| | 031.20 | fabricating, erecting, stripping | |
| | | and moving formwork | |
| | | 031.21 | Foundations |
| | | 031.22 | Slabs on grade |
| | | 031.23 | Columns |
| | | 031.24 | Walls |
| | | 031.25 | Elevated slabs |
| | | | |
| 032.00 | Reinforcing | | |
| | 032.10 | Reinforcing materials and accessories | |
| | 032.20 | sorting and placing reinforcing | |
| | | 032.21 | Foundations |
| | | 032.22 | Slabs on grade |
| | | 032.23 | Columns |
| | | 032.24 | Walls |
| | | 032.25 | Elevated slabs |
| | | | |
| 033.00 | Placing and finishing | | |
| | 033.10 | Materials and accessories | |
| | 033.20 | concrete placement | |
| | | 032.21 | Foundations |
| | | 032.22 | Slabs on grade |
| | | 032.23 | Columns |
| | | 032.24 | Walls |
| | | 032.25 | Elevated slabs |
| | 033.30 | Concrete finishes | |
| | | 033.31 | Horizontal |
| | | 033.32 | Vertical |
| | | 033.33 | Curing |

**FIGURE 1.13**
Sample cost codes.

standardized cost codes (code of accounts), descriptions of each item, and a standard unit of measure. Figure 1.13 shows a few items included in a job costing system. If the estimating process is computerized, the estimator would first select cost codes that pertain to the project and then proceed with the quantity takeoff for each one.

If actual job records are not available, published cost data can be used. For architectural firms and some construction management firms that do not have access to actual cost data, commercially available data can be helpful. The key to a successful application of these data sources is an intelligent comparison of the project at hand with the data that is represented in the publication. Carelessness during this process can yield unrealistic and inappropriate results.

The following is a list of several construction costs books:

*R. S. Means Construction Cost Data*—R. S. Means Company
*Dodge Manual*—McGraw-Hill Cost Information Systems

*Walker's Building Estimator's Reference Book*—Frank R. Walker Company
*National Construction Estimator*—Craftsman Books

Some publishers offer a variety of supplementary publications on specialty construction. Figure 1.14 is a sample page from *R. S. Means Construction Cost Data*. In Fig. 1.14, the crew is a code that identifies the makeup of the crew. (This

## 061 | Rough Carpentry

| | | 061 100 | Wood Framing | CREW | DAILY OUTPUT | MAN-HOURS | UNIT | MAT. | LABOR | EQUIP. | TOTAL | TOTAL INCL O&P | |
|---|---|---|---|---|---|---|---|---|---|---|---|---|---|
| 116 | 8840 | | 3″ x 10″ | F-2 | .31 | 51.613 | M.B.F. | 1,025 | 1,225 | 59.50 | 2,309.50 | 3,150 | 116 |
| | 8860 | | 3″ x 12″ | ↓ | .38 | 42.105 | ↓ | 1,025 | 1,000 | 48.50 | 2,073.50 | 2,750 | |
| 118 | 0010 | FRAMING, COLUMNS | | | | | | | | | | | 118 |
| | 0020 | | | | | | | | | | | | |
| | 0400 | | 4″ x 4″ | F-2 | .52 | 30.769 | M.B.F. | 1,025 | 730 | 35.50 | 1,790.50 | 2,325 | |
| | 0420 | | 4″ x 6″ | | .55 | 29.091 | | 1,025 | 690 | 33.50 | 1,748.50 | 2,250 | |
| | 0440 | | 4″ x 8″ | | .59 | 27.119 | | 1,025 | 645 | 31 | 1,701 | 2,175 | |
| | 0460 | | 6″ x 6″ | | .65 | 24.615 | | 1,300 | 585 | 28.50 | 1,913.50 | 2,375 | |
| | 0480 | | 6″ x 8″ | | .70 | 22.857 | | 1,300 | 545 | 26.50 | 1,871.50 | 2,325 | |
| | 0500 | | 6″ x 10″ | ↓ | .75 | 21.333 | ↓ | 1,300 | 510 | 24.50 | 1,834.50 | 2,250 | |
| 120 | 0010 | FRAMING, ROOFS | | | | | | | | | | | 120 |
| | 6065 | | | | | | | | | | | | |
| | 6070 | Fascia boards, 2″ x 8″ | | F-2 | .30 | 53.333 | M.B.F. | 575 | 1,275 | 61.50 | 1,911.50 | 2,700 | |
| | 6080 | | 2″ x 10″ | | .30 | 53.333 | | 685 | 1,275 | 61.50 | 2,021.50 | 2,825 | |
| | 7000 | Rafters, to 4 in 12 pitch, 2″ x 6″ | | | 1 | 16 | | 545 | 380 | 18.40 | 943.40 | 1,225 | |
| | 7060 | | 2″ x 8″ | | 1.26 | 12.698 | | 575 | 300 | 14.60 | 889.60 | 1,125 | |
| | 7300 | Hip and valley rafters, 2″ x 6″ | | | .76 | 21.053 | | 545 | 500 | 24 | 1,069 | 1,425 | |
| | 7360 | | 2″ x 8″ | | .96 | 16.667 | | 575 | 395 | 19.15 | 989.15 | 1,275 | |
| | 7540 | Hip and valley jacks, 2″ x 6″ | | | .60 | 26.667 | | 545 | 635 | 30.50 | 1,210.50 | 1,625 | |
| | 7600 | | 2″ x 8″ | ↓ | .65 | 24.615 | ↓ | 575 | 585 | 28.50 | 1,188.50 | 1,600 | |
| | 7780 | For slopes steeper than 4 in 12, add | | | | | | | 30% | | | | |
| | 7790 | For dormers or complex roofs, add | | | | | | | 50% | | | | |
| | 7800 | Rafter tie, 1″ x 4″, #3 | | F-2 | .27 | 59.259 | M.B.F. | 605 | 1,400 | 68 | 2,073 | 2,975 | |
| | 7810 | | | | | | | | | | | | |
| | 7820 | Ridge board, #2 or better, 1″ x 6″ | | F-2 | .30 | 53.333 | M.B.F. | 880 | 1,275 | 61.50 | 2,216.50 | 3,050 | |
| | 7840 | | 1″ x 8″ | | .37 | 43.243 | | 880 | 1,025 | 49.50 | 1,954.50 | 2,650 | |
| | 7860 | | 1″ x 10″ | | .42 | 38.095 | | 880 | 905 | 44 | 1,829 | 2,450 | |
| | 7880 | | 2″ x 6″ | | .50 | 32 | | 545 | 760 | 37 | 1,342 | 1,850 | |
| | 7900 | | 2″ x 8″ | | .60 | 26.667 | | 575 | 635 | 30.50 | 1,240.50 | 1,675 | |
| | 7920 | | 2″ x 10″ | | .66 | 24.242 | | 685 | 575 | 28 | 1,288 | 1,700 | |
| | 7940 | Roof cants, split, 4″ x 4″ | | | .86 | 18.605 | | 1,025 | 445 | 21.50 | 1,491.50 | 1,850 | |
| | 7960 | | 6″ x 6″ | | 1.80 | 8.889 | | 1,300 | 212 | 10.20 | 1,522.20 | 1,775 | |
| | 7980 | Roof curbs, untreated, 2″ x 6″ | | | .52 | 30.769 | | 545 | 730 | 35.50 | 1,310.50 | 1,800 | |
| | 8000 | | 2″ x 12″ | ↓ | .80 | 20 | ↓ | 700 | 475 | 23 | 1,198 | 1,550 | |
| 122 | 0010 | FRAMING, SILLS | | | | | | | | | | | 122 |
| | 1810 | | | | | | | | | | | | |
| | 4482 | Ledgers, nailed, 2″ x 4″ | | F-2 | .50 | 32 | M.B.F. | 545 | 760 | 37 | 1,342 | 1,850 | |
| | 4484 | | 2″ x 6″ | | .60 | 26.667 | | 545 | 635 | 30.50 | 1,210.50 | 1,625 | |
| | 4486 | Bolted, not including bolts, 3″ x 8″ | | | .65 | 24.615 | | 1,025 | 585 | 28.50 | 1,638.50 | 2,075 | |
| | 4488 | | 3″ x 12″ | | .70 | 22.857 | | 1,025 | 545 | 26.50 | 1,596.50 | 2,025 | |
| | 4490 | Mud sills, redwood, construction grade, 2″ x 4″ | | | .59 | 27.119 | | 1,450 | 645 | 31 | 2,126 | 2,650 | |
| | 4492 | | 2″ x 6″ | | .78 | 20.513 | | 1,450 | 490 | 23.50 | 1,963.50 | 2,400 | |
| | 4500 | Sills, 2″ x 4″ | | | .40 | 40 | | 545 | 950 | 46 | 1,541 | 2,150 | |
| | 4520 | | 2″ x 6″ | | .55 | 29.091 | | 545 | 690 | 33.50 | 1,268.50 | 1,725 | |
| | 4540 | | 2″ x 8″ | | .67 | 23.881 | | 575 | 570 | 27.50 | 1,172.50 | 1,575 | |
| | 4600 | Treated, 2″ x 4″ | | | .36 | 44.444 | | 765 | 1,050 | 51 | 1,866 | 2,575 | |
| | 4620 | | 2″ x 6″ | | .50 | 32 | | 765 | 760 | 37 | 1,562 | 2,075 | |
| | 4640 | | 2″ x 8″ | | .60 | 26.667 | | 805 | 635 | 30.50 | 1,470.50 | 1,925 | |
| | 4700 | | 4″ x 4″ | | .60 | 26.667 | | 1,425 | 635 | 30.50 | 2,090.50 | 2,600 | |
| | 4720 | | 4″ x 6″ | | .70 | 22.857 | | 1,425 | 545 | 26.50 | 1,996.50 | 2,475 | |
| | 4740 | | 4″ x 8″ | | .80 | 20 | | 1,425 | 475 | 23 | 1,923 | 2,350 | |
| | 4760 | | 4″ x 10″ | ↓ | .87 | 18.391 | ↓ | 1,425 | 440 | 21 | 1,886 | 2,300 | |
| 124 | 0010 | FRAMING, SLEEPERS | | | | | | | | | | | 124 |
| | 0020 | | | | | | | | | | | | |
| | 0300 | On concrete, treated, 1″ x 2″ | | F-2 | .39 | 41.026 | M.B.F. | 1,025 | 975 | 47 | 2,047 | 2,725 | |
| | 0320 | | 1″ x 3″ | ↓ | .50 | 32 | ↓ | 1,025 | 760 | 37 | 1,822 | 2,375 | |

**FIGURE 1.14**

*Means* sample page. (From *Means Building Construction Cost Data 1994*. Copyright R. S. Means Co., Inc., Kingston, MA, 617-585-7880, all rights reserved.)

information can be found in another part of the publication.) The labor productivity is given by worker hours (daily output) per unit and dollars per unit.

## ETHICS IN THE ESTIMATING PROCESS

High ethical standards should be maintained during the estimating process. Guidelines for setting prices and receiving quotations that are fair and equitable to all parties should be developed. Acts of collusion or conspiracy with the implied or express purpose of defrauding clients, suppliers, or subcontrators should be forbidden by the construction company. When dealing with subcontractors, materials suppliers, designers, and owners, the esimator should use business practices that are fair and honest.

The practice called bid peddling or bid shopping by general contractors should be discouraged. These unethical practices can take place before the bid is submitted by the general contractor (called bid shopping) and after the low general contractor is known (called bid peddling). For the purposes of getting a lower subcontract bid, the estimator for the general contractor should not reveal any subcontractor bid to any other subcontractor before the general contractor bid is due. When this does happen, the subcontractors often submit their bids in the last few minutes to those general contractors involved with such practices. If a general contractor has taken the position to participate in bid peddling after they have a contract with the owner, subcontractors often submit a higher bid to those general contractors because they know from past experience that a lower price will be required.

The estimator must also be aware of some unethical practices of architects in placing so-called "weasel clauses" in the specifications. The clauses are designed to place an inequitable or unreasonable amount of risk on the construction firm. The clauses usually contain phrases such as "as needed," "as required," or "at the discretion of the architect." These clauses should be brought to the attention of the architect before the bid opening, and an addendum should be issued that clearly defines the intent of the contract documents.

## COST TO PERFORM AN ESTIMATE

The cost associated with developing a detailed estimate is included in the general contractor's operating expenses. These expenses and other general overhead expenses are part of the bid. In general, the cost will be less than 1 percent of the estimated bid. Obviously, the number of hours that an estimator will spend on a particular bid will vary depending on the complexity of the project, experience and skills of the estimator, and the extent of computerization. If the number of hours for a particular project is multiplied by a rate per hour that includes salary, benefits, and overhead, an approximate cost for estimating a project can be determined. For example, a $2 million project will cost approximately (110 hours × $30/hour) or about $3300 (.165 percent the bid price).

# STUDENT EXERCISES

**1.1.** The following is the systems cost data bank for a company that constructs office buildings.

| Element | Unit cost | Basis |
|---|---|---|
| Overhead | $2.00 | sf of floor space |
| Excavation | 2.00 | Footprint of bldg. |
| Foundations | 5.00 | Footprint of bldg. |
| Structural frame | 6.00 | sf of floor space |
| Exterior walls | 5.00 | sf of exterior wall |
| Interior walls | 8.00 | lf of interior wall |
| Finishes | 6.00 | sf of floor space |
| Roof | 9.00 | Footprint of bldg. |
| Electrical | 3.50 | sf of floor space |
| Plumbing | 4.50 | sf of floor space |
| HVAC | 5.50 | sf of floor space |

Perform a systems estimate for a proposed building that is

50,000 sf of floor space

25,000 sf of foot print

45,000 lf of interior walls

20,000 sf of exterior walls

**1.2.** From the historical data bank of an industrial construction firm the following information is known:

| Element | Piping cost factors |
|---|---|
| Excavation | 0.18 |
| Foundation | 0.23 |
| Framing system | 0.70 |
| Piping | 1.00 |
| Electrical | 0.33 |
| Plumbing | 0.26 |
| Mechanical | 0.42 |

Perform a factored estimate for a project in which the piping cost is $780,000.

**1.3.** For each of the following risks develop a procedure that will minimize or eliminate the risk: (a) mistakes by subcontractors during the bidding process, (b) errors in estimating job overhead, and (c) anticipated labor productivity rates.

# CHAPTER
# 2

# COMPUTERS
# IN CONSTRUCTION
# ESTIMATING

One of the greatest advancements in the estimating process has been the implementation of the computer. The early uses of computers by construction companies were limited to accounting functions. With advances in micro-computering, increased knowledge of computer capabilities, and the development of user-friendly software, construction managers have begun to use computers in everyday construction operations to make quick and accurate decisions.

The computer's potential in construction estimating has progressed from its use as an adding machine to an integrated process of computer-aided design (CAD), estimating software, job costing software, and project scheduling systems. However, the actual use of the computer for estimating is varied within the industry. Some companies use the computer for all projects and with a high degree of sophistication. Others do not use the computer at all. There is a consensus that most construction companies will, within a few years, have some form of computerization in the estimating process to retrieve cost and productivity information from past projects and project them to future ones.

The changes in computer hardware and software are rapid and ongoing. The systems used today will be obsolete in a few years. The estimator will need to stay abreast of developments. Actively participating in professional and trade associations, supporting and communicating with local universities, and reading construction publications will help the estimator keep current.

## IMPACT ON THE ESTIMATING PROCESS

As a company implements the use of the computer in the estimating process, the duties of the estimator will change. Before computerization, the estimator spent the greatest amount of time determining the quantities of materials and performing math calculations. Computers accomplish these tasks rapidly and accurately, allowing the estimator to give more attention to alternative construction methods, subcontractor and material supplier negotiations, predicting the productivity of labor, and developing accurate cost information and bidding strategies. In the future, the estimator will be further assisted by expert system software. With this software the estimator will be able to make better decisions on the most efficient construction method, predicted labor productivity, and equipment selection for the project.

The estimator should never accept everything that comes out of the computer as being totally correct. The computer cannot exercise judgment. Because the estimator does not have to spend as much time in determining quantities and doing math calculations, a good opportunity exists to determine the impact of the construction method on the estimated cost of construction. The estimator should always review the computerized estimate and check for more cost-effective construction methods.

The computer can improve the precision level of the estimate. For example, when an estimate is done manually, the figures need to be rounded off to make the calculations manageable; the computer never has to round off numbers. Another example is the calculation of workers' compensation insurance. Workers' compensation requirements vary from state to state and by craft (i.e., workers' compensation for an iron worker usually costs more than for a carpenter, depending on the state). When estimating manually the estimator will normally use an average of the craft compensation rates. However, when computerized it is possible to use the exact rates for the various crafts.

When the construction company decides to implement computerized estimating, it should run the manual system and computer system in tandem before relying totally on the computerized system. This will allow the estimator to study the differences between the two systems and make adjustments.

## ESTIMATING AND THE SPREADSHEET

The writing of spreadsheet templates reinforces the estimating methodology and can lead to improved techniques. The estimator can develop a good understanding of estimating by first learning the manual process of estimating and then writing estimating programs in a spreadsheet format. This book provides several spreadsheet examples and exercises. It is assumed that the reader knows how to develop a spreadsheet template. The following is a review of the spreadsheet functions and the methods of successfully adapting them to the construction process.

Several spreadsheet programs are available. Some of the more popular ones are Lotus 123, Quattro Pro, and Microsoft Excel. Essentially, a spreadsheet consists of columns and rows forming a grid of cells. The cells can be changed in size and format to allow different mathematical functions to be processed. Many books, manuals, and short courses are available in the use of a spreadsheet. The reader should become familiar with the commands of the spreadsheet program.

To design an effective template, the reader will need to develop a good understanding of two items in a spreadsheet program: using menu commands and writing formulas. Among other things, menu commands allow the user to change the format of the spreadsheet so that a good presentation can be made. The formulas allow the user to perform the mathematics of the estimating process. Consult the program manual and help screens for additional information on the menu commands and formulas.

## Design of the Spreadsheet

The spreadsheet must perform all of the calculations correctly and be in a format that is easily understood. A good spreadsheet template solves problems quickly and improves the estimating process. A person using the spreadsheet template should be able to access it, understand the required input, understand the assumptions made during the calculations, and understand the output. The instruction of the template should be clear and concise. For example, the word "enter" at the top of each column that requires information is an effective method of letting the user know that input information is required.

To illustrate how a concept can be transferred into a mathematical problem and then be solved in a quick and easily understood method, a nonconstruction estimating example is used. The concept is the reconciliation of a checkbook with the monthly bank statement. File CHECK.WK1 is an example spreadsheet solution for this comparison. Figure 2.1 is the first screen that appears to the

```
            CHECKBOOK & THE BANK STATEMENT

This program is designed to allow the user to:
  1.  Enter information into a checkbook REGISTER
  2.  Enter information from the monthly bank STATEMENT

The program will provide:
  1.  The current balance in the checkbook register
  2.  Reconcile the checkbook balance with the monthly bank
      statement and indicate the difference

TO ENTER INFORMATION INTO THE REGISTER PRESS "F5" & "F3" KEYS

TO ENTER INFORMATION INTO THE STATEMENT PRESS "F5" & "F3" KEYS

TO RETURN TO THIS SCREEN PRESS THE "HOME" KEY
```

**FIGURE 2.1**
Spreadsheet CHECK.WK1.

```
Enter - DATE, CHECK #, DESCRIPTION, DEPOSIT AMOUNT, WITHDRAWAL AMOUNT
For deposits, enter any positive number in place of the check # col.
For all cleared transactions place a "Y" in the first column. If
the transaction has not cleared place an "N" in the first column.

      Enter your beginning balance here.....$1,500.00
-------------------------------------------------------------------
CLEA  DATE    CHECK # DESCRIPTION         DEPOSIT   WITHDRAW BALANCE
-------------------------------------------------------------------
 Y    JAN 5    101    Books                          325.00  $1,175.00
 N    JAN 10   102    Rent                           550.00    $625.00
 Y    JAN 12   104    Ace Drug Store                  25.00    $600.00
 Y    JAN 14   105    Max Stereo Shop                200.00    $400.00
 N    JAN 17    1     From Dad            500.00               $900.00
```

**FIGURE 2.2**
Spreadsheet CHECK.WK1 checkbook register.

user. After the instructions are read the checkbook register is brought up. The user should enter all the data that is normally entered when a check is written (see Fig. 2.2). When the bank statement is received, a "Y" is placed next to each of the checks and deposits that have cleared the bank. Place an "N" next to checks that have not cleared. The next step is to bring up the reconciliation screen and enter any service charges or interest gained (see Fig. 2.3). The program will determine whether or not the checkbook is in balance with the bank statement. If it is not, the program will calculate the credit or debit.

The preceding example illustrates a spreadsheet-related design that is simple and easily understood. The instructions are concise, the required information is clear, and the information all fits within the viewing screen. Throughout the re-

```
BANK STATEMENT                       INSTRUCTIONS "HOME" KEY
                                     STATEMENT "F5" & "F3" KEYS

Enter - INTEREST EARNED, SERVICE CHARGES,
        AND BANK STATEMENT BALANCE

Balance from Checkbook               $900.00
Interest Earned      ENTER...          $0.00
Services Charges     ENTER...       ($15.00)
CHECKBOOK TOTAL                      $915.00
------------------------------
BANK STATEMENT BALANCE   ENTER...    $965.00
Deposits not cleared                 $500.00
Withdrawals not cleared              $550.00
BANK BALANCE                         $915.00

After all outstanding deposits and checks have cleared,
The CHECKBOOK TOTAL and BANK BALANCE agree
```

**FIGURE 2.3**
Spreadsheet CHECK.WK1 reconcilation screen.

mainder of the book, example spreadsheets of construction-related activities will be given.

## COMPUTER DISK

Included in this text is a computer disk. The disk contains several spreadsheet files written for either Lotus 123 or Quattro Pro format. The subdirectory contains spreadsheet files that are blank estimating forms.

A variety of spreadsheet files are provided. They will be used throughout the remainder of the book as examples and in the exercises at the end of some of the chapters. The following is a listing of the files with a brief description of what each does. Files on the disk have a .WK1 (Lotus 123) or .WQ1 (Quattro Pro) extension.

| Filename | Description |
|---|---|
| **Root directory** | |
| EXCAVATE | Site excavation quantity takeoff |
| CHECK | Check book |
| CODE | Workspace file |
| MASONRY | Masonry quantity takeoff |
| PRICE | Pricing worksheet |
| PS | Project status report |
| QUAN | Quantity takeoff |
| RECAP | Recap sheet |
| REINF | Reinforcing quantity takeoff |
| SABA | Subcontractor alternate bid analysis |
| TIME | Time card |
| VALUE | Schedule of value calculations |
| WORK_HR | Masonry productivity |
| **Subdirectory—forms** | |
| MASON-WS | Blank masonry worksheet |
| RECAP | Blank recap worksheet |
| SOILS-WS | Blank earthwork worksheet |
| SUB_ANYL | Blank subcontractor worksheet |
| WKSHT-A | Blank worksheet A |
| WKSHT-B | Blank worksheet B |
| WKSH-SUM | Blank summary worksheet |

## DEDICATED CONSTRUCTION ESTIMATING SOFTWARE

There are a variety of estimating computer software programs available. Some simply perform the mathematics of the estimating process; others integrate the estimating operation with other functions of the construction process. No matter how sophisticated the program might be, it is imperative that the estimator understand the calculation methods and assumptions used in the program. The estimator should be properly trained and should know all assumptions before proceeding with an estimate.

The common elements of most estimating programs are the database, quantity takeoff, cost calculations, and bid total. The programs may have different formats, but all will have the basic elements.

*Database.* The database of an estimating program is used to set the estimating standards of the company. Items entered into the database will be used in the pricing of the estimate. For example, the company may have established from past projects that the time to install a hollow metal door with hinges and a passage set is two worker hours. This information is loaded in the database and used for estimating future projects. Not only is there information in the database about labor productivity, but typically the database will contain information about material cost, construction equipment costs, and standard formulas used to calculate quantities.

The database can become very large, so a numbering system must be devised. Many construction companies use the same numbering system that is used in their cost accounting system. Each construction company must develop a numbering system and items in the database to match their methods of construction. Figure 2.4 is an example database numbering format.

*Quantity takeoff.* The quantity takeoff procedure involves the selection of database codes that will be used on the project being estimated. The estimator will enter the quantities for each item selected or enter the variables that calculate the quantities. If variables are entered, formulas within the database are used to calculate the total quantity. For example, a formula used to calculate quantity of concrete in a wall footing will require that the estimataor enter the length, width, and depth of the footing. The computer will then calculate the cubic yards of concrete required.

A digitizing board connected to the computer can also be used to calculate the quantities of materials. A special pen or stylus is used to trace linear items on the drawings and count the elements.

Other technology is available that will transfer quantity information directly from computer-aided design (CAD) programs, which many architectural firms are using, to the estimating program. Paper drawings may soon become obsolete.

*Cost calculations.* The cost calculations are done by the computer after the quantities are entered. By using the database within the software, the cost for labor, material, and equipment is calculated by the computer. Figure 2.5 shows a standard estimate printout from the Timberline Software Corporation Precision Estimating program.

*Bid Total.* The bid total calculates the overhead and requires the estimator to enter the desired markup. Figure 2.6 illustrates the total bid calculations in the Timberline Software Corporation Precision Estimating program.

Your Company Name Here        Phase Report        8-28-92        Page 1

| Group Phase | Phase | Phase Desc | Unit Desc |
|---|---|---|---|
| 3000 CONCRETE | | | |
| | 3051 | Pile Cap Conc. | cuyd |
| | 3053 | Pile Cap Forms | sqft |
| | 3055 | Pile Cap Rebar | ton |
| | 3101 | Footing Concrete | cuyd |
| | 3105 | Footing Forms | sqft |
| | 3108 | Footing Steps | each |
| | 3109 | Keyway | lnft |
| | 3115 | Footing Rebar | ton |
| | 3116 | Set Grade Pins | lnft |
| | 3117 | Dowel at Footing | each |
| | 3118 | Wood Frme-Dowels | mbf |
| | 3121 | Wall Concrete | cuyd |
| | 3125 | Wall Forms | sqft |
| | 3126 | Pilaster Forms | sqft |
| | 3130 | Ledge Blockouts | sqft |
| | 3131 | Pipe Blockouts | sqft |
| | 3132 | Other Blockouts | each |
| | 3135 | Wall Rebar | ton |
| | 3136 | Gang Form Setup | sqft |
| | 3137 | Form Reglets | lnft |
| | 3138 | Form Liner | sqft |
| | 3141 | Column Concrete | cuyd |
| | 3145 | Column Forms | sqft |
| | 3150 | Column Clamps | each |
| | 3155 | Fabr Col Forms | sqft |
| | 3156 | Column Rebar | ton |
| | 3161 | Pier Concrete | cuyd |
| | 3165 | Pier Forms | sqft |
| | 3170 | Pier Rebar | ton |
| | 3181 | S.O.G. Concrete | cuyd |
| | 3188 | Wiremesh | sq |
| | 3193 | S.O.G. Rebar | ton |
| | 3194 | S.O.G. Bulkheads | lnft |
| | 3195 | Perimeter Bheads | sqft |
| | 3196 | Column Blockouts | each |
| | 3201 | Concrete @ Walks | cuyd |
| | 3207 | Bulkheads - Walks | lnft |
| | 3212 | Wiremesh - Walks | sq |
| | 3214 | Rebar - Walks | ton |
| | 3221 | Pit - Misc Concr | cuyd |
| | 3227 | Pit - Misc Forms | sqft |
| | 3235 | Pit - Misc Rebar | ton |

**FIGURE 2.4**
Timberline database. (©1992, Timberline Software Corporation)

R. L. McCoy Construction

**Estimating Standard Report**
**Timberline Headquarters**

3-15-88
3:22 pm

| TAKEOFF QTY | LABOR UNIT PRICE | LABOR AMOUNT | MATRL UNIT PRICE | MATRL AMOUNT | SUB AMOUNT | SUB NAME | EQUIP UNIT PRICE | EQUIP AMOUNT | TOTAL AMOUNT |
|---|---|---|---|---|---|---|---|---|---|
| **2.000  SITEWORK** | | | | | | | | | |
| **2.220  Excavation** | | | | | | | | | |
| **80 Excavate Footing Machine** | | | | | | | | | |
| 22.222 cy | 15.250/hr | 113 | | | | | 27.000/hr | 200 | 313 |
| 80.00 cy | 15.250/hr | 407 | | | | | 27.000/hr | 720 | 1,127 |
| 133.333 cy | 15.250/hr | 678 | | | | | 27.000/hr | 1,200 | 1,878 |
| **85 Excavation-Slab** | | | | | | | | | |
| 88.889 cy | 15.250/hr | 452 | | | | | 18.000/hr | 533 | 985 |
| 266.667 cy | 15.250/hr | 1,356 | | | | | 18.000/hr | 1,600 | 2,956 |
| 533.333 cy | 15.250/hr | 2,711 | | | | | 18.000/hr | 3,200 | 5,911 |
| **95 Backfill** | | | | | | | | | |
| 14.815 cy | 15.250/hr | 75 | 5.500/cy | 83 | | | 18.000/hr | 89 | 247 |
| 60.00 cy | 15.250/hr | 305 | 5.500/cy | 337 | | | 18.000/hr | 360 | 1,002 |
| 80.00 cy | 15.250/hr | 407 | 5.500/cy | 449 | | | 18.000/hr | 480 | 1,335 |
| Memo: Haul any extra to market street job. | | | | | | | | | |
| Excavation | | 6,503* | | 869* | | | | 8,382* | 15,754* |
| **2.230  Base Course** | | | | | | | | | |
| **130 Gravel At Slab, #6** | | | | | | | | | |
| 29.63 cy | 12.500/hr | 74 | 6.000/tn | 134 | | | 18.000/hr | 107 | 315 |
| 88.889 cy | 12.500/hr | 222 | 6.000/tn | 403 | | | 18.000/hr | 320 | 945 |
| 177.778 cy | 12.500/hr | 444 | 6.000/tn | 806 | | | 18.000/hr | 640 | 1,890 |
| Memo: Place any left over in parking lot. | | | | | | | | | |
| **310 Vapor Barrier 6 Mil Poly** | | | | | | | | | |
| 2,400.00 sf | 12.500/hr | 12 | 38.500/rl | 49 | | | | | 61 |
| 7,200.00 sf | 12.500/hr | 36 | 38.500/rl | 146 | | | | | 182 |
| 14,400.00 sf | 12.500/hr | 72 | 38.500/rl | 291 | | | | | 363 |
| Base Course | | 861* | | 1,828* | | | | 1,067* | 3,756* |
| SITEWORK | | 7,364 | | 2,697 | | | | 9,449 | 19,510 |

FIGURE 2.5
Timberline estimating printout. (©1988, Timberline Software Corporation)

```
Your Company Name Here –                    Estimating Standard Report        8-28-92              Page 3
                                               Smith Office Building            11:47 am



                ESTIMATE TOTALS


                      719,308     Labor               71,930.795 hrs
                    1,293,366     Material
                    2,350,000     Subcontractor
                      324,424     Equipment           10,814.133 hrs


        4,687,098


                       64,738     Supervisory Overhead        C         9.00000%
                      187,484     Office Overhead             C         4.00000%
                        9,879     Insurance                   T         2.00000$ /   1,000
                       19,426     Surety Bond.                B
                      179,827     Taxes & Ins on Labor        C        25.00000%
                      272,868     Profit                      T         5.30000%


        5,421,320   TOTAL ESTIMATE
```

**FIGURE 2.6**
Total bid calculations. (©1992, Timberline Software Corporation)

## STUDENT EXERCISE

**2.1.** Write a spreadsheet that will calculate your grade for a course. The spreadsheet should project what your grade will be if you make assumptions on the grades for the remainder of the required assignments and tests. It should do the calculations correctly, be presentable, and be easy to use. Entry Items:

Course, semester, instructor name

15 projects, tests, quizzes, and/or homework assignments

Variable credit for each course requirement

# CHAPTER

# 3

## OVERVIEW OF THE DETAILED ESTIMATE

The most common type of estimate is the detailed estimate. The conceptual estimates described in Chapter 1 provide the project owner and designers with an approximate cost; but the general contractor will sign a contract to construct the building based on a detailed estimate. The general contractor will quantify in detail all the work the construction company intends to perform with its own forces, price the resulting takeoff, and add the subcontractors' bids to arrive at a detailed estimate of the cost of the project. This chapter discusses the general procedures of developing a detailed estimate for a stipulated sum contract by a general contractor and specific information on the principles of detailed quantity takeoff. Chapters 4 through 12 have additional information on the specifics of the detailed estimating process.

## PURPOSE OF THE DETAILED ESTIMATE

The detailed estimate has two basic purposes: to procure work and to serve as the basis of project control. There are many ways that a construction company can procure projects. However, a detailed estimate of a project is usually central to the success of signing a project agreement and successful completion of the project. It is prepared to simulate actual construction operations, identify project resources (i.e., labor, equipment, materials, etc.), and assess the risks involved with the project.

After the contract is signed the construction company will need to develop control programs so that the project does not end up costing more than originally estimated. The detailed estimate is transformed into the budget of the job costing system of the construction company. The project progress is compared to the original budget in the job costing system to determine if the actual cost is comparable to the original estimate. The actual cost data will be placed in the company's historical data bank and used for bidding future projects.

## ORGANIZATION OF
## THE DETAILED ESTIMATE

It is important to organize the estimate so that it is complete and on time. For the competitively bid, stipulated sum contract, the estimate needs to include everything required in the contract documents plus the necessary labor, equipment, overhead, and profit to install all items.

Many general contractors will broadly organize the estimate by the Uniform Construction Index (CSI format). The general contractor will categorize all costs into these divisions. The organization of the general contractor's estimate by the 16 divisions does not always recognize the various scopes of work of subcontractors. The subcontractor's bid may include everything in a division, part of a division, or parts of several different divisions. The estimator should recognize this and must perform a thorough "subcontractor system estimate" of all divisions to make sure that all items are included in their bid to the owner.

Some general contractors refine the CSI division organization to reflect the way that subcontractors normally bid in their geographical location. For example, roofing subcontractors may or may not normally included sheet metal in their bid to the general contractor. The specifications, subcontractor normal bidding patterns, and craft jurisdictions are used to develop the general organization of the estimate. Figure 3.1 is an example of this refined organization.

## MAJOR PHASES OF DEVELOPING
## THE DETAILED ESTIMATE

Whether estimating manually or by computer, the three major phases of quantity takeoff, pricing, and recapitulation are required when developing an estimate. Each of these phases should be organized into 16 index numbers or any other format that the general contractor decides to use. The index numbers should correlate from one phase to another. For example, if index number 3 is concrete on the quantity takeoff, then number 3 should be concrete in the pricing and recapitulation (summary) phases.

The process begins with quantifying the amount of material involved in the project. This can be done by manually counting, adding dimensions, and measuring items on the drawing, or by using computer software that utilizes a digitizer or integrates to the CAD software used in the design process. Common materials are then combined (e.g., several line items of wall footing concrete) and transferred to the pricing process.

During the pricing process the estimator calculates the estimated cost for material, labor, subcontract, equipment, and other (e.g., overhead and profit) costs. See Chapter 4 for additional information on pricing. The costs are summarized by the index numbers and transferred to the recapitulation phase.

ADLER ZONE CENTER
CHAMPAIGN COUNTY, ILLINOIS

| | | | |
|---|---|---|---|
| 1. | Demolition | 22. | Metal doors & frames |
| 2. | Earthwork | 23. | Special doors |
| 3. | Paving & surfacing | 24. | Aluminum windows |
| 4. | Chain link fence | 25. | Hardware |
| 5. | Seeding | 26. | Glass & glazing |
| 6. | Concrete forms | 27. | Lath & plaster |
| 7. | Concrete reinforcing | 28. | Gypsum board |
| 8. | Concrete placement | 29. | Ceramic tile |
| 9. | Concrete finishing | 30. | Acoustical treatment |
| 10. | Masonry | 31. | Resilient tile flooring |
| 11. | Structural steel | 32. | Resilient sheet flooring |
| 12. | Steel joists | 33. | Carpet |
| 13. | Metal deck | 34. | Painting |
| 14. | Metal fabrications | 35. | Toilet partitions |
| 15. | Rough carpentry | 36. | Access flooring |
| 16. | Finish carpentry | 37. | Toilet accessories |
| 17. | Building insulation | 38. | Misc. specialties |
| 18. | PVC roofing | 39. | Food service equipment |
| 19. | Flashing & sheet metal | 40. | Laboratory equipment |
| 20. | Roof accessories | 41. | Window treatment |
| 21. | Sealants & caulking | 42. | General conditions |

**FIGURE 3.1**
Refined organization of estimate.

The recapitulation phase is a summary of the estimate by index numbers. This phase is necessary to calculate many of the overhead items (e.g., taxes, insurance, and bonds). In addition, it provides an overall view of the estimate.

## DEFINING THE WORK ITEMS

Defining the work or line items in the estimate is basic to the estimating process. The decision on the degree of breakdown is somewhat subjective, and what many call one of the *art forms* of the estimating process. The estimator should keep in mind the following general rule when doing a detailed estimate:

*If it is different, keep it separate.*

The type of material, labor productivity, and use of equipment can serve as a guide for keeping items separate in the estimate. These three items can significantly affect the cost if they are varied. The estimator should watch for changes in material, labor, and equipment; if there are changes, the estimator should make a separate line item in the estimate. For example, the material cost of concrete block will vary depending on the size of the block. If the project requires more than one block size, the estimator should keep the different sizes separate during the quantity takeoff and pricing phases. In addition, the labor productivity for block used for a foundation and block used as interior partition walls can also be substantially different. Therefore, blocks that are the same size may have to be further separated in the estimate because of differences of labor productivity.

If the estimator took literally the principle of "if it is different, keep it separate" the estimate would never be completed. The estimator's goal is precision, but in practice, only so much precision can be attained before a point of diminishing returns is reached. Figure 3.2 illustrates this. As more time is allocated to doing the estimate, the precision increases. However, an infinite amount of time would be required to obtain a perfectly precise estimate. Decisions must be made as to the degree of precision and what items to list in the estimate. The degree of precision will be learned from experience and by policies within the company's estimating department. When it is difficult to determine if more time should be spent on a particular estimated item, a quick trial estimate can be made to determine if the cost justifies a separate line item. For example, the estimator may wonder if it is worth making a separate line item for the weep holes in a masonry wall. It is determined that the cost of material and labor to make one weep hole is $.003, or $.30 per 100. This would not justify a separate line item because most projects will have relatively few weep holes. The cost of the weep holes should then be included in the productivity of the masons laying the brick.

For some materials it may appear that the items should be separated by size because of the difference in cost for various sizes. However, in the case of reinforcing bar the size does not constitute a difference in material cost, because reinforcing bar is generally bought and sold by the pound, and usually the cost

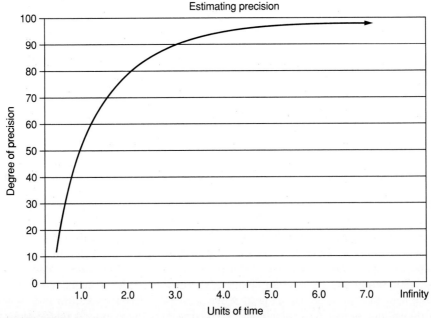

**FIGURE 3.2**
Time versus precision.

per pound is the same for different-sized bars. Therefore, the estimator will need to keep the bar sizes separate only in the takeoff phase to calculate the total weight, and then combine the bar sizes in the pricing phase. However, separate line items should be made in the pricing phase if the cost of labor to install an item is different. For example, the cost of installing reinforcing in a wall will be much more expensive than installation in a wall footing. Therefore, a separate line item in the pricing phase should be made for the wall reinforcing and footing reinforcing.

Weather can also affect the labor productivity rate. The schedule and time of year could dictate separate listing of items constructed during inclement weather.

The equipment used could require that the estimator include separate line items in the estimate to include its cost. For example, it may be practical to place half of an elevated floor slab with a crane and the other half with a pump. This would require two line items in the estimate: one for the part of the slab placed with the crane and the other for the portion of the slab placed by pumping.

Differences in labor, material, and equipment may be detected when the construction method is studied and a schedule is developed. From the project schedule the estimator may detect that two separate line items may be required in the estimate. For example, if the schedule requires two separate activities for placing the exterior 8 inch concrete block (i.e., block below grade and block above grade), the estimate should have two separate line items. The anticipated labor productivity and equipment cost will be different because of scaffolding requirements and ease of placing the block.

In addition, when the schedule is considered, a direct tie between it and the estimate can be made. The anticipated cost, worker hours, and duration can be loaded directly into the network schedule from the estimate. A direct tie can then be made between the network schedule and cost accounting system. This will help in future project cost control.

Consistency is also a key in defining the work items of the estimate. Many construction companies develop standards that should be followed in the estimating process. Many of these standards become a reality as a construction company computerizes the estimating process. Most computer programs require the company to use a coding system that transfers information to the job costing system. The list of standard cost codes gives the estimator a guideline as to the depth of the breakdown to the estimate.

## DOCUMENTATION OF THE ESTIMATE

Another general rule that the estimator should keep in mind: *Another person should be able to duplicate the work in the estimate within a reasonable amount of time*. This requires the estimate to be neat, clear, and easy to follow. Someone else should be able to pick up the estimate and quickly understand the process and confirm the calculations. For example, a job site superintendent should be able to review the estimate and confirm that column footing number B-14 from the working drawings was included in the bid.

Each line item in the estimate should have a description and location of the work. Considering the purpose of the estimate, it should contain as much useful information as is possible and practical. The description does not have to be long, but it should be explicit and definitive. The location of items should be referenced to the set of drawings. The use of column lines, direction arrows, room numbers, and detail numbers on the drawings can be used to describe the location of an estimated item. Sketches on the takeoff and pricing sheets of the estimate can also be useful in describing an item and its location. Figure 3.3 shows the use of some of these methods. The marking of a set of drawings by the estimator for the purpose of showing the location of an estimated item is *not* recommended. For example, if the prints do not have column lines and the estimator places column lines on his or her set of prints to show the location of a column, a person using a different set of prints cannot tell what is being described.

## STEPS IN THE DEVELOPMENT OF A DETAILED ESTIMATE

There are many steps required to develop a detailed estimate. Figure 3.4 is an arrow diagram showing the detail-estimating process. Many of the steps can be done concurrently to save time. The remainder of this chapter is a general discussion of these steps.

### Acquisition of the Contract Documents

When a prospective project is identified by a general contractor the bidding documents must be obtained. Normally, there is no charge to the general contractor for the documents, but a refundable deposit is often required. The deposit will be refunded after the project is bid and the documents are returned.

The bidding documents can also be reviewed at the plan rooms of various contractor organizations and service companies. Specialty contractors and material suppliers extensively use these services for estimating their work.

### Review of Documents and Project Facts

During the review of the documents the estimator should get a "feel" for the building and scope of the project. The documents should be reviewed for clarity, accuracy, and risk associated with the project. The drawings, specifications, invitation to bid, and other documents should be reviewed to determine such general items as bid date, equal employment opportunity (EEO) requirements, prevailing wage requirements, schedule requirements, alternates, contract requirements, and so on.

One method to get the feel of the building is to color code the elements of the building when reviewing the floor plans, wall sections, and elevations. For example, use red to represent brick, blue to represent concrete, and green to represent lumber. This can assist the estimator in understanding the structure of the building.

Much of the general information is then recorded on a report, an example of which is given in Figs. 3.5 through 3.8. The report form has four sections: general project facts, site visitation facts, internal facts, and external facts. After

WORKSHEET A.

| COMPUTED BY: DB | PROJECT: FAIR OAKS MALL | | | | | | | | | DATE: 4-20 |
| CHECKED BY: RL | ARCHITECT: CP ARCHITECTS | | | | | | | | | PAGE: / OF 6 |
| | | | | | | | | | | INDEX NO: |
| REF | DESCRIPTION | QUAN | LENGTH | WIDTH | HEIGHT | QUAN | UN | QUAN | UN | REMARKS |
| | | | | DIMENSIONS | | SUBTOTAL | | TOTAL | | |
| S-2 | COLUMN FOOTINGS | 5 | 7 | 4 | 3 | 240 | CF | 240 | CF | B12 TO B16 |
| S-2 | COLUMN FOOTINGS | 5 | 6 | 6 | 4 | 720 | CF | 720 | CF | B17 TO B21 |
| | | | | | | | | | | |
| | | | | | | | | | | |
| A-26 | ANCHOR BOLTS | 18 | | | | | | 18 | EA | DETAIL 7 |
| | | | | | | | | | | |
| | | | | | | | | | | |
| A-6 | CERAMIC TILE | 3 | 16 | 20 | | 960 | SF | 960 | SF | BAY 12,18,22 |
| | | | | | | | | | | |
| | | | | | | | | | | |
| A-6 | TYPE T WINDOW | 14 | | | | | | 14 | EA | COL LINE 62-68 |
| | | | | | | | | | | |
| | | | | | | | | | | |
| M2-2 | 12" DUCTWORK | 16 | 24 | | | 384 | LF | 384 | LF | ROOMS 2-18 |
| | | | | | | | | | | |
| A-13 | TYPE 2 CARPET | 7 | 30 | 12 | | 2520 | SF | 2520 | SF | CORRIDOR A-G |
| TOTAL FROM PREVIOUS PAGE: | | | | | | | | | | |
| TOTAL: | | | | | | | | | | |

**FIGURE 3.3**
Methods of describing item and location.

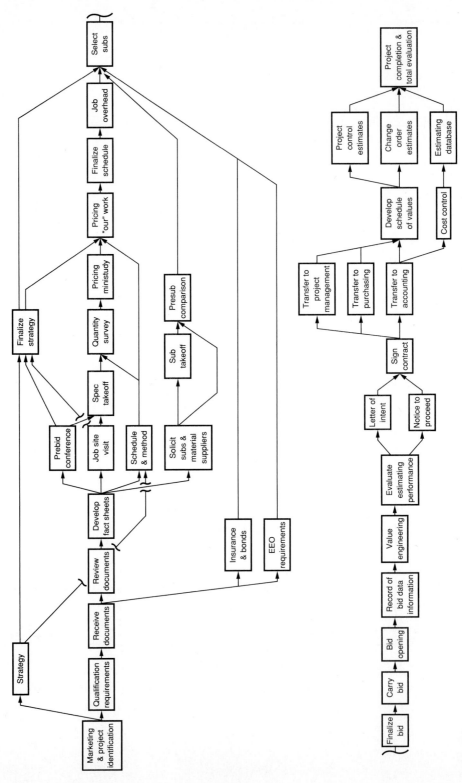

**FIGURE 3.4**
Estimating flow diagram.

52

# PROSPECTIVE PROJECT FACT SHEET

GENERAL FACTS:

PROJECT NAME: _____

ESTIMATOR: _____ BID DATE: _____

PROJECT NUMBER: _____ FACT FINDER'S NAME: _____

OWNER'S NAME: _____ OWNER'S PHONE NUMBER: _____

ARCHITECT: _____ ARCHITECT'S PHONE NUMBER:_____

BID TURN-IN LOCATION: _____ PRE-BID MEETING DATE:_____

HAS LIST OF POTENTIAL BIDDERS BEEN OBTAINED?_____ NUMBER OF POTENTIAL BIDDERS: ____

IS THIS CONTRACT OPEN BID, NEGOTIATED, OR COST-PLUS?_____

IS THIS REPEAT BUSINESS?_____

WHAT TYPE OF WORK — NEW CONSTRUCTION?_____ REMODELING?_____

   AN ADDITION TO AN EXISTING FACILITY?_____

IF REMODELING WORK, WHAT PORTIONS OF THE BUILDING WILL THE OWNER OCCUPY DURING

   CONSTRUCTION?_____

_____

WHAT ARE THE STRUCTURAL CHARACTERISTICS OF THE PROPOSED FACILITY? (TYPE OF

   STRUCTURAL FRAMING, ETC.) _____

PROPOSED SQUARE FOOTAGE: _____

SQUARE FOOTAGE OF BUILDING: _____ FOOTPRINT SIZE IN SQ FT: _____

NUMBER OF FLOORS: _____ HEIGHT OF BUILDING: _____

PERIMETER OF BUILDING — CENTER LINE: _____

WHAT ARE THE PROVISIONS FOR PAYMENT? (HOW, WHEN, WHAT IS THE SOURCE OF FINANCING,

   WHO O.K.'S PAYMENT, WHEN MUST REQUESTS FOR PAYMENT BE SUBMITTED, TO WHOM,

   FORMAT, ETC.) _____

_____

_____

WHAT ARE THE RESULTS OF THE DUN & BRADSTREET REPORT RUN ON THE OWNER? DOES THE

   OWNER HAVE THE ABILITY TO PAY? WHAT IS THE STATE OF THE OWNER'S CREDIT HISTORY?

   SYNOPSIZE THE OWNER'S FISCAL FITNESS. _____

_____

_____

WHAT DIVISIONS OF THE WORK WILL BE SUBCONTRACTED? _____

_____

**FIGURE 3.5**
General project facts.

---

## PROSPECTIVE PROJECT FACT SHEET – CONTINUED

WHAT DO WE KNOW ABOUT THE SUBCONTRACTORS THAT ARE BIDDING ON THIS PROJECT?  HAVE
WE WORKED WITH ANY OF THE SUBS BEFORE?  ARE WE FAMILIAR WITH ANY OF THE SUBS?

_____

_____

WHAT ARE THE CHANCES THAT UNFORESEEN SITE CONDITIONS MAY EXIST?  EXPLAIN.  HAVE ANY
SUCH UNFORESEEN CONDITIONS BEEN ENCOUNTERED IN THE CONSTRUCTION OF ADJACENT
FACILITIES?_____

_____

_____

WHAT IS THE PROBABILITY OF THEFT OR VANDALISM AT THE PROPOSED SITE? _____

_____

DO THE CONTRACT DOCUMENTS CONTAIN ANY EXCULPATORY CLAUSES OR ANY OTHER CONTRACT
LANGUAGE THAT INCREASES THE RISK POTENTIAL TO THE CONTRACTOR?_____

_____

IS THERE AN UNFORESEEN SITE CONDITION CLAUSE IN THE CONTRACT?_____
SUMMARIZE THE LIQUIDATED DAMAGES CLAUSE IN THE CONTRACT DOCUMENTS. _____

_____

ARE THERE ANY POTENTIAL PUBLIC RELATIONS RISKS INVOLVED WITH ACCOMPLISHING THIS
PROJECT?  EXPLAIN._____

_____

IS THE FACILITY DESIGN COMPLETE AND USEABLE?  ARE THE SPECS AND DRAWINGS ADEQUATE?
ARE THEY DETAILED?  DOES THE POTENTIAL FOR AN INORDINATE AMOUNT OF CHANGE ORDERS
EXIST?  EXPLAIN. _____

_____

IF THE PROJECT DURATION IS OVER ONE YEAR, DOES THE ESTIMATE INVOLVE HEDGING ON
CERTAIN COMMODITIES?  (FOR EXAMPLE, PETROLEUM PRODUCTS FOR EXTENSIVE HIGHWAY
CONSTRUCTION)  EXPLAIN. _____

_____

WHAT IS THE POSSIBILITY OF NEGOTIATION IF THE PROJECT BIDS ARE OVER BUDGET? _____
WHAT ARE THE SUGGESTIONS FOR A LOWER PRICE / COST SAVINGS? _____

---

**FIGURE 3.5** (*continued*)

the facts are gathered the risks should be studied and a decision made to either
bid or not bid the project. If the decision is made to bid, the project fact sheet
serves as a basis in the development of a strategic bidding plan for the project.

**PROJECT FACTS.**  The general project facts are taken from the project documents.
These facts are basic and are easily obtained (see Fig. 3.5).

**SITE VISITATION FACTS.**  The facts on the site visitation should be recorded
in the project fact report. The preliminary investigation is the confirmation of

---

# PROSPECTIVE PROJECT FACT SHEET

SITE FACTS:

PROJECT NAME: _____

ESTIMATOR: _____ BID DATE: _____

PROJECT LOCATION: _____

DESCRIBE SITE ACCESS: _____

WEATHER CONDITIONS DURING SITE VISIT: _____ DATE OF SITE VISIT: _____

CONDITION OF ACCESS ROAD SURFACES: _____

IS ALL-WEATHER ACCESS POSSIBLE? _____

IS THERE EVIDENCE OF EXISTING ROCK FORMATIONS? _____

IS THERE ADEQUATE SITE DRAINAGE? _____

IS THE SITE ON A FLOOD PLAIN? _____ ARE THERE ANY SEVERE GRADES? _____

WILL SIGNIFICANT BORROW OR HAUL BE REQUIRED? _____

WERE PHOTOS OF SITE TAKEN? _____ IF SO, ATTACH.

WHAT UTILITIES ARE AVAILABLE AT THE SITE FOR THE CONTRACTOR'S USE? _____

  (WATER, POWER, NATURAL GAS, PHONE, ETC.) _____

WHO PROVIDES THESE TEMPORARY SITE UTILITIES? _____

IF TEMPORARY SITE UTILITIES DO NOT EXIST, CAN TRUNK LINES BE TAPPED FOR TEMPORARY

  USE DURING CONSTRUCTION? _____

IS AN EROSION CONTROL PLAN REQUIRED? _____

ARE THERE ANY SIGNIFICANT EROSION PROBLEMS? (DESCRIBE) _____

ARE THERE ANY EXISTING STRUCTURES ON SITE? _____

WILL THESE REMAIN OR BE DEMOLISHED? _____

_____ SKETCH THE SITE AND ATTACH.

WHAT IS THE DISTANCE IN MILES TO THE NEAREST HOSPITAL : _____ MOTEL: _____

  BORROW PIT: _____ DUMP SITE: _____ POST OFFICE: _____ AIRPORT: _____

  TRAIN/BUS STATION: _____ EQUIPMENT SUPPLIER: _____ RETAIL AREA: _____

  BUILDING SUPPLY STORE: _____ OTHER (SPECIFY AND RECORD DISTANCE IN MILES): _____

ARE ANY TYPES OF HAZARDOUS MATERIALS PRESENT?

  (ASBESTOS, PCB'S, CHEMICAL DRUMS, ETC.) _____

WHAT TYPE OF LAY DOWN OR TEMPORARY STORAGE AREAS ARE AVAILABLE? _____

**FIGURE 3.6**
Site investigation facts.

the conditions as shown in the project documents. However, the investigation should go much further. The estimator will need to study all conditions that are not directly described in the documents but must be done in order to complete the project. Conditions such as traffic patterns in the project area, local labor situations, and other conditions (see Fig. 3.6) must be studied.

**INTERNAL FACTS.** The internal facts of the report in Fig. 3.7 describe the resources the company has available to construct the project. The estimator will need to identify any resources the company has that can significantly affect the

---

# PROSPECTIVE PROJECT FACT SHEET

INTERNAL REVIEW FACTS:

PROJECT NAME: _____

ESTIMATOR: _____ BID DATE: _____

CURRENT JOBS: _____ DOLLAR AMOUNT: $ _____ % COMPLETE: _____

                          _____             _____             _____

                          _____             _____             _____

                          _____             _____             _____

CONTRACT BONDING REQUIREMENTS: _____

AVAILABLE BONDING CAPACITY: _____

HOW WILL THIS PROJECT AFFECT OUR BUSINESS STRATEGIC PLAN? _____

_____

NAMES OF PROJECT MANAGERS AVAILABLE FOR ASSIGNMENT TO THIS JOB: _____

_____

NAMES OF SUPERINTENDENTS AVAILABLE FOR ASSIGNMENT TO THIS JOB: _____

_____

NAMES OF CRAFT FOREMEN AVAILABLE FOR ASSIGNMENT TO THIS JOB: _____

_____

DESCRIBE ANY SKILLED LABOR DEFICIENCIES OR SHORT FALLS EITHER IN-HOUSE OR
IN THE REGION FOR THE PROPOSED PROJECT: _____

_____

WHAT EQUIPMENT REQUIREMENTS EXIST FOR THIS PROJECT?  WHAT PROVISIONS
FOR LEASING, RENTING OR ALLOCATING EQUIPMENT HAVE BEEN MADE, SHOULD
THIS FIRM BE AWARDED THIS JOB? _____

_____

IS THIS PROJECT BEYOND OUR IN-HOUSE TECHNICAL RANGE OR EXPERTISE?
IF SO, EXPLAIN POTENTIAL PROBLEM AREAS: _____

_____

DO WE CURRENTLY HAVE ENOUGH WORKING CAPITAL ON HAND TO MEET
SHORT-TERM PROJECT FINANCING REQUIREMENTS? _____
IF NOT, WHAT ARRANGEMENTS HAVE BEEN MADE FOR SHORT-TERM FINANCING?

_____

WHAT WILL BE THE COST TO ESTIMATE THIS PROJECT? _____
WILL THIS FIRM BE ABLE TO BID COMPETITIVELY ON THIS PROJECT?  EXPLAIN. _____

_____

ARE THERE ANY ASSETS OF THE COMPANY WHICH MAY GIVE US AN ADVANTAGE IN
OBTAINING THIS PROJECT? _____

_____

**FIGURE 3.7**
Internal facts.

```
PROSPECTIVE PROJECT FACT SHEET


EXTERNAL REVIEW FACTS:


PROJECT NAME: _____
ESTIMATOR:_____ BID DATE:_____

WILL USE OF UNION LABOR BE REQUIRED?_____
ATTACH A COPY OF THE PREVAILING UNION WAGE RATES FOR THE AREA (EVEN IF
    UNION LABOR IS NOT REQUIRED, THE UNION WAGE RATES ARE USUALLY
    CONSIDERED THE PREVAILING WAGES BY THE GOVERNMENT WHEN ENFORCING
    THE PROVISIONS OF THE DAVIS-BACON ACT).
ARE THERE CONTRACTUAL REQUIREMENTS FOR EQUAL EMPLOYMENT OPPORTUNITY,
    MINORITY CONTRACTOR WORK, OR AFFIRMATIVE ACTION?
    EXPLAIN. _____

DESCRIBE ANY PAST RELATIONSHIPS WITH THE OWNER. _____

DESCRIBE ANY PAST RELATIONSHIPS WITH THE ARCHITECT. _____

ARE THERE ANY STRINGENT E.P.A. REQUIREMENTS?  EXPLAIN. _____

IS THERE A POSSIBILITY OF NEGOTIATION WITH THE OWNER?_____
WHAT ARE THE OWNER'S NEEDS? _____
WHAT IS THE AVAILABILITY OF SUPPLIERS AND SUBCONTRACTORS?_____

ARE THERE ANY EXTERNAL ASSETS (IN SUBCONTRACTORS) THAT WILL GIVE US AN
    ADVANTAGE IN OBTAINING THIS PROJECT?_____

LIST ANY LICENSING REQUIREMENTS: _____
LIST ANY REQUALIFICATION REQUIREMENTS: _____
```

**FIGURE 3.8**
External facts.

successful bidding and construction of the project. The estimator will also need to identify any resource that is going to be required by the project and is not directly available from the construction company.

**EXTERNAL FACTS.** The external facts listed in Fig. 3.8 are external circumstances that will affect the project. These facts can be outside the construction company's control and can be relationships that have been developed from previous projects. This part of the report may be more difficult because it will require information from a variety of sources.

When reviewing the set of construction drawings the estimator should first make sure that all pages have been included. The specifications should indicate the page numbers of the drawings.

The estimator should review the mechanical and electrical drawings, paying particular attention to how they affect the general construction and the general scope of work to be performed by the various subcontractors. This should be done even when the work is performed under separate contracts. Work may be shown on the drawings for which the general contractor is responsible. For example, concrete pads for equipment may only be shown on these drawings.

## Attending the Prebid Meeting

Many owners and architects require the bidding contractors to attend a prebid meeting. Prebid meetings are helpful to all parties concerned. However, anything that significantly changes or clarifies the project documents must be issued as an addendum. The addendum is the only way that the documents can be changed before the project is bid or the contract signed.

Any unclear or unfair clauses need to be further defined or removed from the documents. Clauses such as "as required," "as needed," and "at the discretion of the architect" affect all bidding contractors, and they need to be clarified. The prebid meeting provides a good opportunity to bring these clauses to the attention of the architect so that they can be corrected or removed.

Alternates can be confusing and may require clarification. The prebid meeting is a good opportunity for the contractors to request a clarification on the relationship of alternates. A project with two alternates that depend on each other is an example of a need for clarification. For example, alternate one is for extending the length of the building, and alternate two is for the cost of a performance and payment bond. Should the estimator assume that alternate one will be accepted to calculate the cost of alternate two? If the estimator calculates the cost of alternate two without the assumption that alternate one will be accepted and the owner then decides to accept both alternates, alternate two will not be correct, and the contractor will lose money on the cost of the bonds.

The prebid meeting is also an excellent time to start developing a bidding strategy. The person representing the construction company should carefully note other general contractors, subcontractors, and material suppliers attending the meeting. The other general contractors should be considered as the competition. The subcontractors and material suppliers should be contacted for their prices during the bidding phase. In addition, the prebid meeting can be a good opportunity to let your competitors know of unfavorable working conditions, site problems, labor disputes, and other information that may adversely affect the project.

## Deciding Whether to Develop a Bid

Someone within the company must make the decision to bid or not bid a project. The decision to bid is based on the facts gathered by the estimator, the analysis of the risk, and whether the project fits the strategic plan of the company. It should be understood that the decision to not bid the project may happen at any time during the bidding process, but rarely changes after the initial decision.

## Bidding Strategy Considerations

An estimator needs to develop a strategy for getting the project at a reasonable price. Every bidding opportunity is a game of trying to outguess and outsmart the opposition. The techniques can include better construction methods, knowledge of competitors, knowledge of the owner's needs, success on similar projects, and a history of building quality projects in a safe manner. The facts report is a key in the development of an empirical strategy for being awarded the bid. From the report, the weaknesses of your competitors and the strengths of your company should become known. Figure 3.9 is an example bidding strategy report. It lists the strengths, risk, recommended strategies, and the value of each strategy.

Statistical methods of bidding strategies have also been developed. The application of bidding procedures based on a systematic analysis of past bidding experience, however, is not common in the construction industry. However, with future developments in the use of computers, a practical statistical-based bidding strategy may be developed.

## Solicitation of Prices from Material Suppliers and Subcontractors

To obtain an accurate price for materials and subcontracts the estimator must request a price from a variety of material suppliers and subcontractors. It is advisable that at least three prices be received for each category of work. A postcard or letter should be sent to those who might be interested. It is important that they be notified early in the process so they have time to prepare a complete and accurate proposal. Computers are helpful in expediting the process. Figure 3.10 is an example of a letter sent to material suppliers.

## Developing the Construction Method, Planning, and Scheduling

The estimate should reflect the method of construction. Different construction methods dictate unique productivity rates and equipment requirements. In addition, the construction schedule indicates the duration of the project. This is useful to the estimator when calculating the cost of job overhead items such as the project superintendent, job site office, and temporary utilities. A plan of construction should be developed during the estimating process.

The theoretical development of a schedule is not an easy process because the completed estimate depends on the schedule and the activity durations depend on the estimate calculations. For this reason, the schedule is developed in steps. The first step is known as the planning process. Planning is the process of determining what activities must be performed in what sequence. After the activities have been identified, the relationships among them need to be developed. This is usually done with the network activity schedule. The next step is to assign durations to the activities. The durations are derived from the labor calculation in the estimate. After the quantity of materials required for a line item of the estimate has been determined, a production rate is assigned and the total duration can be calculated (see Chapter 4). The final step when producing a network schedule is the calculations to determine the total duration of the project. The calculations can become involved if done manually. Several computer programs have been developed to perform these calculations.

It is not usually necessary to develop the schedule in great detail before the bid. The basic schedule should be developed during the bidding process, and then

Bid strategy report

| Strategy number | Strength | Risk | Value | Recommend 1–10 (low–high) |
|---|---|---|---|---|
| 1 | Unique electrical sub bid — said they were bidding only our company | Company has been in business for one year | + $15,000 Better bid, 3% low | 3 |
| 2 | Our company has a better scaffold system | None | + $5,000 | 10 |
| 3 | | | | |

NOTES:

**FIGURE 3.9**
Bidding strategy report.

refined before construction on the project begins. However, on some complicated or time-critical projects the schedule may be very important. For those projects, a detailed schedule may be required at the same time the project is bid.

All of the details of planning and scheduling are not within the scope of this book. However, the estimator should have a good understanding of the

# REQUEST FOR PRICING

### Smith General Construction
### 100 Main Street
### Fairbury, IL 61739


TO:   Thomas Drywall, Inc.
      105 Regency Drive
      Peoria, IL 12345

                                              DATE: April 20


Estimating Dept.:

   We propose to submit a bid for the construction of:

   PEORIA HIGH SCHOOL, PEORIA, IL

Name of Owner: CITY OF PEORIA

Name of Architect or Engineer: JONES & SMITH ARCHITECTS

Date and hour for submission of our bid: MAY 15, 4:00 PM

   You are invited to submit a bid for the following work:

METAL FRAMING, GYPSUM WALLBOARD, INSULATION, CEILING TILE

   Plans and specifications covering the work are available at our office:

100 MAIN STREET, FAIRBURY, IL 61739

   We request that you have your bid in our office no later than:

MAY 14, 5:00 PM

that it be in writing, that it clearly indicate the work covered, and that

in case of alternates, each be listed together with prices therefor.


SIGNED _____          COMPANY _____


TITLE _____           ADDRESS _____


**FIGURE 3.10**
Price solicitation.

basic construction method for the project being bid, and know how to develop a construction schedule.

## Bonding and Insurance Requirements and Costs

There are many different types of insurance and bonds required for a project. Insurance policies provide coverage for a specified loss or liability. Most projects require specialty insurance beyond the usual liability insurance, property insurance, unemployment, and workers' compensation insurance.

A bond acts as an endorsement of the contractor. Under the terms of the bond, the owner is compensated for actual damages sustained from any default of the contractor. If the contractor is in breach of the contract, the surety company guarantees that the project will be completed under the contract terms for up to its face amount of the performance and payment bonds. See Chapter 1 for additional information on bonds.

The estimator will need to include the cost of the insurance and bonds in the bid. The specifications will indicate what type of insurance and bonds are required by the owner. Typically, the cost will be calculated from premium information received from the surety and insurance agents. Basic information will need to be sent to the insurance agent to determine insurance premiums and to the surety company to determine if the project is within the bonding capacity of the construction company. The insurance agent should be under strict instruction from the contractor that all insurance must be supplied in accordance with the contract documents. Information that needs to be sent to the insurance and surety agents consists of the following:

Project name and location

Owner's name

Type of building

Approximate size of project in dollars

Approximate percentage of the project that will be done with the construction company's own labor force

Number of floors to the building

Type of structural frame

Type of exterior

In addition to the cost of the insurance and bonds the estimator will need to include with the bid bond a power of attorney from the surety company. The bid bond and contract bonds seldom, if ever, originate directly from the home office of the surety company. A local representative of the national surety will represent the surety company. A power-of-attorney form should be attached to the bonds. Figure 3.11 is an example of a power-of-attorney form.

### Preparing A Specification Takeoff

The specifications are used to determine the quality of materials and should be thoroughly studied. Many errors have been made because the specifications were

# POWER OF ATTORNEY

ABC INSURANCE COMPANY OF TEXAS
GENERAL INSURANCE COMPANY OF TEXAS
ABC TOWER, DALLAS, TEXAS 79330

No. 28322

KNOW ALL BY THESE PRESENTS:

That ABC INSURANCE COMPANY OF TEXAS and GENERAL INSURANCE COMPANY OF TEXAS, each a Texas corporation, does each hereby appoint

---JOHNATHAN A. PATTERSON; THOMAS J. DOE, Greenville, South Carolina---

Its true and lawful attorney(s)-in-fact, with full authority to execute on its behalf fidelity and surety bonds or undertakings and other documents of a similar character issued in the course of its business, and to bind the respective company thereby.

IN WITNESS WHEREOF, ABC INSURANCE COMPANY OF TEXAS and GENERAL INSURANCE COMPANY OF TEXAS have each executed and attested these presents

this ___5th___ day of ___May___ , 19___.

---

## CERTIFICATE

Extract from the By-Laws of ABC INSURANCE COMPANY OF TEXAS
and of GENERAL INSURANCE COMPANY OF TEXAS:

"Article V, Section 13.--FIDELITY AND SURETY BONDS:...the President, any Vice President, the Secretary, and any Assistant Vice President appointed for that purpose by the officer in charge of surety operations, shall have authority to appoint individuals as attorneys-in-fact or order other appropriate titles with authority to execute on behalf of the company fidelity and surety bonds and other documents of similar character issued by the company in the course of its business... On any instrument making or evidencing such appointment, the signatures my be affixed by facsimile. On any instrument conferring such authority or on any bond or undertaking of the company, the seal, or a facsimile thereof, may be impressed or affixed or in any other manner reproduced; provided, however, that the seal shall not be necessary to the validity of any such instrument or undertaking."

Extract from a Resolution of the Board of Directors of ABC INSURANCE COMPANY OF TEXAS
and of GENERAL INSURANCE COMPANY OF TEXAS adopted July 28, 19--.

"On any certificate executed by the Secretary or an assistant secretary of the Company setting out,
 (i)   The provisions of Article V, Section 7 of the By-Laws, and
 (ii)  A copy of the power-of-attorney appointment, executed pursuant thereto, and
 (iii) Certifying that said power-of-attorney appointment is in full force and effect, the signature of the certifying officer may be by facsimile and the seal of the Company may be a facsimile thereof."

I, James D. Jones, Secretary of ABC INSURANCE COMPANY OF TEXAS and of GENERAL INSURANCE COMPANY OF TEXAS, do hereby certify that the foregoing extracts of the By-Laws and of a resolution of the Board of Directors of these corporations, and a Power of Attorney issued pursuant thereto, are true and correct, and that both the By-Laws, the Resolution, and the Power of Attorney are still in full force and effect.

IN WITNESS WHEREOF, I have hereunto set my hand and affixed the facsimile seal of said corporation

this ___7th___ day of ___May___ , 19___.

D.D.Jones

**FIGURE 3.11**
Power-of-attorney form.

just skimmed. The chances of making a significant error is decreased if the estimator performs a specification takeoff. Division one of the specifications, invitation to bid, advertisement for bidders, instruction to bidders, bid forms, form of owner-contractor agreement, bond forms, general conditions of the contract, supplementary general conditions, and special conditions should be studied to determine the impact on the organization of the estimate and the decision to bid the project. The detail part of the specifications, divisions 2 through 16, will give specific information about the products to be used on the project.

When performing a specification takeoff the estimator should take note of anything that is going to affect the cost of the project or organization of the estimate. The estimator will need to perform a specification takeoff before the quantity takeoff. The following are items that should be included in a specification takeoff:

1. Services to be provided by the contractor, such as field offices for the architect, telephone requirements, and temporary heating.
2. Specified names of manufacturers that are acceptable suppliers.
3. Unusual performance requirements of materials.
4. Items that can affect the organization of the estimate, such as alternates.
5. Special construction phasing requirements by the owner.

The specification takeoff should be reviewed during the pricing phase of the estimate. The estimator will need to adjust the pricing to allow for the quality and general condition items required by the specifications. Figure 3.12 is an example of a specification takeoff.

## Developing a Material Quantity Takeoff

After the specification takeoff and the preliminary construction schedule have been completed the estimator should proceed with the material quantity takeoff. A detailed material takeoff should be completed for each division of work that the general contractor expects to do. The quantity takeoff will serve as a basis for determining material, labor, and equipment prices.

If the estimating process is not computerized the material quantity takeoff step takes the most time of the estimating process. However, with the use of a computer the estimator can digitize the drawings and substantially reduce the amount of time spent in performing a quantity takeoff. The time can then be more effectively used to develop better construction methods and strategies for a successful project.

It is important that the estimator have a good knowledge of the materials and construction methods for each material that is being taken off. The estimator will need to learn the common sizes and physical characteristics of the material, the impact on labor of these characteristics, and the type of equipment necessary for installation of the material. This knowledge is only acquired with an in-depth study of the specified materials and construction methods to be utilized to install them. This will enable the estimator to make correct decisions on the level of

Specifications Takeoff

Project: Lee Hall Renovation
Architect: ABC Architects

| Reference | Item |
|---|---|
| 03300 | Cast-in-Place Concrete |
| 03300-1-12 | Codes and Standards: ACI 301 "Specs for Structural Concrete Buildings," ACI 318 "Building Code Requirements for Reinforced Concrete" |
| 03300-1-21 | Concrete Testing Service: Employ acceptable service and submit test results for concrete materials and mix designs. |
| 03300-1-24 | Quality Control: Contractor shall retain testing laboratory to perform sampling and testing during placement. Sampling ASTM C172 Slump: ASTM C143, one test for each load @ point of discharge. Air Content: ASTM C173, one for each set of compressive strength specimens. Compressive Strength: ASTM C39, one set for each 50 CY or fraction thereof of each class of concrete. 3 cylinders, 1 tested @ 7 days, 1 @ 28 days, 1 retained. |
| 03300-1-42 | Laboratory Reports: Submit 3 copies of test results to architect. |
| 03300-1-48 | Mix Proportions and Design: Comply with ACI 301. Submit written report of each proposed mix design at least 15 days prior to start of work. Any changes in mix design must be approved. Use air-entraining admixture in all concrete, providing not less than 4% nor more than 6% entrained air for concrete exposed to freezing or thawing, and from 2% to 4% for other concrete. |
| 03300-2-12 | Products |
| 03300-2-14 | Concrete Materials Portland Cement: ASTM C-150 Type 1, one brand for total project. Aggregates: ASTM C33, except local aggregates approved by architect. Air Entraining Admixture: ASTM C260 Water Reducing Admixture: ASTM C494, Type F high range water reducer. Approved by architect. |
| 03300-2-30 | Related Materials Vapor Barrier: Clear 8-mils-thick polyethylene. Membrane-Forming Curing Compound: ASTM C309, Type 1, Class B. Concrete Underlayment: High Strength, self-leveling underlayment concrete "Ardex K-15." Concrete Underlayment Primer: "Ardex P-51" Ardex, Inc. |
| 03300-2-46 | Form Materials - Sufficient stability and meet project conditions. |

**FIGURE 3.12**
Specification takeoff.

| Reference | Item |
|---|---|
| 03300-3-2 | Design Mixes:  Normal weight concrete with the following properties:  Building Foundations:  4000 PSI, W/C ratio 0.35, air entrained.  Elevated Structural Slabs:  4000 PSI, W/C ratio 0.35, air entrained.  Building Slabs on Grade:  4000 PSI, W/C ratio 0.35, air entrained.  Air entrain for exterior exposure at slab on grade for new office & tower.  Exterior Walks, Pavements, Site Improvements:  3000 PSI, W/C ratio 0.46 max, air entrained. |
| 03300-3-21 | Reinforcing Materials  Deformed Reinforcing Bars:  ASTM A615, Grade 60.  Waldad Wire Fabric:  ASTM A185 (Sheet stock only). |
| 03300-3-33 | Forming and Placing Concrete |
| 03300-3-45 | Apply form-release agents or wet forms, as requested. |
| 03300-4-5 | Locate construction joints so as not to impair strength and appearance of structure. |
| 03300-4-12 | Vapor Barrier Installation:  Lap joints min. 6" and seal joints with mastic or pressure sensitive tape. |
| 03300-4-40 | Concrete finishes  Walks and Ramps:  Light broom uniform texture. |
| 03300-5-4 | Floor Finished Surface Levelness and Flatness  Conform to F-number requirements as described in ASTM E-1155.  Slabs on Grade:  FF25/FL20 minimum overall for composite values; FF20/FL17 minimum for any individual floor section.  Unshored Elevated Slabs:  FF20 minimum for any individual floor section. |
| 03300-5-44 | Coordinate repair of existing waterproofing membrane where portions of existing balcony construction are removed and replaced and will be exposed to the elements. |

**FIGURE 3.12** (*continued*)

precision of the estimate and the anticipation of all costs. Chapters 5 through 11 describe how to estimate many of the materials that are installed by the general contractor.

## Order And Consistency of Material Quantity Takeoff

The estimator should perform the takeoff in an efficient, accurate, and orderly manner. If the estimator uses a standard procedure, the quality and accuracy of the performance will improve. After the standard procedure is developed the estimator should remain consistent and perform all building takeoffs in the same manner. The material takeoff begins after such activities as a general review of the drawings and contract documents, specification takeoff, and initial schedule development are completed.

Estimators that organize the estimate by the 16 divisions may proceed with using this as the order of the takeoff. However, most estimators start with a division that gives the largest overall view of the project and then proceed to the other divisions. This provides a faster method of becoming familiar with the overall project. The following is a suggested order of divisions to be utilized by a general contractor to develop a detailed material takeoff.

| Division | Description | Order of Takeoff |
|----------|-------------|------------------|
| 1 | General conditions | 8 |
| 2 | Sitework | 3 |
| 3 | Concrete | 1 |
| 4 | Masonry | 2 |
| 5 | Metals | 5 |
| 6 | Wood and plastics | 4 |
| 8 | Doors and windows | 6 |
| 10 | Specialties | 7 |

In addition to orderly overall organization, the estimator should strive for consistency in the procedures of the takeoff. For example:

1. Numbers should be written in a set order (i.e., height—depth—width).
2. Start in the same location of each page of the drawings and proceed in a clockwise or counterclockwise direction.
3. Check off the items on the drawings as they are taken off.
4. Consistently record dimensions on the worksheets in the decimal equivalent.
5. Do not use commas, dollar signs, or parentheses.
6. Avoid scaling the drawings.
7. Do all the takeoff, then proceed to the extension of numbers on the worksheets.
8. Choose a time period to do the takeoff that will allow for the least amount of interruptions.
9. Avoid using scratch pieces of paper by putting the information on the worksheets. All paper, including scratch paper, should be kept in the estimate file. Do not discard any paper pertaining to the estimate.
10. Checklists should be reviewed to reduce or eliminate unintentional omissions. The checklist should contain not only the material items of construction but also those procedural activities required for the construction process. Sample checklists can be found in Chapters 5 through 11.

## Unit of Measure

The estimator will need to learn the common unit of measure for each of the items included in the detailed takeoff. The unit of measure is often the same as the unit of measure in which the material is purchased. For example, concrete is purchased by the cubic yard. The estimator will need to determine the number of cubic yards of concrete in the footings, walls, floors, and so on.

For some items it may be better to use a different unit of measure than that used for ordering the material. For example, formwork for walls is often measured by the square foot of contact area (SFCA). The lumber that is used for the formwork may be ordered by size and number of pieces. However, for estimating purposes it is not practical to take off each piece of form lumber for a common concrete wall. The SFCA will allow the estimator to take off the formwork quickly. A pricing study will need to be performed and included in the company data cost bank on the cost of all the materials per square foot of contact area that make up the typical wall formwork design. The study is periodically updated when the prices of materials change or the components of the forming system substantially change.

When determining the unit of measure the estimator should consider the following:

**1.** What is the unit of measure used to buy the material?
**2.** Is the unit of measure practical in terms of the time required to perform the takeoff?
**3.** Can the field operations provide information on the quantities being installed with the unit of measure? A company cost data bank should be built to estimate future projects. The unit of measure required in the field reporting system should be easily reportable so that a reliable data bank can be built.
**4.** Is there any reason that the unit of measure for the material and the unit of measure for the labor be two different formats? With some items it may be better to use two units of measure in the estimating process: one for material quantities and one for labor quantities. For example, the placement of structural steel may be best measured in pounds for the material pricing and number of steel beams for installation pricing. The numbers can be converted from one to another, but it takes some time. Estimating software programs can convert the dual quantities easily and quickly.

Above all, the unit of measure used for estimating the quantity of an item should be that unit that most readily facilitates accurate pricing.

## Measuring Calculations

The calculations of an estimate need to be done accurately and efficiently. The estimator must have a good knowledge of basic mathematics. This includes algebra, geometry, trigonometry, conversion of numbers, and mensuration. Basic mathematics courses in high school and college cover these subjects.

The following items are issues that are peculiar to construction estimating and will provide an insight on the use of mathematics in this process.

**PRELIMINARY CALCULATIONS.** Preliminary calculations should be made on the overall size of the building. The perimeter calculation should be made at the centerline of the exterior walls. The outside dimensions of the building should be used to calculated the square footage of the footprint of the building. The total number of floors and height of the building should be calculated, and the floor square footage and exterior wall surface square footage should be calculated. All of the information should be recorded on the fact sheet. The information will be

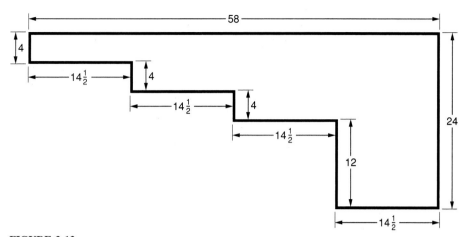

**FIGURE 3.13**
Perimeter of building number 1.

used to help make the decision on whether to bid the project, for calculating the quantities of materials, and for doing quick overall checks on the accuracy of the detailed estimate.

**PERIMETER CALCULATIONS.** The perimeter of the shape that is shown in Fig. 3.13 can be found by adding each individual length.

$$(58 + 24 + 14.5 + 12 + 14.5 + 4 + 14.5 + 4 + 14.5 + 4 = 164)$$

A much simpler method would be to add 2 times the length and 2 times the width.

$$(2 \times 58) + (2 \times 24) = 164$$

For shapes that are similar to Fig. 3.14, additional dimensions must be added.

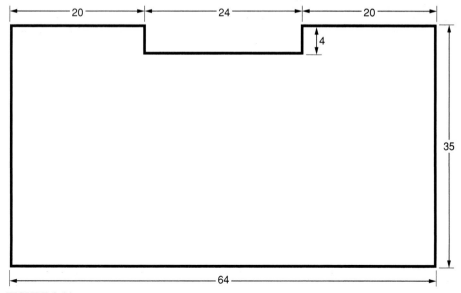

**FIGURE 3.14**
Perimeter of building number 2.

$$(2 \times 35) + (2 \times 64) + (2 \times 4) = 206$$

The centerline of the wall should be used to calculate the perimeter. If the inside dimensions are used, the material for the corners will not be included in the calculations; if the outside dimensions are used, the material for the corners would be doubled (see Fig. 3.15):

$$(2 \times 36) + (2 \times 24) = 120' \text{ Center line distance}$$

**DEDUCTIVE CALCULATIONS.** The use of deductive calculations can save a considerable amount of time and energy. The area of the wall in Fig. 3.16 can be

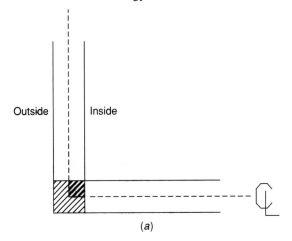

(a)

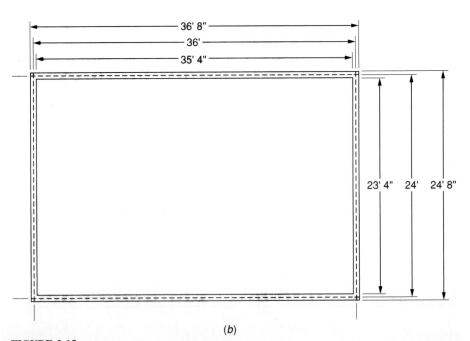

(b)

**FIGURE 3.15**
(a) Centerline at a corner; (b) centerline distance.

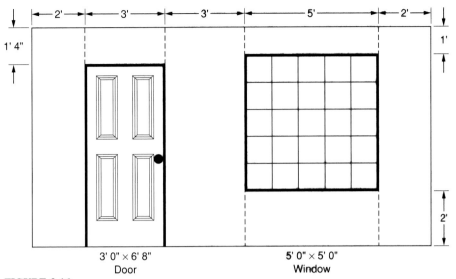

**FIGURE 3.16**
Deductive calculations.

calculated by adding together each solid element or by calculating the total wall
and then subtracting the void areas (window and door).

**CONVERSION OF NUMBERS.** The linear measurement system in the United
States is in inches, feet, yards, and so on. The units are often mixed. For example, a dimension of a wall on a set of drawings could be written 19' 4". To do the
mathematical function of addition, subtraction, multiplication, and division, the
estimator must convert the dimensions to decimal equivalents. Figure 3.17 shows
the basic conversion from inches to feet. The estimator should memorize these

| Inches | Feet |
|:---:|:---:|
| 1 | 0.083 |
| 2 | 0.167 |
| 3 | 0.250 |
| 4 | 0.333 |
| 5 | 0.417 |
| 6 | 0.500 |
| 7 | 0.583 |
| 8 | 0.667 |
| 9 | 0.750 |
| 10 | 0.833 |
| 11 | 0.917 |
| 12 | 1.000 |

**FIGURE 3.17**
Conversion table.

conversions and record only decimal equivalents in the estimate. To memorize the conversions of a fraction of an inch is relatively easy. Simply change the fraction to the nearest $\frac{1}{8}$ inch, put a decimal point and 0 in front of the numerator, and add to the decimal equivalent. To convert $5\frac{5}{8}''$ to the decimal feet equivalent:

$$0.42 + 0.05 = 0.47 \text{ feet}$$

To convert $4'\ 6\frac{3}{4}''$ to decimal feet equivalent:

$$4 + 0.5 + 0.06 = 4.56 \text{ feet}$$

When dimensions are recorded on the quantity takeoff form they should be recorded in the decimal equivalents.

**COMMON DIMENSIONS.** Figure 3.18 is a foundation plan for wall footings that are 2 feet wide by 1 foot deep and 3 feet wide by 1 foot deep. The estimator could take off the length of each wall and find the cubic yards per line item, as shown in Fig. 3.19. However, this is strongly not recommended. The chances of error have dramatically increased because of the amount of calculations required. A better method is shown in Fig. 3.20. Minimal writing and calculations are required. The total length is multiplied once by the width and once by the depth. Also, the cubic yard conversion is not done until all of the wall footings are added. This is the number that will be carried to the pricing sheet.

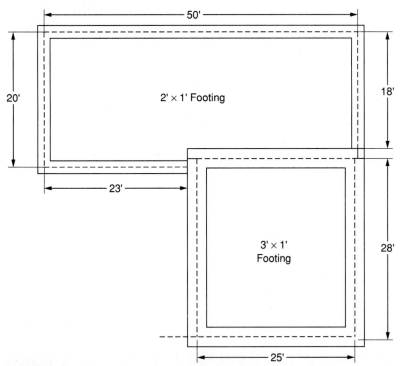

**FIGURE 3.18**
Foundation plan.

PROJECT: SMITH HOUSE
ARCHITECT: AINES

| REF | DESCRIPTION | QUAN | DIMENSIONS | | | SUBTOTAL | | TOTAL | | REMARKS |
|---|---|---|---|---|---|---|---|---|---|---|
| | | | LENGTH | WIDTH | HEIGHT | QUAN | UN | QUAN | UN | |
| | FOUNDATION WALLS | 1 | 50 | 2 | 1 | 100 | CF | 3.7 | CY | 27 CF/CY |
| | | 1 | 20 | 2 | 1 | 40 | CF | 1.5 | CY | |
| | | 1 | 18 | 2 | 1 | 36 | CF | 1.3 | CY | |
| | | 1 | 23 | 2 | 1 | 46 | CF | 1.7 | CY | |
| | | 2 | 25 | 3 | 1 | 150 | CF | 5.6 | CY | |
| | | 2 | 28 | 3 | 1 | 168 | CF | 6.2 | CY | |
| | TOTAL FROM PREVIOUS PAGE: | | | | | 0 | CF | 0 | CY | |
| | TOTAL: | | | | | 540 | CF | 20 | CY | |

**FIGURE 3.19**
Calculation not recommended.

| COMPUTED BY: | AB | PROJECT: | Smith House | | | | | | DATE: | 4.23 |
|---|---|---|---|---|---|---|---|---|---|---|
| CHECKED BY: | RL | ARCHITECT: | AINES | | | | | | PAGE: / OF / | |
| | | | | | | | | | INDEX NO: | |

| REF. | DESCRIPTION | QUAN. | LENGTH | WIDTH | HEIGHT | SUBTOTAL QUAN. | UN. | TOTAL QUAN. | UN. | REMARKS |
|---|---|---|---|---|---|---|---|---|---|---|
| | FOUNDATION WALLS | 1 | 111 | 2 | 1 | 222 | CF | | | |
| | | 1 | 106 | 3 | 1 | 318 | CF | 540 | CF | |
| | | | | | | | | 20 | CY | 27 CF /CY |

| TOTAL FROM PREVIOUS PAGE: | | | | | | | | 0 | CY | |
| TOTAL: | | | | | | | | 20 | CY | |

**FIGURE 3.20**
Recommended calculation.

If the estimate is being done on a computer the efficiency and accuracy is not diminished if each line item is converted to cubic yards. It does not take any additional time to convert each line item, and the computer will not make any math errors.

**ROUNDING OFF NUMBERS.** Careless rounding off of numbers can lead to significant errors in the estimating process. The estimator will need to make decisions when to round off numbers. In general, two digits to the right of the decimal point is considered adequate for most calculations. However, in some instances the use of three or four digits to the right of the decimal point may be necessary. When working with large numerical quantities that are going to be multiplied by a smaller number with several digits to the right of the decimal, the estimator should consider the impact of rounding off the digits. For example:

$$140,000 \times 0.0546 = 7644$$

However, if the estimator rounded off the .0546, the result would be:

$$140,000 \times .05 = 7000$$

The 7000 is off by 8.4 percent. This may be significant and can cause problems with the profitability of the project.

The estimator should keep in mind the following two principles when considering the effect of rounding off numbers.

1. Numbers should not be rounded off that are part of a multiplication or division process that will occur later in the calculations.
2. The multiplication or division of several numbers is only accurate to the number with the least significant digits. For example, the result of $192.2365/14.2 = 13.537781$ should be rounded to 13.5.

When developing the estimate with a spreadsheet program or a dedicated estimating program the question of rounding numbers does not have any significant impact. The computer can carry large decimal numbers for calculations and show only a few decimal points.

**DETERMINING ALLOWANCE FOR WASTE.** Allowances for waste should not be added at the very end of the estimate. Instead, the waste should be calculated within the estimate wherever the wastage can be anticipated.

The estimator will need to add waste to the quantity takeoff for four reasons:

1. Waste may have to be added due to the nature of the material that is being installed. For example, most materials are manufactured in standard sizes. If the project requires material different than the standard size, a wastage will need to be added. If a project requires 2 × 10 lumber 8' 1" long, then 10-foot lumber will have to be used. Since lumber is typically purchased in even foot lengths, the lumber should be taken off as 10-foot lengths instead of 8' 1".
2. Waste may have to be added because of how the material is being placed. For example, concrete that is placed for footings would require more waste than concrete placed in walls due to the unevenness of the ground on which the footings are placed.

3. Waste may have to be added due to the equipment or placing procedures being used. For example, concrete that is placed with a pump often requires additional material.

4. Waste may have to be added due to poor management procedures. Waste due to rework, poor craftsmanship, theft, errors in purchasing, and other inadequate management procedures can be costly. If this type of waste is occurring, the top management of the construction company will have to decide whether to continue to pay for mismanagement or to provide training and control programs to eliminate such waste.

In Chapters 5 through 11 the approximate amount of waste that should be added for various types of materials is discussed. These percentage amounts should be adjusted as needed.

## PRICING STUDIES

A detailed study may have to be performed to determine the unit price for an item. For example, wall formwork is often taken off in square foot of contact area, and then a unit price is applied. The unit price must be determined by adding the cost of all the items that make up the formwork system. A company standard unit price can be developed and used for all projects being bid. However, the unit price should be evaluated from time to time and updated. If the project that is currently being bid has a great deal of formwork, the estimator should reevaluate the price for accuracy for this specific project. See Chapter 6 for an example of a pricing study for wall formwork. Another example of a pricing ministudy is in Chapter 5. This illustrates cycle time calculations to determine the number of trucks required for excavating a site.

## PRICING THE QUANTITY TAKEOFF

There are five different types of cost: material, labor, equipment, subcontract, and miscellaneous (overhead, taxes, insurance, etc.). The estimator will need to determine the price for each of these items. See Chapter 4 for a detailed discussion on the pricing methods and Chapters 5 through 11 for pricing of specific items.

## SUBCONTRACTOR SYSTEM ESTIMATE AND ANALYSIS

During the bidding process the general contractor will receive many subcontractor bids. The estimator will need to perform a subcontractor system estimate and a comparative analysis. An analysis of all of the subcontractors' bids must be made to determine the low bidder, what is their scope of work, and what if anything must the general contractor add to a subcontractor's bid to make a complete bid to the owner. See Chapter 1 for more information on the subcontractor system estimate and Chapter 4 for more information on the subcontractor analysis.

## FORMS USED TO DEVELOP
## A DETAILED ESTIMATE

Each phase of the estimate should be executed on a standard format. Forms should be developed for the quantity takeoff, pricing, and recapitulation phases. Within each phase several different forms could be developed to meet the requirements of the individual circumstances. The standard format serves the purpose of consistency and to gain efficiency (and possibly more accuracy) as the estimator performs the same process over and over. In addition, the standardized forms promote communication between the firm's various estimators and the nonestimating personnel such as project manager, superintendents, and accounting.

A construction firm can either purchase standardized forms from a publishing company that specializes in them, or the company can custom design its own. With either method the forms contain standard columns and headings. It should be understood that the standardized headings are intended to be an aid and not an obstacle. Without them most estimates would be confusing. The estimator should try to use them properly. However, during the estimating process it may become necessary to make changes to or ignore the printed columns. When estimating by computer, significant changes cannot be made to the standard format unless the program is rewritten.

The following are examples of forms that can be used in each of the three estimating phases. A subdirectory called FORMS on the software disk provided with this book contains all of these standard forms. They can be used for the exercises in this book by making a printout.

The quantity takeoff sheets are used to determine the quantity of items that require calculations. It is important that the beginning estimator understand that the goal is not to fill up quantity takeoff sheets, but to get enough information from the drawings and specifications that the cost of the building can be determined. By keeping in mind "If it is different, keep it separate" and "Another person should be able to duplicate your work within a reasonable amount of time," the estimator can make the estimate clear, concise, and detailed. The quantity takeoff sheets provide a paper trail of the complicated calculations. If there is only one item or only a few items such as a flagpole, it is not necessary to list it on the quantity takeoff sheets; it should be listed directly on the pricing sheets.

A variety of different forms can be used for the takeoff. Figure 3.21, worksheet A, should be used when several calculations of width, length, and/or depth are required (e.g., concrete footing takeoff). Figure 3.22, worksheet B, should be used when a listing of like items is required (e.g., reinforcing bar or framing lumber).

Like items are totaled on the quantity takeoff sheets and then transferred as one line item onto the pricing sheet. The pricing sheets are often called summary sheets or spreadsheets. Figure 3.23 is an example of a pricing (summary) sheet.

During the pricing phase subcontractor bids may have to be analyzed. Chapter 4 has additional information on this analysis.

After all of the line items are priced on the summary sheet they are organized by division and entered as line items on the recapitulation sheet. Figure 3.24 is a recapitulation sheet. The purpose of the recapitulation sheet is to summarize

WORKSHEET -A-

| COMPUTED BY: | PROJECT: | | DATE: |
| CHECKED BY: | ARCHITECT: | | PAGE: OF |
| | | | INDEX NO: |

| REF | DESCRIPTION | QUAN. | DIMENSIONS | | | SUBTOTAL | | | TOTAL | | | REMARKS |
|---|---|---|---|---|---|---|---|---|---|---|---|---|
| | | | LENGTH | WIDTH | HEIGHT | QUAN. | UN. | | QUAN. | UN. | | |

TOTAL FROM PREVIOUS PAGE:
TOTAL:

**FIGURE 3.21**
Worksheet A.

78

WORKSHEET -B-

| COMPUTED BY: | | PROJECT: | | | | | | | | | | | | | | | | | DATE: |
| CHECKED BY: | | ARCHITECT: | | | | | | | | | | | | | | | | | PAGE: OF |
| | | | | | | | | | | | | | | | | | | | INDEX NO. |

| REF. | DESCRIPTION | SIZE: | | | SIZE: | | | SIZE: | | | SIZE: | | | SIZE: | | |
|---|---|---|---|---|---|---|---|---|---|---|---|---|---|---|---|---|
| | | NO. | LENGTH | TOTAL | NO. | LENGTH | TOTAL | NO. | LENGTH | TOTAL | NO. | LENGTH | TOTAL | NO. | LENGTH | TOTAL |
| | | | | | | | | | | | | | | | | |

| TOTALS FROM PREVIOUS PAGE: | | | | | | | | | | | | | | | | |
| TOTALS: | | | | | | | | | | | | | | | | |

**FIGURE 3.22**
Worksheet B.

SUMMARY SHEET

COMPUTED BY:  PROJECT:  DATE:
CHECKED BY:  ARCHITECT:  PAGE:  OF
INDEX NO:

| REF | DESCRIPTION | QUANTITY | | MATERIAL COST | | LABOR COST | | | | | | | EQUIPMENT COST | | | TOTAL COST |
| | | TOTAL | UN | UNIT COST | MATERIAL SUBTOTAL | DAILY PROD. OF CREW | CREW MAKE UP | MAN-HOUR PER UNIT | TOTAL MAN HOURS | TOTAL CREW HOURS | AVG WAGE RATE | LABOR SUBTOTAL | RATE PER HOUR | EQUIP. SUBTOTAL | SUB OR OTHER | |
|---|---|---|---|---|---|---|---|---|---|---|---|---|---|---|---|---|
| | | | | | | | | | | | | | | | | |
| | | | | | | | | | | | | | | | | |
| | | | | | | | | | | | | | | | | |

TOTAL FROM PREVIOUS PAGE:
TOTAL:

**FIGURE 3.23**
Pricing sheet.

| INDEX NO. | ITEM | MATERIAL | LABOR | SUBCONTR. | EQUIPMENT | TOTAL |
|---|---|---|---|---|---|---|
| | | | | | | |
| | | | | | | |
| | | | | | | |
| | | | | | | |
| | | | | | | |
| | | | | | | |
| | | | | | | |
| | | | | | | |
| | | | | | | |
| | | | | | | |
| | | | | | | |
| | | | | | | |
| | | | | | | |
| | | | | | | |
| | TOTAL PREVIOUS PAGE | | | | | |
| | SUBTOTAL | | | | | |
| | PAYROLL INSURANCE | | | | | |
| | PAYROLL TAXES | | | | | |
| | SALES TAX | | | | | |
| | ASSUMED BID | | | | | |
| | BUILDERS RISK | | | | | |
| | OWNERS PROTECTIVE | | | | | |
| | PERFORMANCE & PAYMENT BOND | | | | | |
| | GENERAL COMPREHENSIVE | | | | | |
| | TOTAL DIRECT COST | | | | | |
| | GENERAL OVERHEAD | | | | | |
| | PROFIT | | | | | |
| | TOTAL | | | | | |

Recapitulation sheet title: RECAPITULATION SHEET — COMPUTED BY: / CHECKED BY: / PROJECT: / ARCHITECT: / DATE: / PAGE: OF

**FIGURE 3.24**
Recapitulation sheet.

the prices by divisions and add the overhead, taxes, insurance, and profit. In addition, this form can be used to make last-minute changes. Chapter 4 has additional information on the use of the recapitulation form.

## ADDENDUM CONSIDERATIONS

Addenda are often issued during the bidding process that may significantly change the project requirements or clarify the contract documents. The changes, modifications, and clarifications must be in the form of a written addendum. Changes should not be made on the basis of verbal instructions. All contractors that submit a bid to the owner must acknowledge the receipt of the addenda on the bid form. Failure by the general contractor on public works projects to indicate the receipt of an addendum constitutes a nonresponsive bid, which will be rejected.

In addition the general contractor will need to make sure that all subcontractors and suppliers have seen all addenda. A system must be developed by the estimator to ensure that all addenda are forwarded to any subcontractors that have received a set of contract documents from the company.

## FINALIZING THE BID

The estimator should complete as much as possible the day before the bid is due, including all calculations, bid and bond forms, and job overhead. During the final hours before the bid is due, subcontractors and material suppliers call their individual bids to the general contractors. The estimator must do the final analysis of the subcontract bids and apply the general overhead, taxes, insurance, bonds, and fee to the bid. A final check is made and the bid is submitted.

If the estimate is done manually, last minute changes are often performed on what is known as an add/cut sheet. As changes are made they are added to or deducted from the previous bid total. Figure 3.25 is an example of an add/cut sheet.

## DELIVERY OF THE BID

The bid must be delivered to the bid receiving station before the deadline. For all public and most private projects, a late bid will not be considered. Most companies assign someone from the company to hand deliver the bid. The process can become very tense because many subcontractors and material suppliers wait as long as possible to place a bid with the general contractors. It is not unusual for general contractors to receive telephone subcontractor quotations and faxes fifteen minutes or less before their bid is due. The general contractor must analyze the subcontractor's bids and finalize the process before the bid is submitted. The bid carrier must call the home office for the final bid amount. The amount is written on the bid form and deposited at the bid receiving station.

It is important that standard procedures be developed for the process of carrying the bid, as shown in the following list.

---

```
                  Lafayette City Hall
                  Bid due May 7  2:00 PM


Total from recapitulation sheet
   (with overhead profit)              $1,231,543

1:40 PM bid from ACE Mechanical          −10,500
1:45 PM bid from Jackson Elect.           −5,000

         Total                         $1,216,043
```

**FIGURE 3.25**
Add/cut sheet.

1. A briefcase should be provided to the bid carrier with the following contents:
   a. Two extra pens
   b. One hundred dollars to be used in case of a travel emergency
   c. Extra copies of the bid form
   d. Telephone numbers
   e. Location of the bid station and bid opening time
2. Be at the bid receiving station one hour before the bid time.
3. Find the room and if possible the person who is to receive the bid.
4. Synchronize your watch with the official bid receiving clock.
5. Call the home office for any preliminary information and instructions.
6. Call the home office to receive final bid information.
7. Ten minutes before the bid is due record all information on the bid form.
8. Five to ten minutes before bid time, deliver the bid to the receiving station.
9. If telephones are scarce at the location, call the home office early and stay on the line, or carry a cellular telephone. However, conversation on a cellular phone can be heard on a radio scanner.
10. The person receiving the bid should not repeat the bid amount over the phone.
11. Initial all handwritten corrections made on the bid form. If this is not done the bid can be rejected.

## ATTENDING THE BID OPENING

After the deadline has passed the owner or architect proceeds with the opening of the bids. All bids on public projects are opened and read aloud before the public. Most bids for private projects are not read aloud to the public.

The person attending the bid opening from the construction company should take notes on all information that is made available. This information may be valuable in case the low bid for a public works project is contested on the grounds of it being a nonresponsive bid due to not recognizing addenda, not bidding alternates, submitting voluntary alternates, or qualifying the bid. In addition, the information is valuable in the internal final evaluation of the bidding procedures of the company and in future bidding strategy considerations. Figure 3.26 is an example bid tally form that is used to take notes at the bid opening.

## OVER–THE–BUDGET NEGOTIATIONS

After the bid opening the lowest qualified bidder will be contacted by the owner or the architect to begin the contract signing process. However, if the lowest bid is not within the owner's budget the low contractor, and possibly the lowest two or three general contractors, may be asked to participate in a process of negotiating for a lower price. This process is only done on projects that are funded with

S & M CONSTRUCTION COMPANY

PROJECT: LEE HALL RENOVATION
PROJECT #: 920-8749

BID TALLY SHEET

| CONTRACTOR | S & M CONST. | ACE CO. | R. L. CONST. CO. | JACKSON CONST. | AJAX CO. | BELL CO. | SMITH CO. |
|---|---|---|---|---|---|---|---|
| LICENSED | YES | YES | YES | YES | YES | YES | YES |
| BID LICENSE | YES | YES | YES | YES | YES | YES | YES |
| BID BOND W/P OF A | YES | YES | YES | YES | YES | YES | YES |
| ADDENDUM | 1 & 2 YES | 1 & 2 | 1 & 2 | 1 & 2 | 1 & 2 | 1 & 2 | 1 & 2 |
| BASE BID | $830,599 | $916,212 | $915,231 | $965,222 | $969,900 | $872,546 | $951,000 |
| ALT #1 EXHIBITION AREA | $31,317 | $31,856 | $32,589 | $42,000 | $30,800 | $29,383 | $33,218 |
| ALT #2 TIME EXTENSION | $0 | $0 | $0 | $0 | $0 | ($12,544) | $0 |
| ALT #3 EXTEND UTILITIES | $23,902 | $80,495 | $69,145 | $53,500 | $40,960 | $65,123 | $48,977 |
| ALT #4 ADD GLASS DOORS | $2,925 | $8,463 | $8,524 | $7,300 | $8,300 | $8,030 | $6,681 |

**FIGURE 3.26**
Bid tally form.

private money (sometimes known as a form of value engineering). The contractor may be asked if there are any suggestions for lowering the cost of the project. Because of design liability, the contractor should be careful and make it clear that any suggestions given will have to be designed by the architect.

## ASSESSMENT OF THE BIDDING PROCESS

After the project has been bid the estimator should evaluate the reasons for being successful or not successful in the bidding process. The bidding strategy, coordination of the estimating department, effect of project documents on the process, and subcontractor and material supply bidding procedures need to be evaluated. Figure 3.27 is an example form that can be used for the assessment of the bidding process.

PROJECT _____

BID DATE _____

ESTIMATOR _____

Review the following items after the bid is completed and note any items that can be used in future bids.

1  Names of subcontractors and material suppliers that we did not receive a bid from

2  Takeoff errors

3  Pricing of material

4  Pricing of labor productivity

5  Equipment selection and pricing

6  Evaluation of schedule and construction method

7  Profit and overhead calculations

8  Competency of the Architect

9  Evaluation of the Owner

10  Evaluation of the estimating team working relationship

**FIGURE 3.27**
Bidding process assessment form.

## TRANSFER OF ESTIMATE TO PROJECT MANAGEMENT AND ACCOUNTING

A successful bid is transferred to the project management and accounting departments. The work of the estimator will serve as the basis for the budget, cost control system, purchasing strategies, and project schedule. Management systems need to be developed to transfer all the information gained during the estimating phase to the construction phase. Chapter 12 has additional information on this transfer.

## STUDENT EXERCISES

**3.1.** Develop the organization of the estimate for the project assigned by the instructor. Keep in mind the alternates, owner requirements, and schedule requirements of the project.

**3.2.** Complete the specification takeoff of all the documents for the project assigned by the instructor. Include division 1, general conditions, special conditions, and so on.

**3.3.** Be prepared to discuss the construction methods for the project assigned by the instructor during the next class period. List your procedures on how to construct the project.

**3.4.** Complete the project fact sheet for the project assigned by the instructor.

# CHAPTER
# 4

## DEVELOPING THE COST FOR A DETAILED ESTIMATE

All information known about the proposed project is considered in determining the final price of the project. The estimator proceeds with the pricing of the estimate after the specification takeoff, quantity takeoff, bidding strategy, and the construction method have been determined. The costs are classified as either direct or indirect. Material, labor, equipment, and subcontracted costs are direct costs because they are attributable to a specific task of the project. The indirect costs are classified as other. General overhead and job overhead costs such as profit, taxes, and insurance are examples of other costs. These costs cannot be directly attributed to any specific task of the project. When the other costs are added to the cost of material, labor, equipment, and subcontract, the price of the project is determined.

The pricing sheets (summary sheets) and recapitulation sheet are used to determine the direct and indirect costs of a project. See Chapter 3 for examples of forms used in the manual calculations of the cost. Computer files PRICE.WQ1 (or PRICE.WK1) and RECAP.WQ1 (or RECAP.WK1) (Figs. 4.1 and 4.2) are examples of spreadsheet templates that can perform pricing calculations.

This chapter discusses the PRICE and RECAP files and the five types of costs: material, labor, equipment, subcontract, and other. The discussion is based on a general contractor's detailed bid for a stipulated sum contract.

PRICING SPREADSHEET

PROJECT:   ACE OFFICE BLDG.
ESTIMATOR:  ANN
LOCATION:   LAFAYETTE IND.
DATE:   MAY 7
PAGE NO. 1 OF 10

ENTER WAGES:
MECHANIC   $8.55
HELPER   $7.70
FOREMAN   $14.67

ENTER THE REQUIRED INFORMATION

| ENTER ESTIMATE INDEX NO | ENTER ITEM DESCRIPTION | ENTER TOTAL QUANT | UN | MATERIAL | | ENTER CREW MAKEUP | | |
| | | | | ENTER COST/UN | TOTAL MATERIAL $8.952 | # OF MECH | # OF HELPE | # OF FOREM |
| --- | --- | --- | --- | --- | --- | --- | --- | --- |
| 4.00 | CONCRETE FTGS | 20.00 | CY | $50.00 | $1,000 | 1.00 | 1.00 | 1.00 |
| 3.00 | CONCRETE SLAB | 120.00 | CY | $53.00 | $6,360 | 4.00 | 5.00 | |
| 4.00 | BRICK PERIMETE | 5000.00 | EA | $0.04 | $200 | 2.00 | 3.00 | |
| 8.00 | METAL DOORS | 7.00 | EA | $198.90 | $1,392 | | 2.00 | |
| 11.00 | PUMP | | | | $0 | | | |
| 9.00 | CERAMIC TILE INS | | | | $0 | | | |

**FIGURE 4.1**
Pricing spreadsheet.

## MATERIAL PRICING

The price of materials is generated in one of two ways. A lump sum or unit price will be obtained from the material suppliers. The lump sum price is an offer to supply all the materials in a category. For example, a steel supplier may offer to furnish all of the structural steel, steel joists, and roof deck for a price of $150,000. A unit price is an offer from a supplier to furnish the materials at a price per unit. For example, a ready mix concrete supplier may offer to furnish 3000 psi concrete to the project for a price of $55.00 per cubic yard. The estimator will need to take the offered unit price times the required amount of material.

The PRICE file (PRICE.WQ1 or PRICE.WK1) uses the unit price method. The user enters a price per unit, and the computer calculates the total cost of the material.

Regardless of the manner in which the supplier provides the cost, the general contractor has an obligation to furnish the required materials. For this reason the estimator will need to have completed a quantity and specification takeoff for both pricing methods. The estimator will need to confirm:

1. The required material quantity
2. The scope of the offering (has anything been omitted?)
3. That the material meets the required specifications
4. The delivery date
5. That sales taxes have been added
6. The terms and conditions of payment
7. That the material supplier has seen the addenda

The quantity and specification takeoffs have the greatest impact on the total price of the materials for a project. However, the estimator must be aware of many other factors that affect the price of materials.

| | | | | | | | | | | LINE | |
|---|---|---|---|---|---|---|---|---|---|---|---|

* If hours are not entered, the equipment hours will be calculated from labor durations.

| —ENTER ONE PRODUCTION METHOD— | | | | | —EQUIPMENT— | | | ENTER | LINE ITEM | |
| DAILY PRODUCT OF CREW | WORKER HOUR PER UN | TOTAL WORKER HOURS | UNIT PRICE | TOTAL LABOR $15,080 | ENTER RATE PER HOUR | *HOU REQUI HOURS | TOTAL EQUIP. $822 | SUBCONTR $8,000 | TOTAL DAYS | TOTAL $32,854 |
|---|---|---|---|---|---|---|---|---|---|---|
| | | 1.00 | | $10 | $12.00 | 0.000 | $4 | | 0.04 | $1,014 |
| | 1.0000 | | | $969 | $2.00 | | $27 | | 1.67 | $7,356 |
| 120.00 | | | | $13,400 | $2.00 | | $667 | | 41.67 | $14,267 |
| | | | 100.00 | $700 | $1.00 | 125.000 | $125 | | 5.68 | $2,217 |
| | | | | $0 | | | $0 | | 0.00 | $0 |
| | | | | $0 | | | $0 | $8,000 | 0.00 | $8,000 |

**FIGURE 4.1** (*continued*)

## Quantity Discounts

Usually, the larger the quantity purchased the lower the price per unit. The estimator should not assume that the price of concrete for a project that has over 1000 cubic yards is the same as the price for a project that has 35 cubic yards. Suppliers often discount the price for large orders because fixed marketing and overhead expenses can be spread over the larger quantity, they may receive a better price from their suppliers, and they may be able to use a larger and more economical carrier.

## Time

Costs are affected by time, changing markets, fluctuating supply and demand, inflation, recession, and other economic factors. The price of products can also be affected by seasonal demands and the effects of weather on production or delivery.

Timely delivery of the product is essential. The estimator should always request delivery time information from the suppliers during the bidding process. There may be an advantage to accepting a higher quoted price with an earlier delivery time.

## Delivery

The delivery of materials can be costly and is easily omitted during the estimating phase. Sometimes material quotations do not specify what transportation costs are included. This omission leads to misunderstandings and unexpected costs. The estimator must closely scrutinize all material quotations to make sure that these costs are included in the estimate. The transportation costs may be included in the materials supplier's bid, or the estimator may need to make a separate line item in the estimate. Transportation for subcontractor materials will normally be included in the subcontractor's bid.

The material supplier may indicate the material price is delivered FOB. This stands for "free on board" and identifies the location at which title for the merchandise passes from the seller to the buyer. This should be the final destination.

PROJECT: ACE OFFICE BLDG.
ESTIMATOR: JUDY
BID DATE: JAN 15

TO LOCK TITLES PRESS "ALT" L
TO UNLOCK TITLES PRESS "ALT" U

TOTAL SQUARE FOOT = 12406

| INDEX NO. | DESCRIPTION | MATERIAL | LABOR | EQUIP. | SUB. | TOTAL | % OF TDC | S/SF |
|---|---|---|---|---|---|---|---|---|
| 1 | SITE WORK | 2000 | 1000 | 5000 | | 8000 | 2% | $0.64 |
| 2 | CONCRETE | 52800 | 73000 | 2000 | | | | |
| 3 | MASONRY | | | | 47500 | 47500 | 10% | $3.83 |
| 4 | STEEL | 140000 | 37000 | 12000 | | 189000 | 39% | $15.23 |
| 5 | ELECTRICAL | | | | 87500 | 87500 | 18% | $7.05 |
| 6 | PLUMBING | | | | 23700 | 23700 | 5% | $1.91 |
| | | | | | | 0 | 0% | $0.00 |
| | | | | | | 0 | 0% | $0.00 |
| | | | | | | 0 | 0% | $0.00 |
| | | | | | | 0 | 0% | $0.00 |
| | | | | | | 0 | 0% | $0.00 |
| | | | | | | 0 | 0% | $0.00 |
| | | | | | | 0 | 0% | $0.00 |
| | | | | | | 0 | 0% | $0.00 |
| | | | | | | 0 | 0% | $0.00 |
| | | | | | | 0 | 0% | $0.00 |
| | | | | | | 0 | 0% | $0.00 |
| | | | | | | 0 | 0% | $0.00 |
| | | | | | | 0 | 0% | $0.00 |

| | GENERAL CONDITIONS | | | | | | | |
|---|---|---|---|---|---|---|---|---|
| | JOB DURATION IN CAL. DAYS | 365 | | | | | | |
| | SUPT. SALARY @ RATE/HR | $15.00 | 31286 | | | 31286 | | |
| | FULL OR PART TIME | 100.00% | | | | 0 | | |
| | TRAVEL EXPENSES MILES/DAY | 60 | | 3911 | | 3911 | | |
| | FIELD OFFICE @ RATE/WK | $75.00 | | 3911 | | 3911 | | |
| | FULL OR PART TIME | 100.00% | | | | 0 | | |
| | WEEKLY CLEAN-UP NO. HR/WK | 10 | 5214 | | | 5214 | | |
| | WAGE FOR ONE LABOR/HR | $10.00 | | | | 0 | | |
| | FINAL CLEAN-UP TOTAL HOURS | 40 | 400 | | | 400 | | |
| | WAGE FOR ONE LABOR/HR | $10.00 | | | | 0 | | |
| | TOILET @ RATE/WEEK | $35.00 | | | 1825 | 1825 | | |
| | TEMP. ELECT. @ RATE/WEEK | $50.00 | | | 2607 | 2607 | | |
| | TEMP. HEAT @ RATE/MONTH | $300.00 | | | 14600 | 14600 | | |
| | NUMBER OF MONTHS | 4 | | | | 0 | | |
| | DUMPSTER @ RATE/WEEK | $120.00 | | | 5006 | 5006 | | |
| | FULL OR PART TIME | 80.00% | | | | 0 | | |
| | RUBBISH REMOVAL LUMP SUM | $1,250.00 | | | 1250 | 1250 | | |
| | MATL. PROTECTION LUMP SUM | $500.00 | | | 500 | 500 | | |
| | SAFETY EQUIPMENT LUMP SUM | $500.00 | | | 500 | 500 | | |
| | PHOTOGRAPHS LUMP SUM | $400.00 | | | 400 | 400 | | |
| | BUILDING PERMIT LUMP SUM | $800.00 | | | 800 | 800 | | |
| | DUST PARTITIONS LUMP SUM | $850.00 | | | 850 | 850 | | |
| | GUARDRAILS LUMP SUM | $900.00 | | | 900 | 900 | | |
| | SMALL TOOLS @ RATE/WEEK | $50.00 | | | 2607 | 2607 | | |
| | FIRE PROTECTION LUMP SUM | $350.00 | | | 350 | 350 | | |
| | PUNCH LIST LUMP SUM | $500.00 | | | 500 | 500 | | |
| | TOTAL GENERAL CONDITIONS | $77,416 | | | | | 15.9% | |

| | SUBTOTALS | | $194,800 | $147,900 | $59,516 | $158,700 | $433,116 | |
|---|---|---|---|---|---|---|---|---|
| | TAXES | | | | | | 10649 | |
| | PAYROLL INSURANCE | 7.20% | | | | | 20706 | |
| | PAYROLL TAXES | 14.00% | | | | | 13656 | |
| | SALES TAX | 7.00% | | | | | | |
| | BONDS AND INSURANCE | | | | | | | |
| | BUILDERS RISK PER | $0.50 | $100 | | | | 2886 | |
| | OWNERS PROTECTIVE PER | $0.27 | $100 | | | | 1559 | |
| | PERFORMANCE BOND PER | $7.50 | $1,000 | | | | 4331 | |
| | GENERAL COMPREHENSIVE PER | $1.75 | $1,000 | | | | 1011 | |
| | ASSOCIATION FEES | 0.02% | | | | | 116 | |
| | TOTAL DIRECT COST | | | | | | 468012 | |
| | GENERAL OVERHEAD | 8.50% | | | | | 49090 | |
| | PROFIT | 7.00% | | TOTAL BID | | | 40427 | |
| | | | | | | | $677,529 | |

**FIGURE 4.2**
Recap spreadsheet.

If the material is quoted as "FOB-factory," the estimator will need to include the cost of freight charges to the project site or warehouse.

## Handling

After the material is delivered to the job site it must be unloaded. Some material suppliers (such as concrete block suppliers) deliver the products on trucks that are equipped to unload the material. However, many other materials such as structural steel, hollow metal doors, and wood case work must be unloaded and properly stored. Labor and sometimes equipment such as cranes or forklifts are required to unload the material. The labor cost and equipment cost must be included in the estimate.

Subcontractors should make it clear if their bid is made on the assumption that another's material handling equipment is to be used. Proper mutual agreements about any related charges should be understood during the estimating phase.

## Storage

Any costs for storage should be anticipated by reviewing the project schedule. The storage of materials can lead to their loss due to theft, mishandling, or a short shelf life (e.g., special chemicals used on floors). Storage can be expensive and may require special temperature- or humidity-controlled buildings. Other materials may not have to be stored indoors but must be protected from rain. The anticipated cost associated with material storage, insurance, and security should be included in the project material estimate or the job overhead. During the actual construction process the material purchasing and delivery should be coordinated with the project schedule to minimize the storage of materials.

## Terms of Payments and Discounts

The material price is affected by discounts and the required term of payment. Material prices are often quoted as list prices less a percentage (for example, list price less 10 percent). If the product normally is priced at $1000 the quoted price for list less 10 percent would be $900. The estimator should use these discounted prices in the estimate.

The payment terms can also affect the material price. For example, the material supplier may give a 5 percent discount if the material is paid for within fifteen days. These term payment discounts are usually not considered in the estimating phase. It is a function of the cash flow of the construction company. During construction the accounting department should determine if it is prudent to make the early payment to receive the discount.

## The Buyer and Supplier

The creditability of the buyer and the past performance of the supplier can also affect the pricing of materials. If a company has a reputation of not paying bills on time, bid shopping, and other unethical practices, it will likely not receive the lowest price from suppliers. Suppliers often give a better price to companies that they know will treat them fairly.

On the other hand, if a supplier has a poor reputation of delivery, quality control, and not supplying the specified materials, the contractor may not use their bid. It may be less costly to use a supplier whose initial price is higher but who can perform according to the contract requirements. The estimator or other designated individual in the company should develop a list of suppliers and subcontractors who they know, based on past experience and current financial condition, are able to fulfill their responsibilities in accordance with contract provisions.

## Allowance

It is not uncommon for the architect to include a fixed sum in the contract documents for such items as finish hardware, face brick, or electric light fixtures to cover the cost of the material or item of work. The general contractor is to include the allowance in the bid. The allowance establishes an approximate material cost for bidding purposes when the designer has not fully prepared a detailed material specification. In addition to the material allowance, the contractor must include all other costs associated with the item, such as installation, material handling, temporary storage, overhead, and profit. This can cause problems when the estimator develops the cost of installation because the quantity or type of material is not known.

Occasionally, it may be logical for the subcontractor to include the allowance in the bid, such as an electrical fixture allowance in the electrical subcontractor bid. The estimator should make sure that the subcontractor has the material allowance in the bid and not double cover the allowance.

After the contract is let, a final material choice is made. If the material cost is more than the allowance, the contractor's contract will be increased appropriately; if it is under the contract amount, it will be reduced.

## Taxes

Material sales taxes must be paid in the geographical area in which the project is being built. State, city, and/or other local sales taxes may be required. The estimator should contact local authorities to determine if there are any material sales taxes. If the material suppliers have not added the sales tax, the estimator will need to add it in their quotation during the material pricing phase of the estimate. Subcontractors should include the material sales tax in their bid to the general contractor. The estimator should always make sure the subcontractor has done this.

## Government Regulations

The estimator should be aware of government regulations concerning materials. For example, on federal government projects the Buy American Act may require that the contractors purchase materials that were manufactured or produced in the United States. State and local governments may have similar requirements.

The estimator also should not forget government safety laws such as those contained in OSHA and EPA regulations. These regulations specify minimum safety requirements that affect project costs, such as providing perimeter guarding for elevated floor slabs. To prevent accidents, the contractor may desire to utilize accident prevention techniques greater than those specified by the regulatory agencies. The cost of these need to be included in the estimate.

## Owner Supplied Material

It is not unusual for the owner to supply certain materials for the project. For example, the owner may purchase long lead items (materials that take a relatively long time to obtain). The material price for items supplied by the owner is not included in the estimate. However, all other costs associated with the materials for which the general contractor may be responsible, such as delivery, unloading, storage, and installation, must be included.

## Material Pricing Checklist

Figure 4.3 is a checklist that the estimator should use during the pricing phase of the estimate. The general checklist should be reviewed when pricing any material. Specific checklists are provided in later chapters of this book.

## LABOR PRICING

Labor costs are difficult to anticipate and cannot be determined with the same degree of precision as can most other elements of the construction estimate. The estimated price for labor is derived from the quantity of material, anticipated productivity, and the labor wage rates. The quantity of material and wage rates are relatively easy to determine. However, the anticipated production rate is much more difficult to develop.

## Quantity Takeoff Considerations

The quantity of material used in labor pricing is determined during the quantity takeoff phase. The unit of measure is usually the same as that used for the material pricing. However, for some materials it may be advantageous to have a different unit of measure for the material price and the labor price. For example, the unit of measure for reinforcing wire mesh could be in rolls to price material and square foot for labor production. The estimator will need to learn the most appropriate unit of measure for each of the materials that are taken off.

## Wage Rates

The amount that is paid directly to the individual for employment is the wage rate. Indirect costs are also paid by the company on behalf of the employee. These are fringe benefits paid according to wage agreements and statutory requirements. The indirect labor costs are usually calculated in the overhead and profit calculations phase of the estimate. However, some estimating software calculates the indirect cost at the labor calculation phase. Wage rates vary with geographical location. The estimator must determine the local wage rates before calculating the labor price. In addition, the wages may fluctuate from one year to the next.

On some government projects a prevailing wage rate may be required. The Davis-Bacon Act is a federal law that stipulates wage rates that must be paid

|  | Yes | No |  |
|---|---|---|---|
| 1. | ____ | ____ | Is the material per plans and specifications? |
| 2. | Manufacturer of the material (brand name). | | |
|  | _____ | | |
| 3. | ____ | ____ | Delivery included? |
| 4. | ____ | ____ | Taxes included? |
| 5. | ____ | ____ | Shop drawings included? |
| 6. | ____ | ____ | Unloading included? |
| 7. | ____ | ____ | Does the supplier meet any minority requirement? |
| 8. | ____ | ____ | Are there any special storage requirements? _____ |
|  | _____ | | |
| 9. | What are the payment requirements? _____ | | |
|  | _____ | | |
| 10. | What is the expected delivery date? _____ | | |

**FIGURE 4.3**
Material pricing checklist.

workers on federal construction projects. The law states that the wages of workers shall not be less than the wage rates specified in the schedule of prevailing wages as determined by the Secretary of Labor for comparable work on similar projects in the vicinity in which the work is to be performed. The estimator will need to determine from the specifications if the proposed project is covered by the Davis-Bacon Act. In addition, some states have their own prevailing wage laws.

## Productivity

The production rate is basic to the determination of the labor cost. It asks the question, "How many worker hours are required to complete each item of work?" The variables that affect productivity are innumerable. However, the estimator will need to determine optimum crew size and anticipated productivity. When making these decisions the estimator should consider the following information about the activity:

Project schedule
Anticipated weather conditions
Working conditions
Project variations from company historical production data standards
Equipment usage
The effect of the learning curve

Productivity rates should be available from company historical data of previously constructed projects. If the data is not available the estimator will need to consult others in the company and do an in-depth study of all of the tasks related to the installation of the material.

Productivity can be expressed in several different formats. The estimator can define the required labor in terms of worker hours per unit or crew hours per unit; number of units per worker hour or crew hour; unit price; or the estimator may choose to express the labor productivity in total worker hours, crew hours, or total price.

## Worker Hours per Unit and Crew Hours per Unit

The average worker hours per unit is the basic form of a productivity expression. The worker hours per unit or crew hours per unit can be expressed as a number, such as 3 worker hours to hang one door, or it can be expressed in terms of number of units per worker hour or crew hour. For example, a crew can install 200 square feet of roof sheathing per hour. The calculations require the most mathematics during the labor pricing phase, but they offer the estimator the most information.

The average worker hours per unit is the lowest form of productivity calculation. It is equal to the number of workers in the crew times the number of hours in a day divided by the number of units that the crew can install in one day. For example, 5 iron workers can install 10 tons of structural steel in one day. The worker hours per unit is (5 workers × 8 hours)/10 tons = 4 worker hours per ton.

In another example, the average worker hours per unit in which the masons' productivity is 550 bricks per day per mason for 5 masons and 3 laborers working 8 hours is (8 people × 8 hours)/(5 masons × 550 units) = 0.0233 average worker hours per brick. Note that the production rate of the individual is multiplied by the number of productive people (masons). This will give the production rate of the crew. The 0.0233 is the number of hours it takes one person to lay one brick. In this example the crew is a mix of masons and laborers, so the worker hours per unit is an average production rate of the crew.

After the worker hours per unit is calculated the total worker hours and price can be determined. By multiplying the worker hours per unit by the estimated quantity of material the estimator can determine the total number of worker hours.

The worker hours multiplied by the average wage rate will result in the direct cost of labor. From the previous examples:

1. 4 worker hours per ton × 35 tons of structural steel × $18.00 per hour wage rate = $2520. This is the total labor price for installing the 35 tons of structural steel.
2. 0.0233 worker hours per brick × 3,000 bricks × $15.00 per hour average wage rate = $1048.50 total labor price for installing 3000 bricks.

The total number of crew hours can be calculated by dividing the total worker hours by the number of people in the crew. For example:

1. 4 worker hours per ton × 35 tons/5 people in the crew = 28 total crew hours.
2. 0.0233 worker hours per brick × 3,000 bricks/8 people in the crew = 8.7 total crew hours.

The duration of the activity can be determined by dividing the total crew hours by the number of hours worked in a day (i.e., 28 crew hours/8 hours in a day = 3.5 days to install the structural steel, and 8.7 crew hours/8 hours in a day = approximately one day for laying the bricks).

## Unit Price

Pricing the estimated labor by the unit price method is easy and quick. It is preferred by most estimators who are not using a computer to perform the calculations. However, this method can be one of the least accurate if the unit prices are not periodically updated and adjusted to reflect the actual levels of worker production and current wage rates. The development of the unit price is calculated from the same data that is used in the worker hours per unit or crew hours per unit calculations. For example, the unit price for the previous steel and masonry examples are:

1. 4 worker hours per ton × $18.00 per hour = $72 per ton.
2. 0.0233 worker hours per brick × $15.00 per hour = $0.35 per brick. The unit prices are then stored in the company data bank and used as needed.

For a specific project the total labor price is calculated by multiplying the total quantity by the unit price. For example:

1. $72 per ton × 20 tons of material = $1,440.
2. $0.35 per brick × 5,000 bricks = $1,750.

## Total Worker Hours, Crew Hours, or Total Price

For small quantity items the estimator may want to indicate the total worker hours, crew hours, or total price. This method is quick and allows for a great deal of flexibility. However, for large quantities it is recommended that a more in-depth method, such as the worker hours per unit, be used.

The PRICE file (PRICE.WQ1 or PRICE.WK1) allows the user to price the labor by productivity of the crew, worker hour per unit, total worker hours, or unit price. After the wage rates and number of people in the crew are entered the computer will calculate the total cost of labor and the number of days required for the line item.

## EQUIPMENT COST

Costs of equipment used during construction, like labor costs, are difficult to evaluate with any exactness. Equipment costs for civil projects, such as roads and dams, can be substantial, but less significant for building projects. The equipment used on building construction projects are classified as heavy construction equipment, small equipment for a specific task, and job overhead tools.

### Heavy Construction Equipment

The calculations for the cost of heavy construction equipment may take a very specialized and in-depth study of the needs and production capabilities. This may require one or several lines in the pricing sheets to do the calculations. This section includes a discussion of the major factors that affect the determination of the costs of heavy construction equipment.

Estimating the cost of heavy construction equipment is similar to that of labor. The estimator will need to determine what equipment is required and how long it will be needed. In some cases, the equipment will be used for a while, then not used, then needed again. In this case the estimator needs to determine what will be done with it when it is not needed. Will it be sent to another project? Will it be stored on site? If rented, will it be returned to the rental agency?

Most equipment costs are calculated by knowing the production rate of each piece, how long it will be operating, and the hourly cost. Construction companies establish their own hourly equipment costs and production rates, which serve as the historical database.

Construction equipment is either owned by the construction company or rented from another party. In either case, the estimator needs to determine or be provided with the cost of the equipment over a specific time period. If the company has its own equipment, the ownership costs include original equipment cost, maintenance, and investment. The original cost includes all related costs such as sales tax and freight.

Depreciation, which arises out of the use of the equipment, is usually the largest single ownership-related cost. There are many methods of calculating depreciation, with each one giving a different result. As part of the United States Federal Income Tax Code, allowable depreciation methods and periods have been provided. The accounting personnel need to be aware of this information when calculating an annual depreciation rate to be used to determine the ownership costs. It is beyond the scope of this book to present a detailed description of the various depreciation methods.

Maintenance includes major repairs and replacement of parts. The costs of these activities varies with the type of equipment and work to be performed.

These costs are usually noted as a proportion of the annual depreciation because of the relationship between the costs and the working life of the equipment. The accounting department will monitor and track the actual maintenance costs and derive the correct percentage of the depreciation to include in the overall ownership costs.

Investment costs arise from making the investment to purchase and own the equipment. These costs include interest on investment, insurance, taxes, and storage and are usually based on the average annual value of the equipment. Interest on investment may either be interest paid by the construction company to purchase the equipment or, if the equipment is bought for cash, the interest that would have been received if the cash had been invested (including an allowance for inflation).

Insurance is needed to protect the owner against loss. The premiums depend on the type and size of equipment. The insurance company will provide this information. The amount of taxes to include in the ownership costs varies according to the location and regulations of the existing governing bodies. Finally, storage costs include the use of land and any buildings used to store the equipment. As for the other ownership costs, the accounting department will derive them. Operating costs are computed on the basis of the construction company's own experience and consist of items related to the use of the equipment, including fuel, oil, tires, and minor repairs. Equipment manufacturers and vendors provide assistance to construction companies to estimate these costs for the type of equipment and project conditions. The company should, however, track the actual costs so as to use them as historical data for future similar projects.

If the contractor does not have the needed equipment, it can be rented or leased from an outside agency. Renting and leasing are similar, but leasing is usually for a longer period. Whether the equipment is rented or leased, the estimator must consider such factors as available rental agencies for the type and condition of equipment needed, costs, services the agency provides, and what the rental (leasing) agreement includes, especially concerning maintenance and repairs and any minimum on the amount of time for which the contractor will be charged, such as a week or month. These conditions can have a major impact on the estimate.

The rates to rent equipment are usually quoted by the day, week, or month. These costs are usually broken down into costs per hour or unit of work so that they can be included in the estimate.

As previously noted, the major variables that the estimator needs to know to estimate the total cost of the major heavy equipment are as follows:

1. Total amount of work to be performed
2. Hourly cost to own and operate or rent (lease) the equipment
3. Production rate of the equipment

The total amount of work to be performed is obtained from the quantity takeoff. For instance, a quantity takeoff for soil to be removed for the construction of a retaining wall is found to be 320 cubic yards. Relative to the second item, the hourly cost to own and operate one's own equipment is obtained from company records. If the equipment is to be rented or leased, the cost is obtained from the rental agency.

Finally, the hourly production rate is either provided to the estimator or must be determined. The rate depends on many factors:

1. Type and size of equipment
2. Efficiency of equipment
3. Job site conditions (i.e., soil type, weather)
4. Management conditions
5. Type of job to be performed
6. Experience of operator

Since no two jobs are alike, the production rate for any one specific piece of equipment will differ as jobs change. In all cases, the rate of production will be expressed in units moved per a specific time period (usually an hour). For example, a certain size bulldozer may move 200 cubic yards per hour on one project; on another project; however, the same bulldozer may only be able to move 180 cubic yards per hour. It is necessary for the estimator to use an average production rate and then adjust it for the specific job conditions.

To evaluate production rates for a specific project, the estimator will need to know the cycle time for the specific piece of equipment being used. The cycle time is the total amount of time it takes the equipment to complete one cycle of work. For all types of equipment, this time is comprised of a series of times for individual operations. For instance, in the case of hauling earth, a dump truck's cycle time is obtained by summing the individual time to load the truck, transport the soil, dump the material, return the empty truck, and spot it so it is ready to receive the next load. In the case of a crane the cycle time consists of the time to prepare and pick the load, swing the boom, place and unload, and swing back to obtain the next load of material. Every different type of equipment has its own unique cycle time components.

Since job site and management conditions differ for each project and even for similar activities on the same project, cycle times for each piece of equipment have to be estimated based on the conditions connected with the activity in which the equipment is involved. To derive the most accurate time, the estimator should consult with people who have experience in operating and supervising the use of the equipment. These may be in-house personnel or professionals outside the company. In addition, the company's equipment-related historical records may be useful in this task. It is beyond the scope of this book to present an in-depth discussion on obtaining cycle times for various types of equipment.

Besides possibly needing to know cycle times, the estimator will also have to determine the amount of material that can be moved in one cycle. This information depends on the size and efficiency of equipment and the job site and management conditions, including the skill and experience of the operator. The size of the equipment is obtained from the vendor, leasing or rental agency, or company records. This is usually an ideal production rate per cycle and must be adjusted for specific project conditions. For example, a power shovel having a 3.5 cubic yard bucket can ideally move 3.5 cubic yards of material in each cycle. However, if adverse soil conditions are encountered, such as hard, clayey soil, this rate will be reduced. The same may be true for other reasons, such as using poorly maintained equipment, having an inexperienced operator, or operating in an area small enough to result in movement restrictions. The exact reduction of efficiency is site-specific and will have to be determined by those who have experience in the use of the equipment.

Once the cost per hour, the hourly production rate, and the total amount of material to be moved is known, the estimator can derive the total cost of the equipment. Examples of earthwork-related activities are shown below to illustrate the many variables that affect the cost to perform the noted activities. The noted processes also can be applied to other types of equipment.

The estimator should not forget to include the costs associated with moving the equipment to and from the job site and the erection and dismantling of it. This is sometimes referred to as the cost of mobilization and demobilization. The actual costs of these activities depend on many factors, including type of equipment, location and size of job, and company policy relating to equipment allocation costs.

## Examples of Earthwork-Related Activities

*Excavation with backhoe.* The quantity takeoff for the footing excavation was determined to be 300 cy. A specific size backhoe was selected to perform the excavating activity. The cost of the backhoe is $60.00 per hour. Based on the job site and management conditions and the size of the backhoe's bucket, the hourly production rate was estimated to be 10 cy per hour.

The total direct cost to excavate is therefore

$$300 \text{ cy}/10 \text{ cy per hr} \times \$60.00 \text{ per hr} = \$1800.00$$

$$\text{or} \quad \$1800/300 \text{ cy} = \$6.00 \text{ per cy}$$

The following example illustrates how to determine the cost of a single piece of equipment working alone.

*Moving earth with a bulldozer.* On a specific earthmoving job, it was decided because of the type of job and short hauling distance to use a bulldozer. The quantity takeoff resulted in an estimate of 10,000 cy of soil to be moved.

The hourly production of the dozer is determined to be 105 cy/hr. Both the takeoff and production capacity are in terms of bank measure. The equipment cost is $50.00 per hour. The time it will take to move the soil based on the given information is

$$10,000 \text{ cy}/105 \text{ cy per hr} = 95.23 \text{ hours}$$

which will be rounded up to 96 hours. The total cost will then be

$$96 \text{ hrs} \times \$50.00 \text{ per hr} = \$4800.00 \quad \text{or} \quad \$4800/10,000 \text{ cy} = \$0.48 \text{ per cy}$$

The next example is a more detailed illustration of determining the cost of equipment.

*Moving earth with a scraper.* Thirty-six thousand cubic yards of fill are needed. A borrow site was located and is two miles from the job site. Five 30 cy loose measure scrapers will be used to obtain and spread the soil.

Based on job site conditions, the average speed of an empty scraper is 30 mph, and when loaded, 10 mph. The hourly cost of the scraper is $120.00. The fixed time (which is part of the total cycle time apart from travel time) is 3.0 minutes and the swell factor is 0.75 (information about the swell factor can be found in Chapter 5). The efficiency of the scraper is 85%.

The first step is to determine the total time it takes for one scraper to complete one cycle. The travel time when empty is

$$\frac{2 \text{ miles} \times 60 \text{ min per hr}}{30 \text{ mph}} = 4 \text{ min}$$

The travel time when loaded is

$$\frac{2 \text{ miles} \times 60 \text{ min per hr}}{10 \text{ mph}} = 12 \text{ min}$$

$$\text{Total travel time} = 16 \text{ min}$$

Total cycle time:

| | |
|---|---|
| Fixed time | 3.00 min |
| Travel time | 16.00 min |
| Total time | 19.00 min |

The number of trips per hour based on an 85% efficiency is

$$\frac{60 \times 0.85}{19 \text{ min/cycle}} = 2.68 \text{ trips per hour}$$

The hourly output for the fleet of five scrapers is

2.68 trips/hr × 30 cy/scraper × 5 scrapers = 402 cy/hr loose measure

or

$$402 \text{ cy/hr} \times 0.75 = 301.5 \text{ cy/hr bank measure}$$

The total time to move the 36,000 cy of earth is

$$\frac{36,000 \text{ cy}}{301.5 \text{ cy/hr}} = 119.41 \text{ or } 120 \text{ hours}$$

The total cost for the equipment will be

$$120 \text{ hrs} \times \$120.00 \text{ per hr} \times 5 \text{ scrapers} = \$72,000$$

There are many instances on a construction site when different types of equipment must work together. Examples include bulldozers pushing scrapers, shovels loading trucks, and concrete ready mix trucks loading pumping units. In these cases the production of one type can be affected by the operation of the other. For example, in the case of a power shovel loading trucks, if the shovel breaks down, the production rate of both the trucks and the loader will be affected. The following example illustrates how the estimator can calculate the total equipment cost in a situation in which different types of equipment are working together.

*Excavating and moving earth.* The project requires 50,000 cy bank measure of earth to be excavated. Based on the specific job conditions, it was decided to use a power shovel having a probable output of 210 cy/hr bank measure and 10 cy bank measure rear dump trucks. The cost of the power shovel is $105.00 per hour, and each truck costs $35.00 per hour.

A study of company records and job site conditions resulted in an average cycle time per truck of 10 minutes. Assuming the trucks operate an average of 50 minutes per hour, the number of trips one truck can make in an hour is

$$50/10 = 5 \text{ trips}$$

Therefore, the volume of earth hauled per hour per truck is

$$5 \text{ trips/hr} \times 10 \text{ cy/trip} = 50 \text{ cy/hr}$$

The number of trucks required based on the probable output of the power shovel is

$$\frac{210 \text{ cy/hr}}{50 \text{ cy/hr}} = 4.2 \text{ trucks}$$

Using four trucks will slightly reduce the output of the shovel. However, if five trucks are used, the shovel's capacity will be realized, but there will be waiting times for the trucks.

The total number of hours it will take to move the earth with four trucks is

$$\frac{50,000 \text{ cy}}{50 \text{ cy/hr} \times 4 \text{ trucks}} = 250 \text{ hours}$$

The total cost for performing the operation exclusive of the truck drivers and shovel operator is

$$(\$35.00 \times 4 + \$105.00) \times 250 \text{ hrs} = \$61,250.00$$

The final example takes into consideration many of the factors discussed in this section. It also illustrates the need for the estimator to become involved in the details of acquiring information needed to develop the final activity cost.

*Spreading and compacting soil.* Determine the estimated cost of placing and compacting 38,000 cy (bank measure) of soil. The earth will be placed using scrapers. The rate of placement is estimated to be 200 cy per hour. Information from the soil report indicates a required soil moisture content of 12%. The existing moisture content is 7%. The specifications indicate the soil weighs 105 pcf and will be placed in 8″ lifts, measured in a compacted state. In addition, the specifications require spreading the earth with a grader and compacting with ten passes using a sheep's-foot roller.

First, determine the estimated time to complete the job:

$$\frac{38,000 \text{ cy}}{200 \text{ cy/hr}} = 190 \text{ hours}$$

200 cy of earth per hour spread 8″ thick will cover an area of

$$200 \text{ cy} \times 27 \text{ cf/cy} \times 12/8 = 8100 \text{ sf/hr}$$

For the spreading operation a road grader with a 6′-effective-wide blade will be used. Its average speed is 3 mph. It can cover an area of

$$3 \text{ mph} \times 5280 \text{ ft/mile} \times 6' = 95{,}040 \text{ sf/hr in one pass}$$

The road grader will be able to make eleven or twelve passes over an area of 8100 sf. Eleven passes will be used.

Water must be added to raise the moisture content from 7 percent to 12 percent.

Soil spread per hour = 200 cy per hr × 27 cf/cy × 105 pcf = 567,000 lb

Water required per hour = 567,000 lb × 0.05

= 28,350 lb or 3418 gallons (1 gallon weighs 8.33 lb.)

Since the contractor has a 1500 gallon sprinkler truck, he will need 3418/1500 = 2.28 truckloads per hour. The water costs $2.00 per load. The truck must travel five miles for water at an average speed of 15 mph. The average total cycle time is estimated to be sixty minutes, or one complete trip per hour.

For the compacting operation, the area to be covered is 8100 sf/hr. For ten passes, the area is 10 × 8100 = 81,000 sf/hr.

The width of the sheep's-foot roller drum is 5'. The area covered per hour by one roller traveling at 2.5 mph is

$$2.5 \text{ mph} \times 5280 \text{ f/mi} \times 5' = 66{,}000 \text{ sf/hr}$$
$$\text{Rollers needed} = 81{,}000/66{,}000 = 1.23 \text{ or } 2$$

The contractor will use a crawler tractor to pull the rollers.

The labor of the job will be as follows:

| | |
|---|---|
| 1 road grader operator | $ 8.00 per hour |
| 1 tractor operator | $ 8.00 per hour |
| 1 truck driver | $ 7.50 per hour |
| 1 supervisor | $10.00 per hour |

The total hourly labor cost is $33.50 per hour.

The contractor's records indicate the following ownership and operating hourly costs:

| | |
|---|---|
| Road grader | $ 75.00 |
| Water truck | $ 55.00 |
| Crawler tractor | $ 70.00 |
| Sheep's foot rollers | $ 15.00 |
| Total hourly cost | $215.00 |

The transportation costs are estimated to be $1500.00. The total estimated cost is 190 hours ($33.50 per hour + $215.00 per hour) + 190 hours (2.28 truckloads per hour × $2.00 per truck load) + $1500 = $49,582, or $261 per hour.

## Small Equipment For A Specific Task

Equipment in this classification is used for a specific task and normally serves as a support function. Concrete troweling machines, mortar mixers, and concrete vibrators are examples of equipment used for a specific task. This type of equipment is normally owned by the construction company.

The equipment can be priced as an hourly charge-out rate or as a unit price. The estimator will need to establish these charge-out rates. The initial cost of the equipment, expected life of the equipment, and consumables need to be considered when establishing the price.

## Job Overhead Tools

Tools, such as hand tools, wheelbarrows, water hoses, extension cords, and small power tools, will be used for many different activities on the project. They are normally considered to be job overhead equipment and are priced in the job overhead phase of the estimate. A lump sum allowance calculated as a small percentage of the total direct labor cost of the project or a monthly charge is used to establish the estimated cost of these tools. The construction company will need to establish a standard on what is included in the job overhead tools. Figure 4.4

Transit
Jackhammer
Power saw
Power drill
Screw gun
Belt sander
Electric fan
Propane heater
Sump pump
Air compressor
Rigging
Scaffold
Life belt
Screw jack
Hose
Wheelbarrow
Trash cart
Sledgehammer
Shovel
Rake
Broom
Ladder
Dolly
Extension cord
Steel tape measure
Bar clamps
Tamping rod
Rod bender
Fire hydrant wrench
Bolt cutter

**FIGURE 4.4**
Job overhead tools.

is an example of what might be considered job overhead tools. The replacement price for each tool is established. Dividing the total cost of all the tools by a general depreciable life factor, the estimator can establish the monthly cost for all of the tools, or the estimator can divide the total cost of the tools by the total direct labor cost of a typical job to establish the percentage to be added to the estimate.

## SUBCONTRACTOR PRICING

Quotations from subcontractors are an important element in the compilation of a project estimate. The general contractor will generally rely on specialty contractors for a major portion of the total bid. The estimator will need an approximate price to evaluate the sub-bids and must be knowledgeable about the scope of the subcontractors' bids and be able to evaluate the capability of the subcontractors. A subcontractor system estimate and a bid analysis for all subcontracted items should be completed.

### Subcontractor System Estimate

For areas that a general contractor expects to subcontract, a subcontractor system estimate should be performed by the general contractor. The estimate is similar to a system estimate, but it is general in nature. It is not all-encompassing and detailed. For each subcontracted component the quantity of a key element is taken off and all other elements are listed. This will give the estimator an understanding of the scope of work of the subcontractor. A unit price for the key element is then applied to derive the approximate subcontractor bid. Figure 4.5 is an example of a subcontractor system estimate. The general contractor expects to receive a bid

```
Project — Ace Office Building
Estimator — Mike
Bid Date — Feb 23

Roofing Estimate

    Single ply roofing membrane — 30 squares
        Roof insulation
        Metal stop at edge
        Ballast
        Set roof drains — no material
        Flash at skylights
        Flash at firewall
        Set roof hatch — no material


        30 squares × $400 / square = $12,000
```

**FIGURE 4.5**
Subcontractor systems estimate.

for the roofing in Fig. 4.5, but in case one is not received before the bid is due to the owner the $12,000 could be plugged into the bid to cover the cost of roofing. This involves a considerable amount of risk. However, the general contractor will usually not have to do this, because it usually receives several bids for the roofing and sheet metal.

## Subcontractor Capability

Usually, the general contractor has complete freedom in selecting its subcontractors. However, on many public projects the general contractor must award some stipulated percentage of its total contract to minority business enterprises, women-owned businesses, or local firms. In such cases the general contractor must seek out and use the bids of these companies. On private projects the owner may require that the general contractor use only approved subcontractors. Above all, the estimator must make sure of the capability of the subcontractor. The subcontractor's financial strength, integrity, and reputation of past performance in accordance with the project goals must be assessed. The financial strength can be checked by requesting a certified financial statement, bank references, evaluations by information systems such as Dunn and Bradstreet, and discussions with material suppliers of the subcontractor. As mentioned earlier in this chapter, the estimator should develop a list of preferred (qualified) subcontractors.

## Subcontractor Bid Analysis

The general contractor usually solicits bids from several specialty contractors and material suppliers to perform work set out on the drawings and specifications. It is recommended that a minimum of three bids from each specialty area be obtained. When the subcontractor bids are received by the general contractor, the estimator must analyze the bids to determine the lowest bid and make sure that all items are included in the bid. Figure 4.6 is an example of a bid analysis. A blank copy of the form is available in the FORMS subdirectory of the computer disk provided with this book. At the top of the bid analysis form the estimator should list the scope of the subcontract bids. The subcontract system estimates should be reviewed when developing the scope. Some subcontractors may bid all of the items; others may bid only a few of the items. In order to compare one subcontractor's bid with another, the scopes of work must be the same. If a subcontractor does not include an item, the estimator can either combine the subcontractor's bid with another or plug in a number from the subcontractor system estimate. The codes P or C in Fig. 4.6 indicate that an item was either plugged (P) from the subcontractor system estimate or combined (C) with another subcontractor's bid.

## Receipt of Subcontractor and Material Supply Bids

The bids will be received in written format, by fax, or from telephone conversations. All of the bids should have the same basic organization as the estimate. For example, most contractors organize their estimate in the CSI (16 division) format. As the bids are received they should also be organized in this format. The

Subcontractor and Material Supplier Analysis

Project:  ABC STORE
Bid date:  April 1, 19--

| Company name | Bid amount | Items | | | | | | | | Comparative total |
|---|---|---|---|---|---|---|---|---|---|---|
| | | HVAC | Plumb. | Elec. | Temp. control | | | | | |
| Our estimate | | 15,000 | 21,500 | 27,000 | 5,000 | | | | | 68,500 |
| Ace Mech. | 18,000 | * | | | * | | | | | |
| Steven's Elec. | 21,500 | | * | | | | | | | |
| Jackson Plumb. | 22,000 | | * | | | | | | | |
| Jones Inc. | 60,100 | * | * | * | * | | | | | 60,100 |
| Smith Inc. | 43,000 | M18,000 | * | | M | | | | | 61,000 |
| L.D. Inc. | 32,000 | * | * | P27,000 | * | | | | | 59,000 |
| | | | | | | | | | | |
| | | | | | | | | | | |
| | | | | | | | | | | |
| | | | | | | | | | | |

\*      Included in the bid
M $xxx   Combine with another bidder
P $xxx   "Plug"—From our estimate

**FIGURE 4.6**
Subcontractor bid analysis.

bids should be placed in a notebook with 16 divisions. The organization helps to ensure that the estimate is priced on the basis of the most competitive prices and no offer is misplaced or overlooked.

The estimator must be especially careful when receiving telephone quotations. A special form should be developed to ensure that all information is received. Figure 4.7 is an example of a telephone quotation form. The form should be printed on a different color paper from all other paper used during the bidding process. This will help to ensure that bids can be quickly found if misplaced. Whenever possible, the estimator should request all phone quotations be followed up with a written confirmation.

It cannot be overemphasized that the estimator must listen very carefully and all information must be written down during a telephone bid. The estimator should repeat the number back to the bidder in a different context from how it was given. For example, if the bidder said the bid was one hundred fifty-two thousand dollars, the estimator should repeat the number back in numerical format. This will break the mindset of the bidder and the person receiving the bid. It requires each person to listen carefully to what the other is saying.

## OTHER COSTS

The classification of other costs includes costs of overhead and profit. The overhead costs are costs that cannot be attributed to any specific item of work. If the costs can be attributed to an item of work, they should be included in the classifications of labor, material, or equipment of the specific item of the project. The overhead costs are generally subdivided into general overhead and project (job) overhead. All costs associated with the project, either directly or indirectly, need to be included in the bid.

### General Overhead

General overhead costs cannot be associated with any particular project. These costs are often referred to as general and administrative costs. A budget for the operation of the construction company including projected income should be developed based on the strategic plan of the company. Figure 4.8 is an example of a company's budget for operating costs and income. To determine the amount that should be added to each project to account for the cost of general overhead, divide the total projected annual general overhead by the projected annual income. The amount of general overhead for the company described in Fig. 4.8 is

$$\$1,000,000/\$15,000,000 = 0.067$$

Each bid that the company submits should include 6.7 percent for general overhead.

The construction firm should periodically review the calculated overhead rate during the year. If it is apparent five months into the year that the firm's estimated annual volume is too high, an upward adjustment of the overhead rate is probably justified.

**TELEPHONED SUB-BID**

DATE _____

PROJECT _____

SUB-BIDDER _____     ADDRESS _____

PERSON'S NAME _____     PHONE NUMBER _____

SALES TAX INCLUDED      YES ___    NO ___     FOB JOBSITE _____

INSTALLED                YES ___    NO ___     FOB ORIGIN _____

PER PLANS & SPECS        YES ___    NO ___     OTHER _____

WILL HOLD PRICE     60 DAYS ___    (OTHER ___)

ADDENDA RECEIVED _____     BID TAKEN BY _____

| | SECTION | DESCRIPTION | PRICES |
|---|---|---|---|
| I | | | |
| N | | | |
| C | | | |
| L | | | |
| U | | | |
| D | | | |
| E | | | |
| S | | | |
| | | | |
| | | | |
| | | | |
| | | | |
| | | | |
| | | | |
| E | | | |
| X | | | |
| C | | | |
| L | | | |
| U | | | |
| D | | | |
| E | | | |
| S | | | |

**FIGURE 4.7**
Telephone quotation form.

## PROJECTED GENERAL OVERHEAD AND PROFIT – 19XX

| | |
|---|---:|
| Projected Volume | 15,000,000 |
| Desired Profit | 495,000 |

General Overhead

Variable Overhead

| | |
|---|---:|
| Advertising | 25,000 |
| Vehicle expenses | 55,000 |
| Bad debts | 10,000 |
| Communications | 12,000 |
| Interest | 1,800 |
| Office supplies | 21,000 |
| Taxes | 2,400 |
| Travel/entertainment | 8,000 |
| Unapplied labor | 65,000 |
| Unapplied materials | 2,400 |
| Warranty costs | 1,800 |
| **TOTAL VARIABLE COSTS** | 204,400 |

Fixed Overhead

| | | |
|---|---:|---:|
| Contributions | | 3,000 |
| Depreciation | | 117,000 |
| Dues and subscriptions | | 1,500 |
| Insurance | | 47,000 |
| Legal and audit | | 4,625 |
| Payroll taxes | | 72,975 |
| Rent | | 10,000 |
| Repairs / maintenance | | 5,000 |
| Salaries:  President | 70,000 | |
| Vice Pres (2) | 120,000 | |
| Proj Mgr (2) | 100,000 | |
| Chief Est | 50,000 | |
| Sr Est | 40,000 | |
| Jr Est (2) | 50,000 | |
| Field Eng (2) | 50,000 | |
| Secretary (2) | 45,000 | |
| | | 525,000 |
| Shop supplies, tools | | 3,000 |
| Utilities | | 6,500 |
| TOTAL FIXED OVERHEAD | | 795,600 |
| | | |
| TOTAL OVERHEAD | | 1,000,000 |

**FIGURE 4.8**
Company cost/income.

## Job Overhead

The job overhead expenses do not pertain directly to any given construction work item but are nevertheless necessary for ultimate project completion. The job overhead costs are due to requirements in the specifications, drawings, and other contract documents. The documents need to be checked thoroughly for any of these requirements. Job overhead costs may be due to the way the construction company does business. For example, the documents may not require a project sign be erected, but the construction company may want to include one for marketing purposes. Figure 4.9 is a list of job overhead items that may be required for a construction project. Some of the items are fairly straightforward on cost calculations. However, most rely on the duration of the project to calculate the cost. A schedule should be developed by the contractor to determine the duration of the project. Items such as supervisor's salary, temporary offices, and telephones depend on the duration of the project. A wage or rental rate will need to be multiplied by the duration of the project.

The following job overhead items need additional explanation:

*Liquidated damages.* Liquidated damages are often included in the contract terms. If the contractor takes longer to do the project than agreed upon, the contractor must reimburse the owner this amount to pay for costs sustained by the owner. If during the bidding phase it is determined that the project will take longer than required by the contract documents, additional money should be included in the bid to cover the cost of liquidated damages.

*Temporary electrical.* The cost of temporary electricity includes the cost of power, temporary lines on the site, and electrical lamps. Usually, the general contractor will ask the electrical subcontractor to include the cost of installing and removing the temporary lines and the electrical lamps in the sub-bid. The power charges are included in the general contractor's bid. The cost of bringing power to the site should also be checked. Power companies often have a substantial surcharge for this purpose.

*Temporary heat.* The temporary heat can be divided into temporary heat before enclosure and temporary heat after enclosure. Most temporary heat before enclosure is for a specific task, such as installing masonry. The cost for this type of heat should be included in the cost of installing the particular item. Temporary heat after enclosure is usually for general heating. The cost for this should be included in the job overhead. Often the specification will allow for the use of the permanent heat system after the enclosure, but the system will need to be completely cleaned before the owner will accept it.

*Cleanup.* The general contractor will often include two types of cleanup. One is for periodic cleanups during the progress of the project. The other is a final cleaning of the building before it is turned over to the owner. The contract requirements between the general contractor and subcontractors will normally require that they be responsible for their own cleaning.

*Photographs.* Photographs may be required by the owner to be taken by a professional photographer and can be a substantial cost item. Even if the photographs are not required by the owner, it is recommended that progress

## JOB OVERHEAD

**Salary—Supervision**

Construction manager
General superintendent
Concrete superintendent
Excavation superintendent
Welding superintendent
Rigging superintendent
Carpentry superintendent
Equipment superintendent

**Salary—Engineering**

Chief engineer
Office engineer
Schedule engineer
Cost engineer
Materials engineer
Draftsperson
Field engineer
Party chief
Instrument personnel

**Salary/Wages—Other**

QA engineers
Safety engineers
Mechanics
Plant operators
Secretaries and clerks
Computer operators
Training personnel
Lab technicians
Guards
Runners

**Automotive**

Automobiles
Pickups
Tractor-trailers
Cargo trucks
Special purpose trucks

**Temporary Horizontal Construction**

Access roads
Construction bridges
Fencing and gates
Drainage structures
Parking areas
Environmental protection
Laydown areas

**Buildings and Major Equipment**

Project office
Warehouses
First aid station
Tool sheds
Concrete batch plant
Quarry
Carpenter shop
Electrical shop
Paint shop
Machine shop
Equipment maintenance shop
Pipe fabrication shop
Resteel fabrication
Welder test facility
Rigging loft
Hoisting equipment

**Support Systems**

Temporary electrical
Temporary heat
Water supply
Site communications
Compressed air
Inert gas

**General Expense**

General office supplies
Office furniture
Engineering supplies
Engineering equipment
Printing/reproduction
Computer terminal
Telephone/fax/radios
Utilities/portable toilets
Signs
Safety equipment
Permits/licenses/bonds
Advertising and contributions
Job travel expenses
Testing and laboratory
Legal fees
Medical supplies
Progress photos
Move-in costs
Building and grounds maintenance
Drinking water
Taxes/insurance
Payroll burden costs
Backcharges
Consultants
Weather protection
Cleanup
Liquidated damages

**FIGURE 4.9**
Job overhead items.

photos be taken. These could be taken by the supervisor on the project. Photos can be helpful in dispute-resolution proceedings.

## Contingencies

The inclusion of contingencies in a lump sum bid is not recommended. The estimator should develop better estimating procedures for this type of bid. Contingencies are an excuse for using poor estimating practices. If there is a problem with the bid documents, the estimator should request a written clarification from the architect before the bid is submitted. If an item of material, labor, or equipment cost is not known, the estimator should continue to study the problem until a decision can be made on its projected cost.

Some bid documents require a contingency be included in the bid for use by the owner or the architect. These contingencies are listed in the documents as an allowance and should be included in the bid.

## Profit

The estimator's objective when selecting a profit figure is to include the maximum possible profit, yet keep the bid at a competitive level. It can be defined as the return for taking the risk. The owner of the construction company or top management will usually determine the amount of profit that should be added to the estimate.

## Calculations of Other Costs

The calculations of other costs can be performed on the recapitulation sheet. Figure 4.2 (RECAP.WQ1 or RECAP.WK1), which appears earlier in this chapter, is a spreadsheet that calculates job overhead, general overhead, and profit. For job overhead items that are derived from time, the duration in calendar days will need to be included. Note that supervision costs can be estimated at a partial time if the supervisor has other duties that are priced in the labor portion of the estimate.

When the builder's risk, bonds, general comprehensive insurance, general overhead, and profit are calculated manually, an assumed bid must be used (see Fig. 4.10). The assumed bid is necessary because the general contractor will pay for these items based on the total bid. If the assumed bid was not used during the process of calculating the cost of the bond, the estimator could not complete the calculations because the total project bid would not be known. Therefore, an assumed bid is used to do these calculations. If the assumed bid is not close to the actual bid, the estimator should recalculate the bid based on a different assumed bid. The assumed bid is not used on the computer spreadsheet file because of the mathematical process of iteration.

## Alternates

The specifications often require that additional prices be included in the bidding process for alternative methods of construction, materials, or scope of construction.

| | RECAPITULATION SHEET | | | | | |
|---|---|---|---|---|---|---|
| COMPUTED BY: db | PROJECT: **Adler Center** | | | DATE: June 15 | | |
| CHECKED BY: rl | ARCHITECT: Jones & Smith | | | PAGE: 1 of 1 | | |

| INDEX NO. | ITEM | MATERIAL | LABOR | SUBCONTRACT | EQUIPMENT | TOTAL |
|---|---|---|---|---|---|---|
| 1 | DEMOLITION | 698 | 25354 | | 600 | 26652 |
| 2 | EARTHWORK | 9715 | 20326 | | 8190 | 38231 |
| 3 | PAVING & SURFACING | | | 18385 | | 18385 |
| 4 | CONCRETE FORMS | 2538 | 12729 | | 200 | 15467 |
| 5 | CONCRETE REINFORCING | 1626 | 2109 | | | 3735 |
| 6 | CONCRETE PLACEMENT | 18228 | 5660 | | 1380 | 25268 |
| 7 | CONCRETE FINISHING | 1245 | 4810 | | 133 | 6188 |
| 8 | MASONRY | | | 26910 | | 26910 |
| 9 | STRUCTURAL STEEL & JOIST | 46100 | 1392 | 22560 | | 70052 |
| 10 | METAL FABRICATION | 5200 | 1527 | | | 6727 |
| 11 | CARPENTRY | 6576 | 7757 | | 300 | 14633 |
| 12 | BUILDING INSULATION | 277 | 213 | | | 490 |
| 13 | B.U. ROOFING & FLASHING | | | 92981 | | 92981 |
| 14 | ROOF ACCESSORIES | 4614 | 1052 | | 80 | 5746 |
| 15 | SEALANTS & CAULKING | 1667 | 1937 | | | 3604 |
| 16 | METAL DOORS & FRAMES | 12425 | 5278 | | | 17703 |
| 17 | HARDWARE | 13995 | 4916 | | | 18911 |
| 18 | LATH & PLASTER | | | 153387 | | 153387 |
| 19 | FLOOR COVERING | | | 43700 | | 43700 |
| 20 | TOILET ACCESSORIES | 1880 | 461 | | | 2341 |
| 21 | LABORATORY EQUIPMENT | | | 275000 | | 275000 |
| 22 | GENERAL CONDITIONS | | 33275 | | 23724 | 56999 |
| 23 | | | | | | 0 |
| | | | | | | 0 |
| | | | | | | 0 |
| | SUBTOTAL | 126784 | 128796 | 632923 | 34607 | 923110 |
| | PAYROLL INSURANCE | | 6.8% | | | 8758 |
| | PAYROLL TAXES | | 12.5% | | | 16099 |
| | SALES TAX | | 5.0% | | | 6339 |
| | ASSUMED BID | 1068822 | | | | |
| | BUILDER'S RISK | | $0.40/$100.00 | | | 4222 |
| | OWNER'S PROTECTIVE | | $0.27/$100.00 | | | 2832 |
| | PERFORMANCE & PAYMENT BOND | | $9.00/$1000.00 | | | 9619 |
| | GENERAL COMPREHENSIVE | | $1.70/$1000.00 | | | 1817 |
| | | | | | | |
| | TOTAL DIRECT COST | | | | | 972796 |
| | | | | | | |
| | GENERAL OVERHEAD | | 6.7% | | | 65177 |
| | PROFIT | | 3.3% | | | 32102 |
| | TOTAL BID | | | | | 1070076 |

**FIGURE 4.10**
Assumed bid on the manual recap sheet.

The owner originates the alternates and the bidding contractors are required to submit a lump-sum price for each alternate. The alternates must be a complete estimate within themselves and include all applicable direct costs, job overhead, markup, bonds, and tax. The alternates can be chosen at the discretion of the owner.

Alternates that are added to the base bid usually require some deletions of items that were in the base bid. For example, if the owner requested a price for an additional wing to a building, the design would probably require that materials such as a window wall be deducted out of the base bid. The estimator should always ask: "What is the impact on the base bid due to the alternate?" Figure 4.11 is an example of the calculations for an alternate bid.

Occasionally, the low subcontractor used in the base bid can be a different company when an alternate is selected by the owner. Figure 4.12 is an example of this. In the example, Union Plumbing Incorporated is low on the base bid, but Acme Plumbing Incorporated is low if the owner decides to accept alternate number 1. The estimator should study the bids of subcontractors to determine if a different subcontractor is low in the analysis of an alternate. File SABA.WQ1 or SABA.WK1 (subcontractor alternate bid analysis) can be used to do these calculations. Figure 4.13 shows the input screen and the total screen of the subcontractor alternate bid analysis program.

The pricing of alternates can become complicated. The estimator should carefully examine all aspects of the alternate. The alternates should be taken seriously, because they can determine the low bidder.

---

**ALTERNATE BID NUMBER 1**

South Side Shopping Mall
Bid Due Date:   May 7, 19--

Amount to be added to or deducted from the base bid for Asphalt paving in lieu of Concrete paving.

| | |
|---|---|
| Concrete paving | −35,000 |
| Asphalt paving | 28,000 |
| Additional aggregate base | 2,000 |
| Subtotal | −$5,000 |
| Performance bond | −500 |
| Profit and gen. overhead | −100 |
| Total alt. # 1   Deduct | $5,600 |

**FIGURE 4.11**
Alternate bid calculations.

## ALTERNATE BID & SUBCONTRACTORS

**Subcontractor bids**

| | |
|---|---|
| Union Plumbing Inc. base bid = | $45,000 |
| Alt. No. 1 add to base bid = | $5,000 |
| Total | $50,000 |

| | |
|---|---|
| Acme Plumbing Inc. base bid = | $46,000 |
| Alt. No. 1 add to base bid = | $3,000 |
| Total | $49,000 |

**Low base bid**

Union Plumbing Inc.   $45,000

**Low alternate**

Acme Plumbing Inc.   $3,000

**General contractor bid to owner**

| | |
|---|---|
| Base bid | |
| Union Plumbing | −45,000 |
| Acme Plumbing | +46,000 |
| Alternate #1 | |
| Acme Plumbing | +3,000 |
| Subtotal | 4,000 |
| Profit & | |
| Overhead | 500 |
| Total bid | $4,500 |

**FIGURE 4.12**
Using a different subcontractor.

# STUDENT EXERCISES

**4.1.** Edit the file RECAP.WK1 to add four additional job overhead items. Include the necessary formulas to do the calculations on the spreadsheet.

**4.2.** How many iron workers are in a crew if it takes 0.9600 man hours per ton and the crew can install fifty tons in an eight-hour day?

**4.3.** Given: four masons and two laborers. Each mason can install 135 units/day. Total crew hours = 1250. Average wage rate = $11.00/hr. Find: the total labor cost.

**4.4.** What is the total duration in days of a masonry project that has 25,000 bricks, a ten-hour work day, a crew size of five masons and three laborers, and 0.1025 man hours per unit? Also, what is the necessary production rate of the masons in units per day? (Masons are considered to be the only productive people in the crew.)

**4.5.** Modify the PRICE.WQ1 or PRICE.WK1 file to include a lump sum entry in the material column.

Screen 1:

### SUBCONTRACTOR ALTERNATE BID ANALYSIS

Project: Ace Office
Estimator: Suzette
Bid Date: May 17

Enter the data in the chart below

| Subcontractor Name | Base Bid | Alt. No. 1 | Alt. No. 2 | Alt. No. 3 |
|---|---|---|---|---|
| Smith Plumbing | $36,000 | $1,562 | ($1,000) | $1,500 |
| Jones Plumbing | $40,000 | $2,500 | ($800) | ($3,000) |
| Sam's Plumbing | $35,500 | $2,523 | ($200) | $1,800 |
| Mike and Sons | $38,000 | $3,500 | $0 | $500 |

** PRESS ALT "T" FOR TOTALS **

Screen 2:

### TOTALS SUBCONTRACTOR ALTERNATE BID ANALYSIS

| BASE BID | Bid Amount | Subcontractor |
|---|---|---|
|  | $35,500 | Sam's Plumbing |

* Add to the base bid the following alternates *

| ALTERNATE | | Bare Cost | Subcontractor |
|---|---|---|---|
| Alternate | 1 | $2,062 | Sam's Plumbing |
| Alternate | 2 | ($500) | Smith Plumbing |
| Alternate | 3 | $1,500 | Jones Plumbing |

NOTE – The general contractor should add taxes, insurance, overhead, and profit to the above base bid and alternates
** PRESS ALT "D" TO ENTER TOTALS **

**FIGURE 4.13**
Subcontractor alternate bid analysis.

**4.6.** Modify the PRICE.WQ1 or PRICE.WK1 file to include a different quantity field for use in labor calculations.

**4.7.** Develop a spreadsheet that will automatically use the information in the PRICE.WQ1 or PRICE.WK1 file to establish the recap sheet.

**4.8.** Expand SABA.WQ1 or SABA.WK1 to include two additional alternates and two additional subcontractors.

# CHAPTER

# 5

## EARTHWORK

Division 2, site work, of the Uniform Construction Index (CSI format) includes a wide variety of subject areas. The following major areas of division 2 are covered in this chapter: site work, building excavation, backfilling, and related earthwork activities.

The intent of this chapter is to (1) provide sufficient background so that the estimator understands the general items in division 2; (2) establish a basis for estimating earthwork associated with general construction; and (3) provide an introduction for those interested in the heavy/highway segment of the construction industry. All buildings require some form of earthwork before the commencement of construction, from a few cubic yards of excavation for footings to thousands of cubic yards of site cut and fill.

Financially, earthwork is one of the most risky phases in the construction of a project because of the multitude of unknowns. Weather and subsurface conditions such as rock, underground water, and soil type add to the uncertainties. These variables not only affect labor productivity but also equipment selection and production. Excavation can be by hand or by the use of large tractors, scrapers, or draglines.

The exact amount of excavation is sometimes difficult to determine because of the varying field conditions. For example, the actual amount of extra excavation required on the outside of a basement wall for working space will often be determined as the work is being performed. The materials purchased for the project (such as sand and gravel) are also difficult to determine because of variations in moisture content, material consistency, and waste factors. However, the estimator must include the cost of these items in the bid.

The earthwork estimate is not as precise as other items in the bid. This does not mean that the estimator can be careless in calculating the quantities for earthwork. The estimator should be consistent in performing earthwork calculations and strive for specific procedures that will increase the company's accuracy in the earthwork portion of the project.

This chapter introduces earthwork measurements and focuses on calculations of quantities and costs to perform several different types of work.

## TAKING OFF EXCAVATION WORK

The quantity takeoff of excavation is in cubic feet and converted to cubic yards (27 cubic feet = 1 cubic yard). The estimator needs to know if bank yards or swelled yards are being used in the calculations. A bank yard is the measurement of the soil as it lies undisturbed in the ground. When the soil is excavated it will expand and assume a larger volume. This expansion is called the swell factor. It is measured as a percentage increase above the undisturbed volume. Once excavated soil is placed and compacted on the project, it will be compressed into a smaller volume. The degree of compaction and the type of soil will affect the amount of shrinkage. The estimator needs to compensate for swell and shrinkage when hauling earth off the site or bringing additional material and compacting it on the site.

The swell and shrinkage factors vary greatly depending on the type of material. The estimator should refer to the soils report or consult with a soil engineer to determine the exact swell and/or shrinkage factors for each specific project. Some representative percent swells are noted in Fig. 5.1. For example, if we must remove 350 cubic yards of wet clay, the total cubic yards that must be transported from the site is 350 × 1.35, or 473 cubic yards.

Fine and coarse aggregates are taken off in cubic feet and then converted to tons. Figure 5.2 shows the weights of various types of granular material. For

| Type of soil | Percent swell |
|---|---|
| Dry clay | 35 |
| Wet clay | 35 |
| Dry gravel | 12 |
| Wet gravel | 14 |
| Dry sand | 15 |
| Wet sand | 15 |
| Well-blasted rock | 60 |

**FIGURE 5.1**
Typical swell percentages.

| Material | Weight — lbs per cubic foot |
|---|---|
| Bank sand | 93 |
| Torpedo sand | 100 |
| Crushed stone | 93 |
| Crushed stone screenings | 93 |
| Gravel | 100 |

**FIGURE 5.2**
Weights of granular materials.

example, if 529 cubic feet of crushed stone is required to be placed under a slab on grade, the total weight is

$$\frac{529 \times 93}{2000} = 25.6 \text{ tons}$$

## Sitework Takeoff

Most construction projects require the movement of earth on the site. This will result in altering the existing elevation to a different or finish elevation. To determine the amount of soil to be moved, the estimator first needs to have a plot plan or topographic survey. This drawing is developed by plotting the readings (elevations) obtained from a topographic field survey usually performed by a licensed land surveyor. Figure 5.3 is an example of a plot plan. The different contour

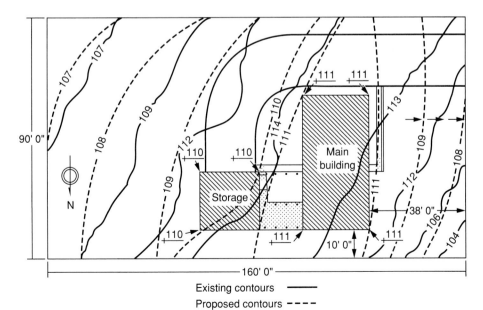

Existing contours ——
Proposed contours - - - -

**FIGURE 5.3**
Plot plan.

lines represent changes in elevation. The dashed lines usually indicate existing elevations; the solid lines represent proposed or finish elevations. However, the reverse can apply. The estimator should check the legend before beginning the takeoff.

Before the excavation can begin the site will have to be cleared of unwanted trees and underbrush. It will be necessary for the estimator to visit the site to determine the extent of clearing and grubbing. By visiting the site and using the drawings, the estimator can determine how much land needs to be cleared.

The specifications usually require that top soil be removed from all proposed building and paved areas and stockpiled for future redistribution. For instance, six inches of soil may be required to be removed before excavating or filling can begin. The estimator will need to calculate the total volume in cubic yards of topsoil removed and the total cubic yards required for distribution after construction is completed. For example, the amount of topsoil (6" deep) removed from a construction area measuring 100 feet by 300 feet would be

$$\frac{100 \text{ ft} \times 300 \text{ ft} \times 0.5 \text{ ft}}{27 \text{ cf per cy}} = 555.6 \text{ cy}$$

Two methods are used to calculate the quantity of earth to be moved on a site. The area average end method is normally used for heavy and highway work, and the grid method is usually used for building construction.

**AREA AVERAGE END METHOD.** The first step in the area average end method is to divide the plot plan into a series of grids, as shown in Fig. 5.4. The existing and finish elevations are noted at the intersection of grid lines. For this example, a 50' grid was selected. However, the estimator can use any interval. The next step is to determine how the sections will be cut. The estimator can select a north-south or east-west direction. It is usually less cumbersome in developing the necessary calculations to select the shortest overall dimension—in the case of the example, the N-S (150') direction. Cutting a series of sections at each 50' N-S grid line will result in six cross sections, or stations.

Using the existing and final elevations, the estimator plots a cross section at each station and calculates the respective areas. Finding the areas may be a simple task of dividing the total cross section into a series of simple figures to remove the need to use trigonometry or calculus. Other methods of determining the area can also be used. One is plotting each cross section to scale, determining the area in square inches, and converting it to square feet using the designated scales. Another common method uses a device called a planimeter. The cross section is plotted to scale, and the planimeter is used to obtain the area in accordance with the directions provided by the manufacturer. Figure 5.4 illustrates how to find the areas of the cross sections at stations 1 and 2 using the idea of simple figures and geometry.

Once all the areas have been determined, the next step is to find the volume of earth to be moved between any two adjacent stations. The following relationship is used to calculate the volume:

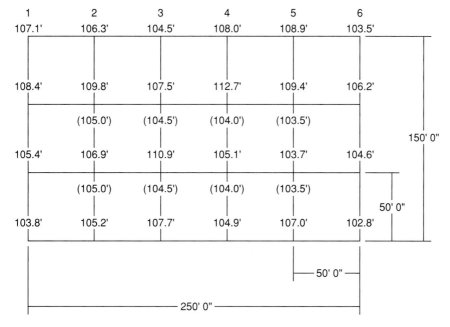

Note: Existing and final elevations the same at the perimeter
of the plan.
Final elevations shown in parentheses.

### Grid Row 1— Area

Along grid row 1, since the existing and final elevations are the same,
there will be no change, and thus the area equals zero.

### Grid Row 2 — Area

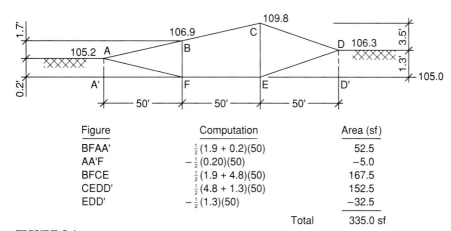

| Figure | Computation | Area (sf) |
|---|---|---|
| BFAA' | $\frac{1}{2}(1.9 + 0.2)(50)$ | 52.5 |
| AA'F | $-\frac{1}{2}(0.20)(50)$ | −5.0 |
| BFCE | $\frac{1}{2}(1.9 + 4.8)(50)$ | 167.5 |
| CEDD' | $\frac{1}{2}(4.8 + 1.3)(50)$ | 152.5 |
| EDD' | $-\frac{1}{2}(1.3)(50)$ | −32.5 |
| | Total | 335.0 sf |

**FIGURE 5.4**
Area average end method.

Volume of earth between grid rows 1 and 2:

$$V_{12} = \frac{A_1 + A_2}{2} \times 50$$

$$V_{12} = \frac{0 + 335 \text{ sq ft}}{2} \times 50 \text{ ft} = 8375 \text{ cf or } 310.2 \text{ cy}$$

Grid Row 3 — Area

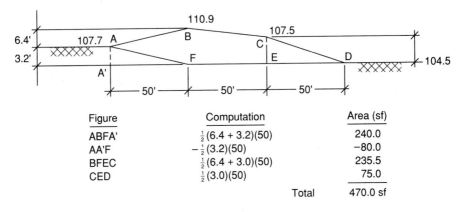

| Figure | Computation | Area (sf) |
|---|---|---|
| ABFA' | $\frac{1}{2}(6.4 + 3.2)(50)$ | 240.0 |
| AA'F | $-\frac{1}{2}(3.2)(50)$ | −80.0 |
| BFEC | $\frac{1}{2}(6.4 + 3.0)(50)$ | 235.5 |
| CED | $\frac{1}{2}(3.0)(50)$ | 75.0 |
| | Total | 470.0 sf |

Volume of earth between grid rows 2 and 3:

$$V_{23} = \frac{A_2 + A_3}{2} \times 50 \quad =$$

$$\frac{335.0 \text{ sq ft} + 470.0 \text{ sq ft}}{2} \times 50 \text{ ft} = 20125 \text{ cf or } 745.4 \text{ cy}$$

Total volume between grid rows 1 and 3 is therefore:

$$V_{13} = 310.2 \text{ cy} + 745.4 \text{ cy} = 1055.6 \text{ cy}$$

Using the same procedure, the estimator can obtain the total volume of earth to be moved on the entire site.

**FIGURE 5.4 (*continued*)**

$$V_{12} = \frac{A_1 + A_2}{2} \times \text{Perpendicular distance between stations}$$

This process is repeated for each set of cross sections. The volumes are then summed to obtain the total volume to be moved.

**GRID METHOD.** A much easier method for calculating cut and fill requirements for general building and site work is the grid method. This method does not require section drawings or complicated area formulas. Figure 5.5 illustrates the grid method.

The first step in this method is to draw grid lines on the site plan. The grid is usually square, but it can take the shape of rectangles or other geometric figures.

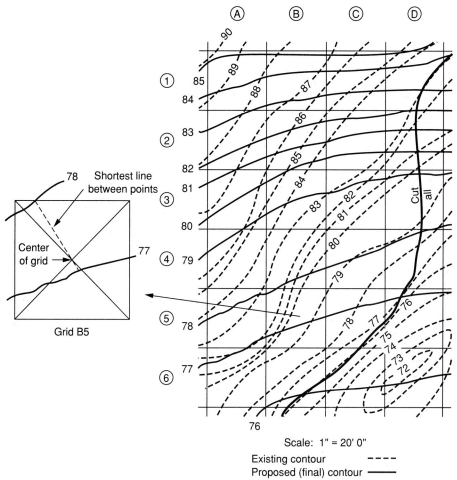

**FIGURE 5.5**
Grid method.

The size of the grid is a function of the scale of the drawing, the interval of the contours, and the close proximity of one contour line to another. A small grid will produce a more precise cut-fill estimate, but it should be kept within the relative accuracy of the total earthwork. For example, if the grid is drawn so small that in many cases no contour lines fall within a grid, then the grid should be drawn larger. To start the evaluation, a common grid size is one-inch squares.

The next step is to make readings of the existing and proposed elevations and record them on a chart. The readings are the average elevations for each grid. The average elevation can be obtained by one of two methods. If the grid has a relatively consistent slope, then the visual center of the grid is established and the reading is an interpolation between the two closest contour lines. In grid B5 (Fig. 5.5 enlargement) the proposed contour of the land is in a relatively consistent slope from the southeast to the northwest. The elevation contour lines marked 77 and 78 are closest to the center. By visually drawing the shortest line that will touch these two contour lines and go through the center of the grid, the interpolation will show that 77 is closer to the center than 78. A judgment is made that the center is one-fourth of the distance between 77 and 78. The reading is then recorded as 77.25.

The second method of obtaining the elevation is calculated by averaging the four corners of the grid. If the land is not at a constant slope, it may be necessary to take several readings and find the average. The center of grid C6 for the proposed contours may not represent the average elevation of the grid. Readings are made and recorded in the same manner as the previous method for each of the corners of the grid, and an average is determined.

The existing and proposed elevations are recorded in a chart (see Fig. 5.6). The proposed elevation is subtracted from the existing elevation and recorded in the appropriate column. If the difference is positive, the grid will have to be cut and the number recorded in the cut column. If the difference is negative, the grid will have to be filled and the number recorded in the fill column.

The next step is to record the area of the grid in square feet. The grid area is then multiplied by the cut or fill columns and recorded in the appropriate cut or fill volume column in cubic feet. The sum of the volume columns will give the total cut and fill on the project.

Figure 5.5 also shows a cut-fill line, at which neither cut nor fill is required. This line can be established by simply interpreting the location point of grids that show little or no cut or fill. A cut-fill line is then drawn between the points. This line can help the contractor establish the traffic patterns on the site for the cut and fill operations.

The area of the building is often table topped, and footings are excavated after the site earthwork is completed. Tabletopping is the cutting and filling of a site to make a flat space within the building area. The tabletop elevation is established at the bottom of the sand or gravel under a concrete slab on grade. In Fig. 5.7, the tabletop elevation has been established by the estimator to be 683.84:

| | |
|---|---|
| Finish floor | 684.50 ft |
| Concrete floor (4″) | − 0.33 ft |
| Under-slab gravel (4″) | − 0.33 ft |
| | 683.84 ft |

An adjustment column is on the cut and fill takeoff sheet to account for structures such as roads, drives, and parking lots. If the parking lot in Fig. 5.7 is made up of three inches of asphalt and six inches of base, a total of nine inches will need to be recorded in the adjustment column and subtracted from the finish elevation. Grid A3 (Fig. 5.7) is all parking lot. An adjustment of −0.75 is necessary. In grid B3 (Fig. 5.7) the parking lot is in only about two-thirds of the grid. The adjustment factor is then $-0.75 \times 0.66 = -0.5$. The adjustment

COMPUTED BY: KB  
CHECKED BY: RL  
PROJECT: Sam's Place  
ARCHITECT: A1A International  
DATE: 1-7  
PAGE: 1 OF 1  
INDEX NO:

| GRID ID | EXISTING ELEVATION FOUR CORNERS | | | | CENTER OR AVERAGE | PROPOSED ELEVATION FOUR CORNERS | | | CENTER OR AVERAGE | ADJUSTMENT TO PROPOSED | FILL FEET - | CUT FEET + | GRID SIZE | NET FILL VOLUME CF | NET CUT VOLUME CF |
|---|---|---|---|---|---|---|---|---|---|---|---|---|---|---|---|
| A1 | | | | | 88.7 | | | | 84.2 | | | 4.5 | 20 x 20 | | 1800 |
| A2 | | | | | 87.6 | | | | 82.4 | | | 5.2 | | | 2080 |
| A3 | | | | | 86.5 | | | | 79.9 | | | 6.6 | | | 2640 |
| A4 | | | | | 84.8 | | | | 78.7 | | | 6.1 | | | 2440 |
| A5 | | | | | 83.0 | | | | 77.7 | | | 5.3 | | | 2120 |
| A6 | | | | | 79.2 | | | | 76.6 | | | 2.6 | | | 1040 |
| B1 | | | | | 87.3 | | | | 83.8 | | | 3.5 | | | 1400 |
| B2 | | | | | 85.4 | | | | 81.5 | | | 3.9 | | | 1560 |
| B3 | | | | | 83.8 | | | | 79.2 | | | 4.6 | | | 1840 |
| B4 | | | | | 81.7 | | | | 78.3 | | | 3.4 | | | 1360 |
| B5 | | | | | 79.5 | | | | 77.3 | | | 2.2 | | | 880 |
| B6 | | | | | 77.2 | | | | 76.3 | | | 0.9 | | | 360 |
| C1 | | | | | 85.6 | | | | 83.7 | | | 1.5 | | | 600 |
| C2 | | | | | 83.6 | | | | 80.9 | | | 2.7 | | | 1080 |
| C3 | | | | | 81.4 | | | | 78.8 | | | 2.6 | | | 1040 |
| C4 | | | | | 78.9 | | | | 78.0 | | | 0.9 | | | 360 |
| C5 | | | | | 77.7 | | | | 76.9 | | | 0.8 | | | 320 |
| C6 | 78.0 | 74.0 | 73.0 | 74.4 | 74.8 | | | | 76.2 | | 1.4 | | | 560 | |
| D1 | | | | | 83.3 | | | | 83.5 | | 0.2 | | | 80 | |
| D2 | | | | | 81.5 | | | | 80.8 | | | 0.7 | | | 280 |
| D3 | | | | | 79.4 | | | | 78.7 | | | 0.7 | | | 280 |
| D4 | | | | | 77.6 | | | | 77.8 | | 0.2 | | | 80 | |
| D5 | | | | | 74.8 | | | | 76.8 | | 2 | | | 800 | |
| D6 | 74.0 | 73.0 | 74.6 | 73.0 | 73.7 | | | | 76.0 | | 2.3 | | | 920 | |
| TOTAL FROM PREVIOUS PAGE: | | | | | | | | | | | | | | 0 | 0 |
| TOTAL: | | | | | | | | | | | | | | 2440 | 23480 |

**FIGURE 5.6**  
Grid method worksheet.

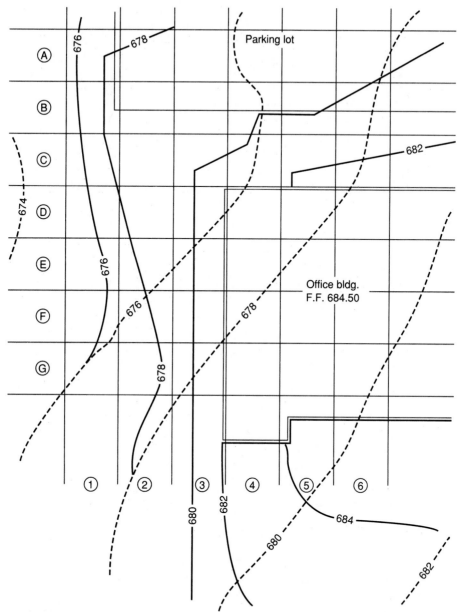

**FIGURE 5.7**
Cut-fill calculation.

column is then added to the difference between the existing elevation and proposed elevation and recorded in the appropriate cut or fill column (see Fig. 5.8).

The grid method is made up of many simple calculations that can be completed quickly and accurately with a computer spreadsheet. File EXCAVATE.WQ1 (EXCAVATE.WK1) is an example of such a template using Quattro-Pro. Figure 5.9 is a printout of the site cut and fill report.

COMPUTED BY: KB
CHECKED BY: RL

PROJECT: Brier Cafe
ARCHITECT: A1A National

DATE: 1-7
PAGE: 1 OF 1
INDEX NO:

| GRID ID | EXISTING ELEVATION FOUR CORNERS | CENTER OR AVERAGE | PROPOSED ELEVATION FOUR CORNERS | CENTER OR AVERAGE | ADJUSTMENT TO PROPOSED | FILL FEET - | CUT FEET + | GRID SIZE | NET FILL VOLUME CF | NET CUT VOLUME CF |
|---|---|---|---|---|---|---|---|---|---|---|
| A3 | | 86.5 | | 79.9 | 0.75 | | 7.35 | 20x20 | | 2940 |
| B3 | | 83.8 | | 79.2 | 0.5 | | 5.1 | 20x20 | | 2040 |
| | | | | | | | | | | |
| TOTAL FROM PREVIOUS PAGE: | | | | | | | | | | 0 |
| TOTAL: | | | | | | | | | | 4980 |

**FIGURE 5.8**
Cut-fill sheet.

**FIGURE 5.9**
Computer-generated cut-fill report.

PROJECT NA  ACE OFFICE
ESTIMATOR: Julie
BID DATE: Dec 29

| STANDARD GRID SIZE IN FEET | |
|---|---|
| VER | HORZ |
| 10 | 10 |

TOTAL    16 CY    TOTALFI    22 CY

TAB "RIGHT" →

| ENTER GRID L | ENTER EXISTING EXISTING ELEVATION | | | | ADJUSTMENTS SIZE OF SQUAR IN % | DEPTH OF SQ. IN FT. | ENTER FINISH FINISH ELEVATION | | | | ADJUSTMEN SIZE OF SQUAR IN % | DEP IN FEE | ENTER ADJUSTMENTS IN SIZE OF GRID IF DIFFERENT FROM STANDARD IN FT. HORZ. | VERT. | NET FILL IN CUBIC YAR | NET CUT IN CUBIC YAR |
|---|---|---|---|---|---|---|---|---|---|---|---|---|---|---|---|---|
| | CENTER OF SQUARE AND/OR THE FOUR CORNERS CENT | FOUR CORNERS | | | | | CENTER OF SQUARE AND/OR THE FOUR CORNERS CENTER | FOUR CORNERS | | | | | | | | |
| A1 | 100.0 | 105.0 102.0 105.0 105.0 | | | | | 104.0 | | | | | | | | 0.00 | 2.22 |
| A2 | 101.0 | | | | | | | 105.0 104.4 104.0 106.0 | | | | | 12.00 | 12 | 0.00 | 14.26 |
| A3 | | 108.0 107.0 107.0 108.0 | | | | | 104.0 | | | | | | | | 18.67 | 0.00 |
| A4 | 105.0 | | | | | | 104.0 | | | | | | | | 3.70 | 0.00 |

**FIGURE 5.10**
Mass excavation photo.

## Building Excavation Quantity Takeoff

For some buildings, mass excavation may be required (see Fig. 5.10). For others, trenching for foundation walls or footings may be needed (see Fig. 5.11).

**MASS BUILDING EXCAVATION.** The quantity of mass excavation is obtained from the details of the design. The overall size of the building and the size of the footings need to be known before the size of the excavation is calculated. The

**FIGURE 5.11**
Trenching excavation photo.

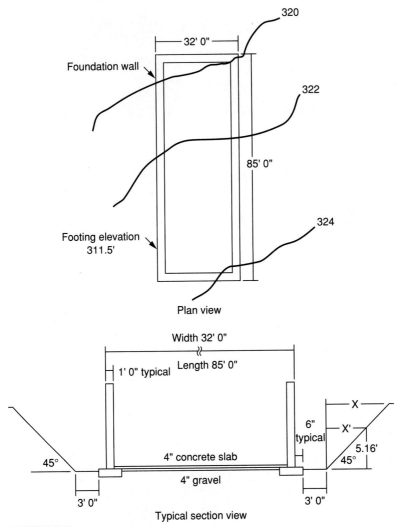

**FIGURE 5.12**
Plan and sectional view of building foundation.

construction method and the safety of the workers will also need to be considered when determining the size of the excavation.

The depth of the excavation is the difference between the existing elevation and the lowest point of the materials to be placed. For most building sites, the average existing elevation of the total building area can be used to establish the top of the excavation. If the earth slopes a great deal in the area of the building, it may be necessary to break the building down into smaller sections. The estimator will have to subtract from the existing grade the depth of the topsoil if it has been removed during the site work. The lowest point is normally the bottom of the granular material under the concrete slab. Figure 5.12 shows a plan and sectional view of a building's foundation. The depth of the excavation is

| | |
|---|---|
| Existing average elevation | 322.00 ft |
| Strip top soil | − 0.50 ft |
| Elevation: top of footings | −311.50 ft |
| Under-slab gravel | − 0.33 ft |
| Total depth of excavation | 10.33 ft |

It should be noted that additional finish hand excavation will be necessary to excavate to the bottom of the footings.

The length and width of the excavation can be determined by adding the outside dimensions of the building, the footing projections, and the amount of working space required to safely install the footings, walls, waterproofing, and so on. The amount of working space required depends on the work activity, depth of the excavation, type of soil, and the method of protecting against cave-ins. In Fig. 5.12, the overall plan dimensions of the excavation are

**Length**

| | |
|---|---|
| Outside dimensions of building | 85′ 0″ |
| Footing projections, 2 × 6″ | 1′ 0″ |
| Working room, 2 × 3′ 0″ | 6′ 0″ |
| Length of excavation | 92′ 0″ |

**Width**

| | |
|---|---|
| Outside dimensions of building | 32′ 0″ |
| Footing projections, 2 × 6″ | 1′ 0″ |
| Working room, 2 × 3′ 0″ | 6′ 0″ |
| Width of excavation | 39′ 0″ |

The total mass excavation quantity is

$$10.33 \text{ ft} \times 92.0 \text{ ft} \times 39.0 \text{ ft} = 37{,}064 \text{ cf} \quad \text{or} \quad 1373 \text{ cy}$$

There are several ways to protect against cave-ins. One is to drive metal sheet piling around the perimeter of the building before the excavation begins. This method is expensive, but it is sometimes required because of the close proximity of other structures.

A more common method is to slope the edges of the excavation back to the angle of repose. This is known as "laying back" the sides of the excavation. The angle of repose (also known as the angle of internal friction) is the angle between a horizontal line and the sloping surface of the earth at which it will generally remain stable (or not slide) unless disturbed. The angle of repose depends on the type of soil and its moisture content. It can be obtained from the soil report or the soils engineer. Figure 5.13 shows the angle of repose for several different types of soil. Whatever method is used to protect against cave-ins, the contractor must adhere to the most recent OSHA 1926 safety standards on excavation.

When the estimator encounters the need to lay back the sides of the excavation, the extra soil to be excavated must be taken into consideration. To calculate

| Soil type | Density of soil | Angle of repose—degrees |
|---|---|---|
| Coarse sand or sand & gravel | Compact Loose | 40 35 |
| Medium sand | Compact Loose | 40 30 |
| Fine, silty sand or sandy silt | Compact Loose | 30 25 |
| Clayey silt | Soft to medium | 20 |
| Silty clay | Soft to medium | 15 |
| Clay | Soft to medium | 0–15 |

**FIGURE 5.13**
Angles of repose.

the total quantity, the estimator can either divide the entire volume into simple figures or consider the entire volume as one figure. One will need to apply geometric and/or trigonometric principles in either case. The following example utilizes the second method.

Referring to Fig. 5.12, with the sides of the excavation laid back at a 45-degree angle, a geometric figure known as a prismoid is formed. The formula for a prismoid is

$$\text{Volume} = \frac{h}{6} \times (\text{AB} + 4\text{AM} + \text{AT})$$

The height is obtained from the cross-sectional view. The areas of the base (AB), midsection (AM), and top (AT) are obtained by the application of geometric principles.

Utilizing some of the information from Fig. 5.12, the dimensions of the base are 39' 0" × 92' 0". Therefore,

$$\text{AB} = 39.0 \text{ ft} \times 92.0 \text{ ft} = 3588 \text{ sf}$$

To obtain the area at the top of the excavation, first calculate the dimensions. The estimator will have to add to the bottom dimensions the horizontal distance the soil is laid back measured at the top of the excavation (distance $X$ in Fig. 5.12).

Using trigonometry,

$$\tan 45° = \frac{10.33 \text{ ft}}{X}$$

$$X = \frac{10.33 \text{ ft}}{\tan 45°} = 10.33 \text{ ft}$$

The dimension applies to both the width and length since the sides are laid back at a 45-degree angle all around the excavation. If this wasn't the case, different calculations would have to be made.

$$\text{Width} = 39.0 \text{ ft} + 2 \times 10.33 \text{ ft} = 59.66 \text{ ft}$$

$$\text{Length} = 92.0 \text{ ft} + 2 \times 10.33 \text{ ft} = 112.66 \text{ ft}$$

The area at the top of the excavation is

$$\text{AT} = 59.66 \text{ ft} \times 112.66 \text{ ft} = 6722 \text{ sf}$$

Finally, the area at the midsection, or halfway between the top and bottom of the excavation, is determined by first obtaining the midheight of the excavation and then the horizontal distance to the setback at that height ($X$, in Fig. 5.12).

$$\text{Midheight} = \frac{10.33 \text{ ft}}{2} = 5.16 \text{ ft}$$

$$X = \frac{5.16 \text{ ft}}{\tan 45°} = 5.16 \text{ ft}$$

The outside dimensions at midheight of the excavation are

$$\text{Width} = 39.0 \text{ ft} + 2 \times 5.16 \text{ ft} = 49.33 \text{ ft}$$

$$\text{Length} = 92.0 \text{ ft} + 2 \times 5.16 \text{ ft} = 102.32 \text{ ft}$$

The resulting area at midheight is

$$\text{AM} = 49.22 \text{ ft} \times 102.32 \text{ ft} = 5048 \text{ sf}$$

The total volume is

$$\text{Volume} = 10.33 \text{ ft}/6 \times (3588 + 4 \times 5048 + 6722) \text{ sf} = 52,515 \text{ cf} \quad \text{or} \quad 1945 \text{ cy}$$

**BUILDING WALL AND FOOTING EXCAVATION.** If the project does not have a floor level below grade, it is necessary only to excavate for the footings. The procedures for wall footing excavation are similar to those of mass excavation. The first step is to determine the length of the footings. The best procedure is to use the centerline dimensions of the foundation around the perimeter of the building. This procedure was explained in Chapter 1. The depth of the excavation is determined similar to the method of establishing the depth of mass excavation. The thickness of the topsoil must be subtracted from the existing elevation if it has been removed during the site work.

The estimator will then have to decide how the sides of the footings are to be formed to hold the concrete until it has cured. Two procedures of forming can be used. One is to carefully excavate the footings and let the sides of the excavation serve as the form (earth form). The other is to build a side form of wood or other appropriate material and then remove it after the concrete has been placed and cured. The specifications should be checked carefully because many times it is not permitted to earth form the footings. If the footings are earth-formed, it will be necessary to carefully shape the sides of the footings. If the sides of the footings are formed, additional excavation is necessary to allow for a larger working space. For either earth-formed or built footing forms, a line item should be included in the pricing sheets that indicates the lineal footage or square footage of footings that require crumbing. Crumbing is required to remove clumps of soil or boulders before the concrete is placed.

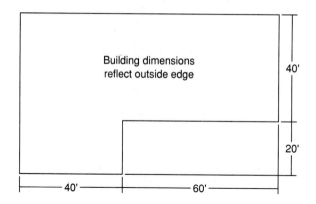

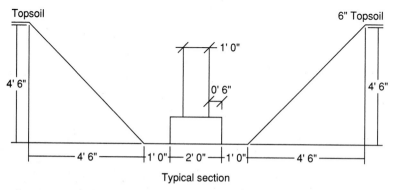

Typical section

Centerline dimension of foundation wall = 99' + 59' + 39' + 20' + 60' + 39' = 316 ft
Area of excavation:
   Rectangular portion = 4' × 4.5' = 18.0 sf
   Triangular portions = 2 × $\frac{1}{2}$(4.5')(4.5') = 20.25 sf
   Total area = 18.00 sf + 20.25 sf = 38.25 sf
Volume of excavation = 316 ft × 38.25 sf = 12,087 cf or 448 cy

**FIGURE 5.14**
Calculations for footing and wall excavations.


As in mass excavation, the sloping of the sides of the excavation is necessary to prevent cave-ins. Figure 5.14 shows the calculations required for footing
excavation.


## BACKFILLING

After the foundation has been completed, soil must be placed in the void that remains. This operation usually takes place after the building has been substantially
completed.

Two methods are commonly used to calculate the quantity of material
required for backfilling. The first method is to subtract the volume of the building below grade (including the basement, foundation system, and any fill under the

building) from the volume of the soil removed during the building excavation. For example, the estimator calculated that 1450 cubic yards of excavation is required for the building in Fig. 5.15. The total backfill required is

| | | |
|---|---|---|
| Volume of excavation | = | 1450.0 cy |
| Volume of building $(45' \times 78' \times 9')/7$ | = | $-1170.0$ cy |
| Volume of ftg. projection: | | |
| $[(45' + 45' + 78' + 78') \times 0.5' \times 0.5']/27$ | = | $-2.3$ cy |
| Total backfill | | 277.7 cy |

The second method is to calculate the actual volume of backfill required. This method is particularly used for buildings that do not have a basement and the material used for backfilling is different on either side of the foundation wall. The estimator will need to make a sketch (see Fig. 5.16) before calculating the amount of backfill.

Area of A and D:
$(2)(\frac{1}{2})(4')(6.25')$   = 25.00 sf
Area of B and C:
$(2)(1.5')(5.25')$   = 15.75 sf
Area of E and F:
$(2)(1')(1')$   =   2.0 sf
        Total area   = 42.75 sf

The volume of backfill is

$$165 \text{ ft} \times 42.75 \text{ sf} = 7053.75 \text{ cf} \quad \text{or} \quad 261.25 \text{ cy}$$

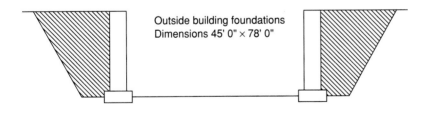

Outside building foundations
Dimensions 45' 0" × 78' 0"

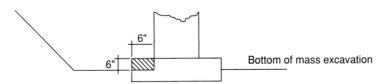

6"

6"   6"   Bottom of mass excavation

**FIGURE 5.15**
Backfilling.

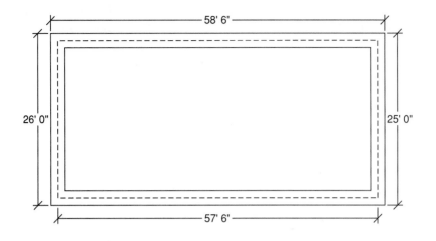

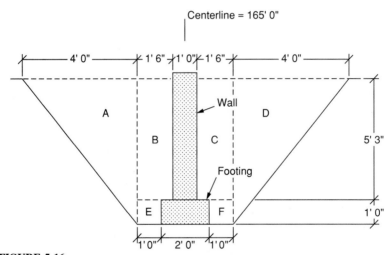

**FIGURE 5.16**
Cross section for backfill.

## EXCESS OR BORROW

After all the excavation and filling calculations, it is necessary to determine if excess material will have to be taken off or additional material will have to be brought onto the site. The total amount of cut is subtracted from the total amount of fill. For example:

**Cut**

| | |
|---|---|
| Site cut | 235 cy |
| Topsoil removed | 66 cy |
| Building excavation | 63 cy |
| Footing excavation | 20 cy |
| Hand exc. at slab turndown | 5 cy |
| Excavation for sidewalks | 13 cy |
| Excavation for signs | 5 cy |
| Total cut | 341 cy |

Slab turn down          Thickened slab

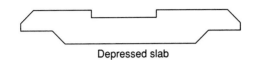

Depressed slab

**FIGURE 5.17**
Underslab requirements.

**Fill**

| | |
|---|---|
| Site fill | 105 cy |
| Topsoil replaced | 66 cy |
| Backfill at building | 40 cy |
| Total fill | 135 cy |

**Haul-off or borrow**

| | |
|---|---|
| Cut | 341 cy |
| Fill | −135 cy |
| Total haul-off | 206 cy |

Using a 15 percent average swell factor for the material being excavated, the total quantity to be hauled off the site is

$$206 \times 1.15 = 233 \text{ cy}$$

If the difference between the cut and fill is negative, a shortage of material on the site exists and borrow is necessary.

## UNDERSLAB REQUIREMENTS

The design of concrete slabs on grade often requires the slab to be turn-down, thickened, or depressed. Figure 5.17 illustrates the sectional view of these three conditions, which usually involve hand excavation. For the purpose of developing the estimate, the turn-down should be assumed to be excavated at a 45-degree angle. Placing gravel under the slab will also require hand grading or possibly the use of a small tractor. The estimator will need to calculate the cubic yards of hand excavation and the square footage of hand grading.

## OTHER EARTHWORK-RELATED ACTIVITIES

### Grading

Various types of grading are required on most projects. The grading is needed to smooth the area and prepare it for the next construction operation. The estimator needs to calculate the square footage of grading for

- Rough site grading to prepare for topsoil
- Finish grading of topsoil to prepare for landscaping
- Fine grading of underslab gravel to prepare for concrete slab

## Trenching

The contractor often uses a trenching machine to excavate long, narrow trenches (less than one foot wide and no deeper than four or five feet). The estimator will need to calculate the linear feet of trench required. For larger trenches, a backhoe may have to be used, and the estimator will need to calculate the cubic yards of excavation.

## Rock Excavation

Rock excavation is a matter of loosening, excavating, and transporting the material. Rock can be classified as soft, medium, or hard, according to the difficulty of loosening and removing it. For calculating yardage, measurements are taken of the rock in its original position and before loosening. The volume will be larger after loosening and breaking. The swell figure can be up to 60 percent of the original bank measure.

When excavating rock the following factors need to be considered:

Kind of rock (soft, medium, or hard)
Amount of each kind of rock in cubic yards
Open-cut excavation or tunneling
Bracing or timbering
Water considerations
Loosening method to be used (e.g., machine drilling and blasting, ripping)
Materials and equipment needed for drilling and blasting
Delays
Loading by hand labor or power equipment
Length of haul and kind of road for transporting broken rock
Transportation method (barrows, trucks)
Equipment needed for transportation
Transportation delays, especially those caused by drilling and blasting
Disposal, dumping, leveling, spreading
Special rules, regulations, and safety requirements to be complied with

## Filling and Compacting Soil

When placing fill material for the purpose of supporting slabs, pavements, and backfilling, the technical specifications will most likely require that the activity be performed in a particular manner and that the final results meet a specified compaction requirement. To ensure that the requirement has been met, an inde-

| Compactor type | For soil type |
|---|---|
| Pneumatic — large tire | All types |
| Pneumatic — small tire | Sandy clays and silts<br>Gravelly sand<br>Clays with small amount of fines |
| Sheep's foot | Clay, silty clay, gravel with<br>clay binder |
| Steel tandem: 2 axle | Sandy silts, granular material<br>with clay binder |
| Steel tandem: 3 axle | Same as for 2 axle |
| Steel — three wheel | Granular or granular plastic<br>material |
| Vibratory | Sand, silty sands, silty gravels |

**FIGURE 5.18**
Compaction equipment.

pendent testing laboratory will test the soil and report on its findings. This should be included in the estimate.

To determine the cost of filling and/or compaction, the estimator must first refer to the technical specifications to obtain any information that will affect the cost. The specifications may contain a soils report indicating the type of soil and the moisture content. Also, the specifications may indicate the degree of compaction of the cohesive soils (i.e., clay) as measured by the standard or modified Proctor tests, or the relative density for cohesionless soils (i.e., sands and gravels). The specifications on the method of filling and compacting soil may be very detailed, including the required type of equipment, the thickness of the layers of soil to be placed (known as lifts), the moisture content of the earth, and other related data. Figure 5.18 provides a summary of the different types of compaction equipment and the types of soil each can compact effectively.

## PRICING EXCAVATION WORK

Establishing the price of excavation is different from the pricing of other work for a building project. For most items in the project, material is purchased and installed. Excavation usually does not require the purchase of many materials. The greatest cost in earthwork is the equipment necessary to redistribute the soil. From previous experience, company records, or published data average production times of equipment are identified. As discussed in Chapter 1, the estimator will need to consider such parameters as cycle time and type of soil to adjust the average production times to fit the specific site conditions.

The total hours required for excavation can be derived by dividing the cubic yards of excavation by the productivity of the crew, including equipment. For example, 600 cubic yards of footing is to be excavated by a crew of one laborer, one equipment operator, and a one-half cubic yard tractor backhoe that can excavate (for the existing site conditions) 200 cubic yards per day. The time required for the crew is

$$\frac{600 \text{ cy}}{200 \text{ cy}} \times 8 \text{ hrs/day} = 24 \text{ crew hours}$$

If the laborer wage rate is $10.00 per hour, the operator wage rate is $15.00 per hour, and the backhoe rate is $30.00 per hour, the direct cost of the excavation activity is

$$24(\$15.00 + \$10.00) + 24 \times \$30.00 = \$1320.00$$

Figure 5.19 is an example of a summary sheet for excavation.

When developing an estimate a reminder list such as the one shown below would be helpful. The first part of the list contains the major items that a contractor may do with his own forces along with the unit of takeoff. The second part notes other considerations that affect the final estimate. The third part of the list is items that will normally be performed by a specialty contractor.

## Site work reminder list

| Quantity takeoff | |
|---|---|
| **Item** | **Unit of measure** |
| Site cut and fill | cy |
| Building excavation | cy |
| Footing excavation | cy |
| Hand excavation | cy |
| Crumbing of footings | lf/sf |
| Shaping of earth form footings | lf/sf |
| Backfilling outside walls | cy |
| Backfilling inside walls earth | cy |
| Backfilling inside walls granular | ton/cy |
| Backfilling isolated footings | ton/cy |
| Backfilling curbs | cy/lf |
| Grading—site rough | sf |
| Grading—site finish | sf |
| Grading—for granular underslab | sf |
| Grading—granular for slab | sf |
| Trenching | lf/cy |
| Borrow | cy |
| Haul-off excess | cy |
| Dewatering | time |
| Wellpoints | time/u |
| Excavate for slabs and sidewalks | cy/sf |
| Excavate flagpoles | ea/cy |
| Excavate signs | ea/cy |
| Excavate curbs | cy/lf |
| Excavate tanks | cy |
| Excavate guard rails | ea/cy |
| Fill for tanks | cy/ton |

# Site work reminder list (*continued*)

## Other considerations that can affect costs

Minimum rental times
Distance to dump sites or barrow pits
Swell factors
Shrink factors
Equipment hauling and setup time
EPA regulations
Over excavation for working space
Safety
Shoring or lay excavation back
Dump fees
Equipment downtime and service
Subsurface reports
Rock removal
Equipment demobilization

## Specialty contractor bid to general contractor

Asphalt paving
Grading for base of paving
Paving base
Paving binder
Paving topping
Paving sealer
Painting and stripping for paving
Pile driving
Number of setups
Move in and move out
Subsurface exploration
Borings
Core drillings
Standard penetration tests
Seismic exploration
Tunneling
Demolition
Site utilities
Landscaping
Marine work
Railroad work
Irrigation systems
Cleanup
Minority-owned business
Union or merit shop contractor
Certificate of insurance
Performance and payment bonds
Safety performance record
Documented total quality management program

COMPUTED BY: KB  PROJECT: ACE Manufacturing  DATE: 1-7
CHECKED BY: RL  ARCHITECT: John Smith  PAGE: 1 OF 1  INDEX NO:

| REF. | DESCRIPTION | QUANTITY TOTAL | UN. | MATERIAL COST UNIT COST | MATERIAL SUBTOTAL | DAILY PROD. OF CREW | CREW MAKE-UP | MAN-HOUR PER UNIT | TOTAL MAN HOURS | TOTAL CREW HOURS | AVG. WAGE RATE | LABOR SUBTOTAL | RATE PER HOUR | EQUIP. SUBTOTAL | SUB. OR OTHER | TOTAL COST |
|---|---|---|---|---|---|---|---|---|---|---|---|---|---|---|---|---|
| | Strip Top Soil | 150 | CY | 0 | 0 | 300 | 2 | .1533 | 8 | 4 | 16.50 | 132 | 85 | 340 | | 472 |
| | Site Cut | 758 | CY | 0 | 0 | 600 | 2 | .027 | 20.2 | 10.1 | 16.50 | 333 | 85 | 859 | | 1192 |
| | Site Fill | 1220 | CY | 0 | 0 | 600 | 2 | .027 | 32.5 | 16.3 | 16.50 | 537 | 85 | 1382 | | 1919 |
| | Wall Ftg. Exc. | 276 | CY | 0 | 0 | 140 | 2 | .114 | 31.5 | 15.8 | 16.50 | 520 | 45 | 710 | | 1230 |
| | Crumb Footing | 400 | LF | 0 | 0 | 600 | 1 | .013 | 5.33 | 5.33 | 15.00 | 80 | | 0 | | 80 |
| | Back Fill | 226 | CY | 0 | 0 | 800 | 3 | 0.12 | 27.12 | 9.04 | 16.00 | 434 | 45 | 406 | | 840 |
| | Slab Turn down | 9 | CY | 0 | 0 | 5 | 1 | 1.6 | 14.4 | 14.4 | 15.00 | 216 | | 0 | | 216 |
| | Sand @ SOG | 181 | TON | 12 | 2172 | 150 | 3 | 0.16 | 28.96 | 9.7 | 16.00 | 463 | 45 | 434 | | 3069 |
| | Fine Grade Slab | 10270 | SF | | | 3000 | 3 | 0.002 | 20.5 | 6.9 | 15.10 | 308 | | 0 | | 308 |
| | Replace Top Soil | 150 | CY | | | 300 | 2 | .053 | 8 | 4 | 16.50 | 132 | 85 | 340 | | 472 |
| | Barrow | 550 | CY | 3 | 1650 | | | | | | | 0 | | 0 | | 1650 |
| | Layout | 3 | AC | 100 | 300 | | 3 | | 24 | 8 | 16.50 | 396 | | 0 | | 696 |
| TOTAL FROM PREVIOUS PAGE: | | | | | 6 | | | | | | | 6 | | 0 | | 0 |
| TOTAL: | | | | | 4182 | | | | | | | 3561 | | 4471 | 0 | 12144 |

**FIGURE 5.19**
Summary sheet for excavation.

# STUDENT EXERCISES

**5.1.** After reviewing Chapters 4 and 5, write a spreadsheet template that will calculate the number of trucks required for earth removal with the following input:

Quantity of earth to be hauled off

Round trip time of the truck

Time at loading

Capacity of truck

Time at dump site

Productivity of end loader

**5.2.** How does the soil swell and shrink affect the earth takeoff?

**5.3.** Given the site plan shown in Fig. 5.20, and using a 50-foot grid, use the four-point method described in the chapter to calculate the total cubic yards of cut-and-fill work required.

**5.4.** Assume a contractor has to dig a massive excavation for a building foundation. He uses four dump trucks and a large backhoe. The backhoe excavates material and in turn loads a dump truck with five cubic yards of material. When a truck is loaded it leaves the excavation site, hauls the material to a dump site, and then returns empty to be loaded again. Assume that once a truck leaves the excavation site, it takes 20

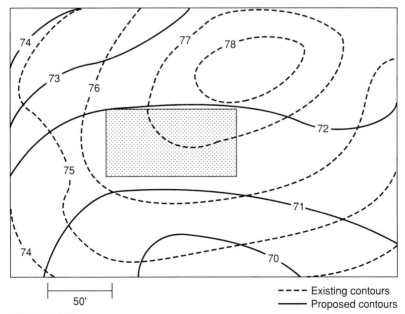

**FIGURE 5.20**
Site plan.

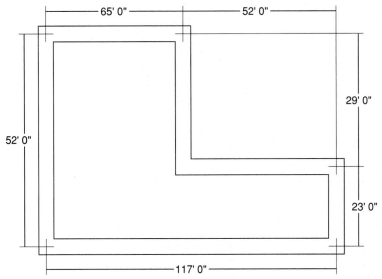

Note: All dimensions to centerline

Plan view

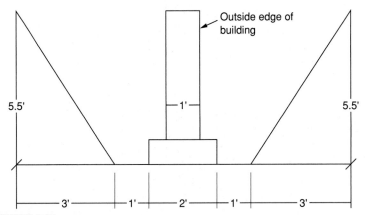

**FIGURE 5.21**
Foundation wall.

minutes to return. The contractor has determined that the backhoe can load a dump truck in six minutes, assuming a truck is available to be loaded. Assuming that the backhoe costs $100 per hour and that each truck costs $45 per hour, determine the estimated cost for excavating 20,000 cubic yards of material.

**5.5.** Given the information in Fig. 5.21, determine the cubic yards of earth to be removed for the footing excavation.

# CHAPTER
# 6

# CONCRETE

Division 3, concrete, of the Uniform Construction Index (CSI format) includes items relating to concrete construction. The major concrete-related items covered in this chapter are formwork, reinforcing steel, concrete (cast-in-place and precast), finishing, curing, and protection.

Estimating concrete can vary depending on whether the concrete is cast-in-place on the project or is purchased as precast units. If the concrete is cast-in-place, the estimator must consider various activities in developing the cost, including installing formwork, reinforcing steel (and other embedded items), concrete, finishing, curing, protecting concrete, and removal and cleaning (and possibly coating) of the forms. If, on the other hand, precast concrete items are specified, the estimator determines the cost of the specific item and then considers the cost of placing it into its final position. There are many different types of commercially available precast units. In addition, manufacturers of precast components can custom make any size and style needed. Concrete can be precast on or off the job site. Specialty contractors usually install precast units.

The purpose of this chapter is to (1) provide sufficient background so that the estimator understands the general items in division 3; (2) establish a basis for estimating concrete work associated with general construction; and (3) provide an introduction to the specialty of concrete construction. This chapter will present the method of taking off and pricing formwork and its removal (including cleaning and coating), reinforcing steel and other embedments, concrete (including placing and finishing, curing, and protection), and precast concrete.

## TAKING OFF FORMWORK

Estimating formwork can be a tedious and time-consuming task. There are hundreds of different formwork systems, not to mention the various types of materials of which they are constructed. Forms can be built on the job (referred to as job-built forms) or prebuilt. Job-built forms are usually constructed of wood; prebuilt forms are usually made of steel and wood. Some prebuilt forms, however, can be made of fiberglass (beams and columns), all metal (floor systems), or paper products (columns). Figure 6.1 shows examples of job-built and prebuilt formwork systems.

Relative to job-built forms, the various types and sizes of components are determined by the member being formed and from the results of a formwork design. In the case of prebuilt forms, they are purchased or rented by prefabricated sections for the type and size of member and installed on the job site. In either case, cutting, fabricating, placing, alignment, and bracing are possible in constructing formwork. Stripping and cleaning may also need to be included in the estimate if the formwork is to be reused.

It is to the contractor's advantage to reuse the same form, whether job–built or prebuilt, as many times as possible. This will result in a lower per unit cost. The number of reuses depends on the durability of members, the care taken in erecting and removing them, and the number of times the same member or section of formwork can be used. One can usually obtain more reuses from prebuilt forms than from job-built ones. The issue of reuse is considered in pricing the formwork.

In developing the formwork estimate, the following items should be considered:

1. Type of member being formed
2. Whether a job-built or prebuilt form will be used
3. Location and other characteristics that make the form unique
4. What is included in the takeoff, which may differ by company

Taking off the quantities of formwork is somewhat more difficult than other materials because the drawings do not indicate the location or quantity of forms to be installed. The estimator must be able to determine what concrete needs to be formed, including requirements for bracing, scaffolding, or similar formwork components not shown on the drawings. This requires the estimator to have experience in formwork construction and/or be provided detailed formwork design drawings.

In most cases, formwork is taken off by computing the actual surface area of the form that comes into contact with the concrete, measured in square feet. The "square foot contact area" (sfca) is then categorized by the type of member being formed (beam, column, slab, etc.). An exception to this would be for moldings, cornices, sills, reglets, chamfers, and copings, which are taken off by the linear foot.

Most buildings will have openings in the concrete. These openings are accounted for by "blocking out" the form so that the fluid concrete does not flow into the space. The material for blockouts must be included in the takeoff.

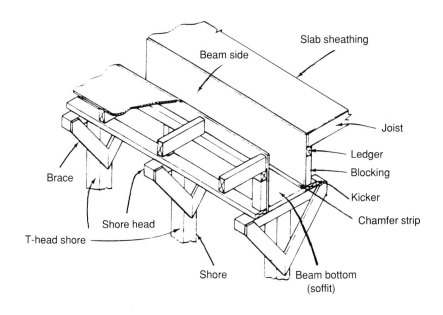

Job-built system

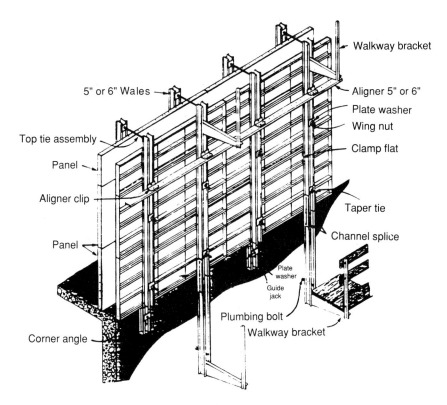

Prebuilt system

**FIGURE 6.1**
Formwork systems. (Courtesy of The Burke Company.)

149

The formwork takeoff must also include related materials such as bracing, scaffolding (falsework), fasteners, wire, ties, form liners, form oil, and other items necessary to erect and secure the formwork. The estimator will obtain the types and quantities from the formwork design or from the supplier.

## Job-Built Forms

Taking off the quantity of job-built forms begins with a formwork design to determine the size, spacing, and quantity of sheathing, studs, joists, wales, ties, and other formwork components. The quantity to be taken off is based on the square foot contact area. (See Fig. 6.6 for a ministudy illustrating job-built forms quantity takeoff.)

Figure 6.2 contains an illustration of a job-built wall form, and Fig. 6.3 is the completed worksheet documenting the quantity takeoff of the components.

## Prebuilt Forms

Prebuilt or prefabricated forms (see Fig. 6.4) can be purchased or rented depending on how often they will be used. If a contractor will use the formwork for only one small project, it is probably better to rent it. If the forms are going to be used for many projects or for one very large project, it may be more economical to purchase them.

The actual type and size of prefabricated formwork required depends on the item being formed. The estimator, using the formwork design calculations and the project drawings and specifications, works with the supplier to identify the required material items based on the square foot contact area with the concrete. Items such as bracing, ties, and other accessories are furnished in adequate quantities with the forms, so the amounts of the various accessories do not have to be taken off by the estimator. Figure 6.5 shows an example of a takeoff of the prebuilt formwork shown in Fig. 6.4.

## PRICING OF FORMWORK

The total cost of erecting formwork includes materials, labor, and equipment. Since job-built or prebuilt forms can be used for most formwork, the estimator will need to perform a cost–benefit analysis to determine which is more economical. In this analysis it is important that the estimator consider the number of times the forms can be reused. Many variables must be considered when determining the number of reuses. Some of the major ones include complexity of the formwork, size, number of repetitions of the same size, quantity of formwork to be installed, and quality of the formwork materials.

## Formwork Material Cost

The costs of materials are obtained from the supplier of the formwork components or systems. In the case of job-built forms, the estimator should determine the cost of the material for one section of the formwork, calculate a unit square foot cost,

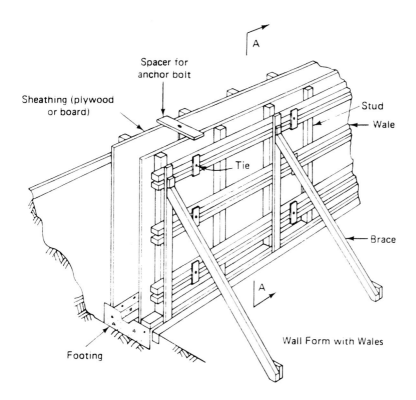

Spacer for
anchor bolt

Sheathing (plywood
or board)

Stud

Wale

Tie

Brace

Footing

Wall Form with Wales

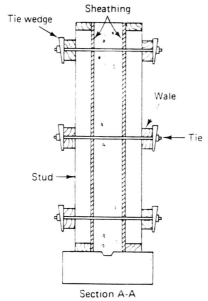

Tie wedge

Sheathing

Wale

Tie

Stud

Section A-A

**FIGURE 6.2**
Job-built wall form.

| COMPUTED BY: KB | | PROJECT: | Cobbs Crossing | | | | | | | | DATE: 9-26 |
| CHECKED BY: RL | | ARCHITECT: | AIA International | | | | | | | | PAGE: 1 OF 1 |
| | | | | | | | | | | | INDEX NO: |

| REF | DESCRIPTION | QUAN | DIMENSIONS LENGTH | WIDTH | HEIGHT | SUBTOTAL QUAN | UN | TOTAL QUAN | UN | REMARKS |
|---|---|---|---|---|---|---|---|---|---|---|
| | Plywood Sheathing | 2 | 100 | | 8 | 1600 | SF | 50 | EA | 32 SF/Sheet |
| | 2"x4" Studs | 100 | 8 | | | 800 | LF | | | |
| | 2"x4" Wales | 2 | 600 | | | 1200 | LF | | | 100 LF/4 Ft o.c. |
| | 2"x4" Bracing | 50 | 8 | | | 400 | LF | | | |
| | 2"x4" Bracing | 50 | 10 | | | 500 | LF | | | |
| | 2"x4" Brace Plate | 2 | 110 | | | 200 | LF | | | |
| | | | | | | | | | | |
| | Subtotal 2"x4" | | | | | 3100 | LF | 2067 | BF | 0.67 BF to LF |
| | | | | | | | | | | |
| | Ties | 150 | | | | | | 150 | EA | |

| TOTAL FROM PREVIOUS PAGE: | | |
| TOTAL: | | |

**FIGURE 6.3**
Quantity takeoff for job-built formwork.

152

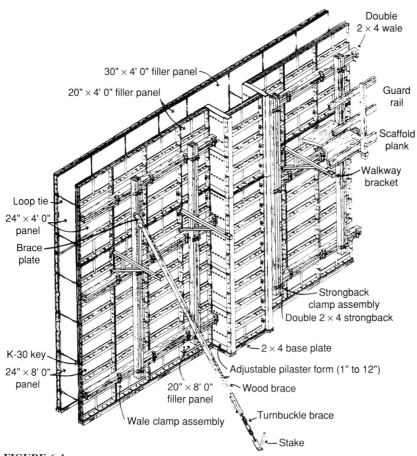

**FIGURE 6.4**
Example of prebuilt form. (Courtesy of The Burke Company.)

and use this number to determine the total material cost from the takeoff of the total square foot contact area for the specific form.

Using the example formwork takeoff in Fig. 6.3, the material pricing is shown in Fig. 6.6. After the prices of the individual components are calculated, the items are added and the sum divided by the total square foot contact area. If the formwork is to be used more than once, the price per square foot of contact area is divided by the number of reuses, as shown in Fig. 6.6. This price is then increased by approximately 10 percent to account for any formwork damaged during removal. The final unit price is then applied to the total square footage of formwork required for the project. This process is called a ministudy. The estimator should perform a ministudy when there is substantial difference in the type or size of material or there is a change in the waste requirements. For most construction companies the process of determining the cost of formwork using a ministudy will be done two or three times a year, or when bidding on a project that

| COMPUTED BY: KB | PROJECT: Cobbs Crossing | DATE: 7-26 |
|---|---|---|
| CHECKED BY: RL | ARCHITECT: AIA International | PAGE: 1 OF 1 |
| | | INDEX NO: |

| REF | DESCRIPTION | QUAN. | DIMENSIONS | | | SUBTOTAL | | TOTAL | | REMARKS |
|---|---|---|---|---|---|---|---|---|---|---|
| | | | LENGTH | WIDTH | HEIGHT | QUAN. | UN. | QUAN. | UN. | |
| | Formwork Panels | 2 | 100 | | 10 | 2000 | SF | | | |
| | Pilaster Panels | 20 | 1 | | 10 | 200 | SF | | | |
| | Subtotal Panels | | | | | | | 2200 | SF A | |

| TOTAL FROM PREVIOUS PAGE: |
|---|
| TOTAL: |

**FIGURE 6.5**
Example worksheet for prebuilt formwork.

| Item | Quantity* | Unit | Unit price | Total material |
|---|---|---|---|---|
| $\frac{3}{4}$ Plywood sheets | 1600 | sf | 1.25 | $2,000.00 |
| 2 × 4 Studs | 533 | bf | 0.50 | $ 266.50 |
| 2 × 4 Wales | 800 | bf | 0.50 | $ 400.00 |
| 2 × 4 Bracing — 8' | 267 | bf | 0.50 | $ 133.50 |
| 2 × 4 Bracing — 10' | 333 | bf | 0.50 | $ 166.50 |
| 2 × 4 Base plate | 133 | bf | 0.50 | $ 66.50 |
| | | | Total | $3,033.00 |

| | |
|---|---|
| Total per square foot = $ 3,033/ 1,600 sf = | $ 1.90 per sf |
| 3 Reuse of forms = $ 1.90 / 3 = | $ 0.63 per sf |
| Add for damage = $ 0.63 × 1.10 = | $ 0.70 per sf |
| Total sfca price | $ 0.70 |

*Note: All quantities include waste.

**FIGURE 6.6**
Job-built form ministudy.

has forms that are different from those covered by the most recently performed ministudy.

## Formwork Labor Cost

To obtain the labor cost, the estimator will need to know the labor productivity and wage rates of the crew. The productivity is obtained from company historical records and adjusted for the specific project. Many items affect the productivity rates, including:

1. What is included in formwork
2. Number of forming irregularities
3. Whether or not formwork will need to be cleaned and oiled
4. Complexity of the fabrication of prebuilt forms
5. Complexity of the construction of job-built forms
6. Amount of reshoring needed for elevated slabs and beams
7. Size and shape of member to be formed
8. Height of member to be formed above ground
9. Number of reuses
10. Removal of the formwork

In formwork construction some tasks do not require material, such as stripping and cleaning. These activities should be documented separately on the summary sheet from those related to the erection of the forms, which include a material component. Some companies, however, include these two activities in their labor pricing.

## Formwork Equipment Cost

For very large formwork projects, heavy equipment may be needed to assist in the erection and removal process. In addition, special formwork systems such as flying forms or gang forms require the use of heavy equipment.

The equipment is priced by the type and size required and the number of hours needed. Operator time and wages also need to be considered, either as part of the equipment costs or listed in the labor category. Figure 6.7 shows an example of a summary sheet using the information from the worksheet shown in Fig. 6.5.

## TAKEOFF OF REINFORCING STEEL AND OTHER EMBEDMENTS

The reinforcing steel used in concrete may be reinforcing bars and/or welded wire mesh. Other items in reinforcing or formwork, known as embedments, include anchor bolts, plates or inserts for the future connection of other items of work, corner protection angles, supports for the reinforcing bars in the forms, and sleeves for the passage of pipes, conduit, and ductwork.

Reinforcing bars are designated by the bar number, which corresponds to the bar diameter in eighths of an inch. Figure 6.8 lists the different sizes and physical properties of the commonly used reinforcing bars. Reinforcing bars are available in many different types and grades of steel. They can also be purchased with a plastic coating.

The reinforcing bars can be purchased from the mill or warehouse where they can be cut to size, bent, bundled, and tied. These suppliers can also provide shop drawings that aid in the handling and placement of reinforcing bars on the job site. For smaller jobs, the contractor might find it more economical to purchase straight bars and cut and bend them on the job. This activity is seldom done because it is usually more expensive and results in more waste.

Mesh reinforcing may be welded wire mesh or expanded metal. Welded wire mesh is usually furnished in a rectangular or square arrangement of wires welded together. The wire mesh designation uses spacing and wire gauge. For example, for a designation of 6×6–W1.4×W1.4, the first two numbers indicate the size of the grid, in this case a square of 6″ (longitudinal direction) × 6″ (transverse direction). The second set of numbers relates to the standard number size for the specific gauge of wire. Figure 6.9 lists some of the common wire mesh designations.

Welded wire mesh is sold in rolls or flat sheets. The rolls are 5 feet wide and 150 feet long. The flat sheets are available in a variety of sizes. In addition, the mesh is available in different materials, the most common being plain or galvanized steel. One can also purchase plastic coated mesh.

Expanded metal reinforcement is a special type of mesh used primarily for concrete floor, roof, and bank vault construction. The estimator should check with the supplier to determine units of takeoff.

Reinforcing bars are held in the forms by bar chairs, spacers, or bolsters, or they may be suspended by wires. These supports may be plastic, or galvanized

# SUMMARY SHEET

COMPUTED BY: KB  
CHECKED BY: RL  
PROJECT: Occone Bank  
ARCHITECT: A/A Architects  
DATE: 9-26  
PAGE: 1 OF 1  
INDEX NO:

| REF | DESCRIPTION | QUANTITY TOTAL | UN | MATERIAL COST UNIT COST | MATERIAL SUBTOTAL | DAILY PROD OF CREW | CREW MAKE-UP | MAN-HOUR PER UNIT | TOTAL MAN HOURS | TOTAL CREW HOURS | AVG WAGE RATE | LABOR SUBTOTAL | RATE PER HOUR | EQUIP SUBTOTAL | SUB OR OTHER | TOTAL COST |
|---|---|---|---|---|---|---|---|---|---|---|---|---|---|---|---|---|
| | Prefab Panels | 2200 | SF | 2 | 4400 | 500 | 2 | | | 35 | 25 | 1750 | | 0 | 0 | 6150 |
| | Water Shingles | 1067 | BF | 0.25 | 267 | 400 | 2 | | | 22 | 18 | 792 | | 0 | 0 | 1059 |
| | TOTAL FROM PREVIOUS PAGE: | | | | 0 | | | | | | | 0 | | 0 | 0 | 0 |
| | TOTAL: | | | | 4667 | | | | | | | 2542 | | 0 | 0 | 7209 |

FIGURE 6.7
Summary sheet.

| Bar number | Pounds per foot | Inches, diameter | Area, square inches |
|:---:|:---:|:---:|:---:|
| 2 | 0.167 | 0.250 | 0.05 |
| 3 | 0.376 | 0.375 | 0.11 |
| 4 | 0.668 | 0.500 | 0.20 |
| 5 | 1.043 | 0.625 | 0.31 |
| 6 | 1.502 | 0.750 | 0.44 |
| 7 | 2.044 | 0.875 | 0.60 |
| 8 | 2.670 | 1.000 | 0.76 |
| 9 | 3.400 | 1.128 | 1.00 |
| 10 | 4.303 | 1.270 | 1.27 |
| 11 | 5.313 | 1.410 | 1.56 |

**FIGURE 6.8**
Reinforcing bar chart.

or zinc-coated steel with plastic legs and other materials. All of these accessories are included in the embedments category. Figure 6.10 shows some of the more common types of reinforcing bar supports. To determine the type, size, and quantity of bar supports, the estimator should refer to the technical specification and consult with experienced people within the company.

Reinforcing bars are taken off in linear feet by type and size and converted to weight. Figure 6.8 can be used to convert length to weight using the unit weight numbers. For example, ten #8 bars 12' 0" long weigh a total of

$$10 \times 12' \times 2.67 \text{ lb/ft} = 320.4 \text{ lb} \quad \text{or} \quad 321 \text{ lb}$$

| | Steel area sq. | | Approx. wt. per 100 lbs/sf |
|:---|:---:|:---:|:---:|
| | **Long.** | **Trans.** | |
| **Rolls** | | | |
| 6×6-W1.4 × W1.4 | 0.028 | 0.028 | 21 |
| 6×6-W2.0 × W2.0 | 0.040 | 0.040 | 29 |
| 6×6-W2.9 × W2.9 | 0.058 | 0.058 | 42 |
| 6×6-W4.0 × W4.0 | 0.080 | 0.080 | 58 |
| 4×4-W1.4 × W1.4 | 0.042 | 0.042 | 31 |
| 4×4-W2.0 × W2.0 | 0.060 | 0.060 | 43 |
| 4×4-W2.9 × W2.9 | 0.087 | 0.087 | 62 |
| 4×4-W4.0 × W4.0 | 0.120 | 0.120 | 85 |
| **Sheets** | | | |
| 6×6-W2.9 × W2.9 | 0.058 | 0.058 | 42 |
| 6×6-W4.0 × W4.0 | 0.080 | 0.080 | 58 |
| 6×6-W5.5 × W5.5 | 0.110 | 0.110 | 80 |
| 4×4-W4.0 × W4.0 | 0.120 | 0.120 | 85 |

**FIGURE 6.9**
Welded wire mesh table.

| Symbol | Bar Support Illustration | Bar Support Illustration Plastic Capped or Dipped | Type of Support | Typical Sizes |
|---|---|---|---|---|
| SB | 5" | 5" Capped | Slab bolster | $\frac{3}{4}$, 1, $1\frac{1}{2}$, and 2 inch heights in 5 ft. and 10 ft. lengths |
| SBU* | 5" | | Slab bolster upper | Same as SB |
| BB | $2\frac{1}{2}$" $2\frac{1}{2}$" | $2\frac{1}{2}$" $2\frac{1}{2}$" Capped | Beam bolster | 1, $1\frac{1}{2}$, 2, over 2" to 5" heights in increments of $\frac{1}{4}$" in lengths of 5 ft. |
| BBU* | $2\frac{1}{2}$" $2\frac{1}{2}$" | | Beam bolster upper | Same as BB |
| BC | | Dipped | Individual bar chair | $\frac{3}{4}$, 1, $1\frac{1}{2}$, and $1\frac{3}{4}$" heights |
| JC | | Dipped      Dipped | Joist chair | 4, 5, and 6 inch widths and $\frac{3}{4}$, 1 and $1\frac{1}{2}$ inch heights |
| HC | | Capped | Individual high chair | 2 to 15 inch heights in increments of $\frac{1}{4}$ inch |
| HCM* | | | High chair for metal deck | 2 to 15 inch heights in increments of $\frac{1}{4}$ inch |
| CHC | 8" | 8" Capped | Continuous high chair | Same as HC in 5 foot and 10 foot lengths |
| CHCU* | 8" | | Continuous high chair upper | Same as HC |
| CHCM* | | | Continuous high chair for metal deck | Up to 5 inch heights in increments of $\frac{1}{4}$ inch |
| JCU** | Top of Slab, $\frac{3}{4}$" MIN, #4 or $\frac{1}{2}$, HEIGHT, 14" | Top of Slab, $\frac{3}{4}$" MIN, #4 or $\frac{1}{2}$, HEIGHT, 14" Dipped | Joist chair upper | 14" Span heights −1" thru +3$\frac{1}{2}$ vary in $\frac{1}{4}$" increments |
| CS | | | Continuous support | $1\frac{1}{4}$" to 12" in increments of $\frac{1}{4}$" lengths of 6'-8" |

* Usually available in Class 3 only, except on special order.
* Usually available in Class 3 only, with upturned or end bearing legs.

**FIGURE 6.10**

Reinforcing bar supports. (Courtesy of the Concrete Reinforcing Steel Institute.)

Reinforcing steel bars are taken off in an order consistent with the specific members identified on the drawings using a special worksheet (see Fig. 6.13). Following this method will result in capturing all the reinforcing bar requirements for each member. Be sure to keep the various bar sizes separate by grade of material, location, and use.

Since bars are available only in certain lengths, they may need to be connected through splicing or lapping. The American Institute of Concrete or other prevailing code must be used to determine the acceptable connecting technique. If lapping, an allowance must be made for this depending on the length of the overlap. The estimator should document the lap calculations on the worksheet. In terms of waste, as little as 1 percent should be included for precut bars and as much as 10 percent when the bars are cut and bent on the job site. In addition, when there are no special design requirements, the estimator can use 5 percent to take care of the additional bar length needed for laps. File REINF.WK1 or REINF.WQ1 is a spreadsheet that can be used for reinforced bar takeoff (see Fig. 6.11).

---

### REINFORCING QUANTITY TAKEOFF

**ENTER PROJECT INFORMATION**

| | |
| --- | --- |
| ALT I   = | INSTRUCTION |
| ALT W   = | WORKSHEET |
| ALT L   = | LOCK TILES |
| ALT U   = | UNLOCK |
| ALT S   = | SUMMARY |
| ALT T   = | TOTAL |

PROJECT:       West High School
ESTIMATOR:     Bob Smith
SHIPPING LENGTH: =          40 FEET
BAR LAP REQUIR. =           30 B.D.

| ITEM | LOCATION | BAR # | # of BARS | LENGTH | TOTAL LENGTH | TOTAL WEIGHT | ITEM TOTAL |
| --- | --- | --- | --- | --- | --- | --- | --- |
| FOOTINGS | Col. line 1 | 4 | 1 | 10 | 10 | 7 | |
| | West | 6 | 5 | 3.7 | 19 | 29 | |
| | East | 5 | 20 | 100 | 2078 | 2167 | |
| | Center | 4 | 2 | 10 | 21 | 14 | |
| SUBTOTAL | FOOTINGS | | | | | | 2217 |
| SLAB | | | | | | | |
| | West | 18 | 3 | 10 | 34 | 465 | |
| | Classroom | 5 | 2 | 5 | 10 | 11 | |
| SUBTOTAL | SLAB | | | | | | 476 |
| COLUMNS | | | | | | | |
| | walkway | 4 | 6 | 12 | 74 | 50 | |
| | entry | 3 | 5 | 20 | 102 | 38 | |
| SUBTOTAL | COLUMNS | | | | | | 88 |

**FIGURE 6.11**
Spreadsheet for reinforced bar takeoff.

Welded wire mesh is taken off by the various sizes specified and the number of square feet required of each type. In the placement process the mesh is usually required to be lapped at at least one grid. This allowance must be included in the takeoff. There is very little waste (1 percent or less) considered in the welded wire mesh takeoff. Once the total square footage is calculated, this quantity is converted to rolls or sheets, depending on how it is purchased. In the first case, the estimator would divide the total number of required square feet by 675 to obtain the number of rolls. This quantity includes waste and laps. A similar method is used for sheets, adding approximately 10 percent for laps and waste.

Embedments are taken off per unit by type and size. The quantity of each is listed by type and size on the worksheet, with 5 percent added for waste.

Figure 6.12 is a sectional drawing of reinforcing steel, and Figure 6.13 is an example of a takeoff for reinforcing bars.

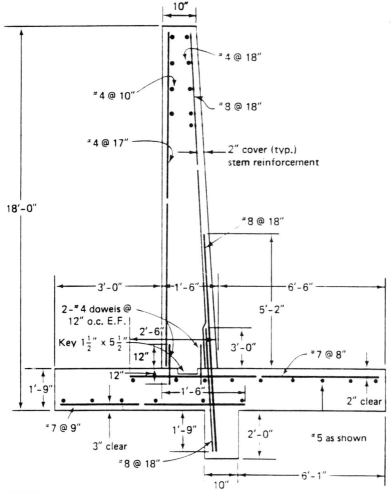

**FIGURE 6.12**
Reinforcing steel drawing.

COMPUTED BY: DB  
CHECKED BY: RL  
PROJECT: RETAINING WALL  
ARCHITECT: JOSEPH ENGINEERS  
DATE: 9-26  
PAGE: 1 OF 1  
INDEX NO:

| REF. | DESCRIPTION | SIZE: #4 NO. | LENGTH | TOTAL | SIZE: #5 NO. | LENGTH | TOTAL | SIZE: #7 NO. | LENGTH | TOTAL | SIZE: #8 NO. | LENGTH | TOTAL | SIZE: NO. | LENGTH | TOTAL |
|---|---|---|---|---|---|---|---|---|---|---|---|---|---|---|---|---|
| 6-12 | WALL STEEL | | | | | | | | | | | | | | | |
| | HORIZONTAL | 9 | 100 | 900 | | | | | | | 67 | 16.5 | 1106 | | | |
| | VERTICAL | 71 | 16.5 | 1172 | | | | | | | 67 | 9 | 603 | | | |
| | | | | | | | | | | | 67 | 7 | 469 | | | |
| | DOWELS | 200 | 2 | 400 | | | | | | | | | | | | |
| | SUBTOTAL | | | 2472 | | | | | | | | | 2178 | | | |
| | CONVERSION FACTOR | | | .668 | | | | | | | | | 2.670 | | | |
| | SUBTOTAL | | | 1651 | | | | | | | | | 5815 | | | |
| 6-12 | FOOTING STEEL | | | | | | | | | | | | | | | |
| | HORIZONTAL | | | | 15 | 100 | 1500 | 134 | 4.5 | 603 | | | | | | |
| | | | | | | | | 150 | 9 | 1350 | | | | | | |
| | SUBTOTAL | | | | | | 1500 | | | 1953 | | | | | | |
| | CONVERSION FACTOR | | | | | | 1.043 | | | 2.044 | | | | | | |
| | SUBTOTAL | | | | | | 1565 | | | 3992 | | | | | | |
| | TOTALS FROM PREVIOUS PAGE: | | | 0 | | | 0 | | | 0 | | | 0 | | | 0 |
| | TOTALS: | | LB | 1651 | | LB | 1565 | | LB | 3992 | | LB | 5815 | | LB | 0 |

**FIGURE 6.13**  
Takeoff of reinforcing steel items.

# PRICING REINFORCING STEEL

## Reinforcing Material Cost

Reinforcing steel is usually purchased by weight. The exception may be for welded wire mesh and embedment items. The estimator should contact the supplier to determine the unit of purchase for the embedded items.

Normally the general contractor receives a price for all the reinforcing. The estimator should make sure that all bending, shop drawings, and shipping are included. For small projects, the reinforcing contractor may quote a unit price for the reinforcing. The estimator takes the total weight times the quoted unit price. Again, the estimator should make sure that all bending, shop drawings, and shipping are included.

## Reinforcing Labor Cost

The labor productivity and wage rates must be known to determine the labor cost. Company historical productivity factors altered for the specific project will be utilized along with current wage rates. It is important that the estimator separate the various labor production functions as the takeoff is being performed. The productivity for placing reinforcing in a wall footing will be higher than the productivity required for a wall. Remember the rule: "If it is different, keep it separate." In addition, the estimator should not forget the handling of the reinforcing steel once it arrives on the job site. It may also have to be inventoried and stored, which incur labor costs.

## Reinforcing Equipment Cost

Heavy equipment may be needed to unload and handle the reinforcing steel. The cost of the equipment, such as a crane or fork lift, should be included in the estimate. Figure 6.14 is a summary sheet for pricing the installation of reinforcing steel.

# TAKING OFF CONCRETE

Concrete may be either ready-mixed or mixed on the job. Most of the concrete used in building construction is ready-mixed and delivered by the ready-mix company. However, on very large building projects or civil construction projects such as highways and dams, the concrete is usually produced on site using field batching plants. Since most concrete used for buildings is ready-mixed, job-mixed concrete will not be discussed in this text.

There are various types of concrete. The specifications indicate the types required for each project. Besides the basic ingredients of cement, coarse and fine aggregate, and water, the specifications may require additional ingredients (such as coloring agents). These additional ingredients are known as admixtures. In the case of ready-mixed concrete, this information is provided to the ready-mix

SUMMARY SHEET

COMPUTED BY: T.F.  
CHECKED BY: RL  
PROJECT: OCCONE BANK  
ARCHITECT: AAA ARCHITECTS  
DATE: 9-26  
PAGE: 1 OF 1  
INDEX NO:

| REF | DESCRIPTION | QUANTITY | | MATERIAL COST | | LABOR COST | | | | | | | EQUIPMENT COST | | SUB OR OTHER | TOTAL COST |
|---|---|---|---|---|---|---|---|---|---|---|---|---|---|---|---|---|
| | | TOTAL | UN | UNIT COST | MATERIAL SUBTOTAL | DAILY PROD OF CREW | CREW MAKE-UP | MAN-HOUR PER UNIT | TOTAL MAN HOURS | TOTAL CREW HOURS | AVG WAGE RATE | LABOR SUBTOTAL | RATE PER HOUR | EQUIP SUBTOTAL | | |
| 6.12 | Wall Steel | | | | | | | | | | | | | | | |
| | #4 Rebar | 1651 | LB | 1.1 | 1816 | 2000 | 4 | | | 6.6 | 21 | 139 | | 0 | 0 | 1955 |
| | #8 Rebar | 5815 | LB | 1.25 | 7269 | 1500 | 4 | | | 31 | 21 | 651 | | 0 | 0 | 7920 |
| | Subtotal | | | | 9085 | | | | | | | 790 | | | | 9875 |
| | | | | | | | | | | | | | | | | |
| | Footing Steel | | | | | | | | | | | | | | | |
| | #5 Rebar | 1565 | LB | 1.15 | 1800 | 1800 | 4 | | | 7 | 21 | 147 | | 0 | 0 | 1947 |
| | #7 Rebar | 7192 | LB | 1.2 | 4710 | 1500 | 4 | | | 20 | 21 | 420 | | 0 | 0 | 5210 |
| | Subtotal | | | | 6590 | | | | | | | 567 | | | | 7157 |

| | TOTAL FROM PREVIOUS PAGE: | 0 | | | 0 | | | | | | | 0 | | | | 0 |
| | TOTAL: | | | | 15,675 | | | | | | | 1,357 | | | | 17,032 |

FIGURE 6.14
Summary sheet.

supplier, whose responsibility it is to ensure that the concrete meets all specifications.

Ready-mix concrete is taken off by the cubic foot and converted into cubic yards, since that is how it is purchased. Foundations, columns, beams, and girders are taken off by determining the linear footage of each item times its cross-sectional dimensions. The cubic footage of each item is tabulated and converted to cubic yards. Slabs and pavements (including sidewalks) are taken off by area for any one thickness and then converted to cubic feet and then cubic yards. Irregular shapes will have to be subdivided into areas that have known geometric relationships for the purpose of calculating the volume.

When taking off concrete, keep the various types of members (beams, columns, footings, etc.) separate since labor productivity rates to construct them may differ. Also keep the different types or strengths of concrete separate.

Deductions are not made for openings less than one square foot in size. A waste factor of 5 to 10 percent should be included depending on the complexity of work and the forming conditions. For example, concrete placed on an irregular surface such as a subgrade for a concrete slab will require a much higher waste factor than concrete that is placed in wall forms.

Figure 6.15 shows a concrete plan, and Fig. 6.16 is an example of a concrete takeoff.

## PRICING CONCRETE

### Concrete Material Cost

The ready-mix supplier will provide the cost per cubic yard of each type of concrete specified. The type of admixtures, strengths, and general quantities will affect the cost of the concrete. The estimator should make sure that the ready-mix concrete supplier has the capability to deliver the specified concrete.

### Concrete Labor Cost

The cost for labor depends on the productivity and wage rates. Company historical data, revised for the specific job, is used along with current wage rates. In determining the labor cost, the estimator should keep in mind that the concrete has to be physically moved on the job site. To determine the amount and cost of labor involved, one must first determine the method by which the concrete will be moved. Will it be by wheelbarrow, chute, crane and bucket, conveyor, or pump? The method will most likely be dictated to the estimator or be known based on past experience for the specific type of work and project.

Another labor-intensive activity is tamping or vibrating the concrete for proper consolidation and striking off the concrete to its designated elevation. The estimator must consider the activity requirements when establishing the labor productivity.

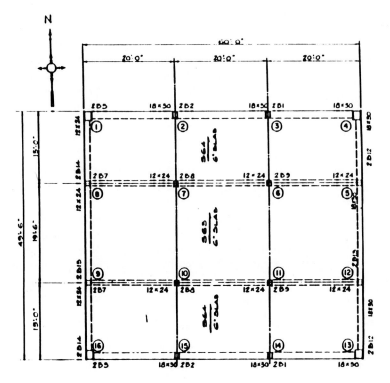

ROOF FRAMING PLAN

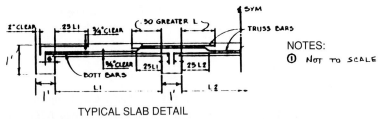

TYPICAL SLAB DETAIL

**FIGURE 6.15**
Drawing of concrete work.

## Concrete Equipment Cost

For many concrete jobs, heavy equipment is needed to move the material on the job site. The estimator must determine what equipment will be used and for how long. Knowing this information and the hourly cost to own and operate or rent the equipment, a total cost can be derived and documented on the summary sheet.

Based on the concrete takeoff (Fig. 6.16), a pricing example is shown in Fig. 6.17.

WORKSHEET A

| COMPUTED BY | DB | | | | | | DATE | 9-26 |
| CHECKED BY | RL | | | | | | PAGE | 1 OF 1 |
| PROJECT | Occone Bank | | | | | | INDEX NO. | 136 |
| ARCHITECT | AAA Architects | | | | | | | |

| REF | DESCRIPTION | QUAN | DIMENSIONS | | | SUBTOTAL | | TOTAL | | REMARKS |
| --- | --- | --- | --- | --- | --- | --- | --- | --- | --- | --- |
| | | | LENGTH | WIDTH | HEIGHT | QUAN | UN | QUAN | UN | |
| 6.15 | 6" SLAB | 1 | 60 | 47.5 | .5 | 1485 | CF | | | |
| | 12" BEAM | 4 | 58 | 1 | .5 | 116 | CF | | | EAST TO WEST |
| | 12" BEAM | 2 | 49.5 | 1 | .5 | 50 | CF | | | NORTH TO SOUTH |
| | SUBTOTAL | | | | | 1651 | CF | 62 | CY | 27 CF/CY |
| | WASTE | | | | | | | 3 | CY | 5% |
| | TOTAL | | | | | | | 65 | CY | |
| | | | | | | | | | | |
| TOTAL FROM PREVIOUS PAGE | | | | | | | | 0 | CY | |
| TOTAL | | | | | | | | 65 | CY | |

**FIGURE 6.16**
Concrete takeoff worksheet.

COMPUTED BY: DB
CHECKED BY: RL

PROJECT: COBBS CROSSING
ARCHITECT: AIA INTERNATIONAL

DATE: 4-26
PAGE: 1 OF 1
INDEX NO.:

| REF | DESCRIPTION | QUANTITY TOTAL | UN | MATERIAL COST UNIT COST | MATERIAL SUBTOTAL | DAILY PROD. OF CREW | CREW MAKE-UP | MAN-HOUR PER UNIT | TOTAL MAN HOURS | TOTAL CREW HOURS | AVG WAGE RATE | LABOR SUBTOTAL | RATE PER HOUR | EQUIP. SUBTOTAL | SUB OR OTHER | TOTAL COST |
|---|---|---|---|---|---|---|---|---|---|---|---|---|---|---|---|---|
| | CONCRETE FLOOR | 65 | CY | 51 | 3315 | 100 | 7 | | | 5.2 | 18 | 655 | 130 | 715 | | 4685 |
| | | | | | | | | | | | | | | | | |

TOTAL FROM PREVIOUS PAGE: 0

TOTAL: 4685

FIGURE 6.17
Concrete summary sheet.

## TAKING OFF FINISHING, CURING, AND PROTECTING CONCRETE

After the concrete is placed into the forms, vibrated, and screeded to the proper elevation, the next task is the proper finishing of the exposed surfaces in accordance with the technical specifications. The question of where does the placing operation end and the finishing activity begin must be answered by the estimator so as to ensure a complete estimate. Most contractors consider the placing operation through floating and the balance of the tasks in finishing. However, this may differ with the specific construction company.

The method, tools, and equipment used depends on the specified finish. Finishing operations may also include rubbing, patching (i.e., walls), and application of certain types of materials such as a surface hardening agent.

In addition, to control the rate of setting (hydration) the concrete must be cured. Proper curing ensures that the concrete attains its design strength. Curing methods include leaving the forms in place, sprinkling, ponding, spray mists, moisture retention covers, and seal coats. Sometimes a combination of these methods can be used.

Finally, concrete may have to be protected from such things as precipitation on slab surfaces, freezing temperatures, and other activities or environmental conditions that can damage the material or exposed surfaces. The method used depends on the potential damage. For instance, heat may need to be provided to keep the concrete from freezing, or a plastic cover may need to be placed over a newly placed slab to protect it from rain.

Since the activities of finishing, curing, and protecting are mostly labor intensive, there is little material involved. Finishing is usually taken off by the square foot. The total area to be finished has probably already been calculated during the formwork or concrete estimating process. The estimator should take care to separate each area requiring a different finish. If any special materials are needed, they should be noted in the appropriate units (those in which they are purchased) on the worksheets.

Taking off the curing activity depends on the method of curing to be used. This may be specified in the technical specifications. Once the method is known, the estimator can then determine the materials needed to perform the task. The quantities of required materials depend not only on the specific material and the unit in which it is purchased but also the manufacturer's instructions in the case of coatings and the surface area to be cured. In some cases, such as leaving the forms in place, there will be no additional material costs; in the case of water spraying or ponding, the material cost will be negligible.

The takeoff of any protecting items depends on the item. The estimator will need to determine if any materials are required and, if so, what units they will be purchased, so that they can be correctly documented on the worksheets. In many cases, such as providing heat to an enclosed space for adequate curing of a slab during subfreezing temperatures, material and labor for building the enclosure will have to be included in the estimate.

Figure 6.18 shows a concrete slab drawing, and Fig. 6.19 shows a completed worksheet for finishing the concrete.

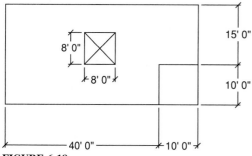

**FIGURE 6.18**
Drawing of concrete to be finished.

## PRICING FINISHING, CURING, AND PROTECTING CONCRETE

The estimator must first determine the total costs of any materials needed in the finishing, curing, and protecting activities. These costs can be obtained from the material supplier and documented on the summary sheet.

The cost of labor depends on the productivity rates and current wage rates. Company historical rates, adjusted for specific job site conditions, should be used. In most cases, heavy equipment will not be needed to perform the tasks. The contractor will most likely use some powered tools for the finishing operation. The cost of these can be placed in the equipment category.

Figure 6.20 shows a summary sheet for the finishing, curing, and protection activities covered in the worksheet shown in Fig. 6.19.

## TAKING OFF PRECAST CONCRETE

As noted earlier in this chapter, precast concrete is formed and cured at a location other than its final location of placement. The contractor can produce the precast items, but they are more commonly purchased. Precast concrete can also be prestressed or posttensioned. If the contractor produces the precast members, the estimating methods discussed in this chapter should be used. The cost of transportation to the project and moving on the job site need to be included.

If the contractor purchases a precast component, there is no need to make a detailed takeoff of the formwork, reinforcing steel, concrete, and related items. However, the estimator will have to consider handling and other costs incurred in erecting and fastening the member into its final resting position.

To take off precast concrete members, the estimator must determine the number and size of each and document them on the worksheet. It is important that each different member be listed separately. This information will be used to obtain quotes from precast manufacturers.

Sometimes, additional material will be required to fasten the precast members in place. An example is posttensioned concrete construction. The steel reinforcement (tendons) are grouted in place after the concrete member is set in place.

| | | | | | | | | | |
|---|---|---|---|---|---|---|---|---|---|
| COMPUTED BY: | KB | | PROJECT: | Occore Bank | | | | DATE: | 4-26 |
| CHECKED BY: | RL | | ARCHITECT: | AAA Architects | | | | PAGE: | 1 OF 1 |
| | | | | | | | | INDEX NO: | |

| REF. | DESCRIPTION | QUAN. | DIMENSIONS | | | SUBTOTAL | | TOTAL | | REMARKS |
|---|---|---|---|---|---|---|---|---|---|---|
| | | | LENGTH | WIDTH | HEIGHT | QUAN. | UN | QUAN. | UN | |
| | Concrete Finishing | | 50 | 25 | | 1240 | SF | | | |
| | <deduct> | | <10> | <10> | | <100> | SF | | | |
| | <deduct> | | <8> | <8> | | <64> | SF | | | |
| | Subtotal | | | | | 1086 | SF | 1086 | SF | |

| | | | | | | | | | | |
|---|---|---|---|---|---|---|---|---|---|---|
| TOTAL FROM PREVIOUS PAGE: | | | | | | | | 0 | | |
| TOTAL | | | | | | | | 1086 | SF | |

FIGURE 6.19
Concrete finishing worksheet.

171

SUMMARY SHEET

COMPUTED BY: DB  
CHECKED BY: RL  
PROJECT: OGGONE BANK  
ARCHITECT: AAA ARCHITECTS  
DATE: 9-26  
PAGE: 1 OF 1  
INDEX NO:

| REF | DESCRIPTION | QUANTITY TOTAL | UN | MATERIAL COST UNIT COST | MATERIAL SUBTOTAL | DAILY PROD OF CREW | CREW MAKE-UP | MAN-HOUR PER UNIT | TOTAL MAN HOURS | TOTAL CREW HOURS | AVG. WAGE RATE | LABOR SUBTOTAL | RATE PER HOUR | EQUIP. SUBTOTAL | SUB OR OTHER | TOTAL COST |
|---|---|---|---|---|---|---|---|---|---|---|---|---|---|---|---|---|
| | CONC. FINISHING | 1086 | SF | 0 | 0 | 725 | 2 | | | 12.0 | 15 | 360 | 5 | 60 | | 420 |

TOTAL FROM PREVIOUS PAGE: 0  
TOTAL: 420

**FIGURE 6.20**
Summary sheet.

172

If the contractor is performing this activity, the estimator will have to take off the material required (grout, steel reinforcing, etc.). In addition, several pieces of miscellaneous steel may be required. The estimator should make sure that either the precast supplier or steel supplier has included the cost of these items in the bid.

## PRICING PRECAST CONCRETE MEMBERS

The material price is obtained from the manufacturer. Any other material prices need to be obtained from the supplier. The quoted price for precast units is by the linear foot or per unit.

The labor cost to install the units depends on the current wage rates and company historic productivity rates adjusted for the specific job. The major categories of labor costs include lifting the precast item into place, aligning it into its final position, and fastening it. These activities are similar to those of installing structural steel.

In most cases, heavy equipment is needed to handle and set the precast concrete members. To determine the equipment costs, the estimator needs to know the type and size of the equipment to be used, how long it will be used, and the cost per hour to own and operate or rent the equipment.

## ESTIMATING OTHER DIVISION 3 ITEMS

There are other items in division 3, as shown in the reminder list below. To estimate these items, the estimator must first know what unit the takeoff will be based on. The reminder list presents units for the major items in division 3. Once the units are known, the balance of the estimating process involves tasks similar to those described in this chapter.

When developing the estimate for the items in division 3, the estimator needs to consider not only the direct costs of the materials, labor, and equipment but also factors that may affect these costs. In addition, the estimator needs to be concerned with specific items that are usually subcontracted.

### Concrete reminder list

| Quantity takeoff | |
| --- | --- |
| Item | Unit of measure |
| Formwork | |
| Accessories | ea/lb/lf/set/c/gal/cwt |
| Expansion joint | lf/lb |
| Forms in place, general | sfca |
| Forms in place, stairs | sf/lf/riser |
| Shores | ea/sf/flr |
| Slipforms | sfca |
| Waterstop | lf/ea |

(*continued*)

## Concrete reminder list (*continued*)

| | |
|---|---|
| Reinforcing steel | |
| Accessories | mlf/m/clf/c/cwt/ea |
| Galv. reinforcing | cwt |
| Prestressing steel | lb |
| Reinf. in place | ton/ea/lb |
| Welded wire fabric | csf/ton/roll/sheet |
| Cast-in-place concrete | |
| Aggregate | ton/bag/cy/cwt |
| Cement | bag/cwt |
| Admixtures/surface treatments | lb/gal/ton/bag |
| Concrete—ready-mix | cy |
| Curing | csf/sf |
| Finishing | sf |
| Patching | sf |
| Waterproofing/dampproofing | sf |
| Precast concrete | |
| Beams, columns, joists | lf |
| Slabs | sf |
| Stairs | riser/flight |
| Tees | sf |
| Tilt-Up | sf/lf |
| Wall panels | sf |
| Cementitious decks | |
| Channel slabs | sf |
| Plank | sf |
| Formboard | sf |
| Insulating | cy/sf |
| Wood fiber | sf |

### Other considerations

Site access for concrete trucks
Special concrete handling equipment
Weather conditions
Capability of concrete supplier to provide the needed quantities
Special forming requirements
Hoisting and unloading of formwork and reinforcing
Shop drawings for reinforcing

### Specialty contractors

Financial capability
Ability to meet the schedule
Minority-owned business
Safety performance
Past performance

# STUDENT EXERCISES

**6.1.** Perform a takeoff of the concrete turn-down slab in Fig. 6.21.

**6.2.** Take off the welded wire mesh and reinforcing bars in Fig. 6.21.

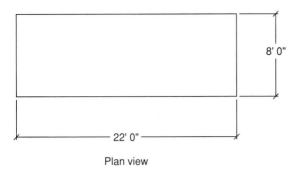

8' 0"

22' 0"

Plan view

1' 0"

1' 0"

4" Conc. slab w/
6 × 6 W1.4 × 1.4 WWF on
6 mil VB on 4" gravel

2 #4 Bars cont.

**FIGURE 6.21**
Concrete slab plan and detail.

**6.3.** Develop a summary sheet for the takeoffs in Exercises 6.1 and 6.2 using the following cost and productivity information.

Slab edge form
    Material $1.25 per square foot
    Labor $1.75 per square foot

Wire mesh
    Material $0.35 per square foot
    Labor $0.20 per square foot

Reinforcing bars
    Material $0.25 per pound
    Labor $0.20 per pound

Concrete
    Material $50.00 per cubic yard
    Labor 1.1 worker hours per cubic yard
    Wage rate = $20.00 her hour

Finish
    Material $0.15 per square foot
    Labor $0.25 per square foot

**6.4.** Perform a takeoff of all formwork, concrete, and reinforcing steel for the drawings provided by the instructor.

**6.5.** Determine the costs of the items resulting from the takeoff in Exercise 6.4 using the cost and productivity information from the instructor.

**6.6.** Develop a speadsheet that can be used for taking off welded wire mesh. The spreadsheet should have data for the following: name of project, bid date, description of item, location of item, number of item, size of mesh, and waste and lap additions. The spreadsheet should give the total number of rolls for each category of work and size of welded wire mesh.

**6.7.** Make a copy of file REINF.WK1 or REINF.WQ1 and modify it to include the weight of reinforcing hooks.

# CHAPTER
# 7

# MASONRY

Division 4, masonry, of the Uniform Construction Index (CSI format) includes a variety of relatively small building units assembled to form a larger building element such as a wall. Division 4 items covered in this chapter are brick, block, mortar, and accessories.

The large variety of masonry units available requires that the estimator be certain to bid exactly what is required. The specifications and drawings should be checked carefully, and local suppliers should be contacted about availability, cost, and special requirements. The most common masonry units are clay bricks and concrete blocks. These masonry units are used extensively throughout the United States. Stone and tile are not as commonly used. However, the rehabilitation of older buildings may require the use of clay tile to match existing walls.

Brick and block are often used for structural and aesthetic reasons. They can be used in load-bearing walls, non-load-bearing walls, or applied as a veneer to other building systems. Depending on the design requirements, the use of masonry can cost less, be more durable, or require less maintenance than other materials.

In most cases masonry requires extensive field labor; no other material is as labor-intensive. Therefore, it is necessary for the estimator to develop accurate labor production rates for masonry. In addition to placing the brick or block, the mason is usually responsible for the installation of stone sills, copings, and other embedded items such as lintels, flashing, reinforcing bars, and horizontal reinforcing.

The purpose of this chapter is to (1) provide sufficient background so that the estimator understands the general items in division 4; (2) establish a basis for

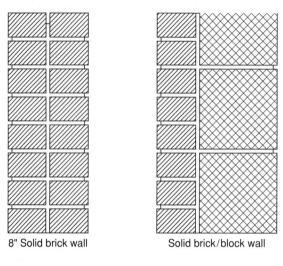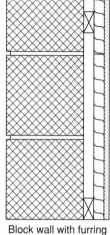

8" Solid brick wall          Solid brick/block wall          Block wall with furring
                                                             strips & gyp board

**FIGURE 7.1**
Types of masonry walls.

estimating masonry work associated with general construction; and (3) provide an
introduction to the specialized area of masonry construction.

## WALL TYPES AND BOND PATTERNS

The type of wall and bond pattern affect the cost of the masonry. The wall can
be laid with concrete block or brick in a simple running bond pattern to the more
complex composite wall laid in a common bond pattern. Figure 7.1 shows various
brick and block wall types, and Fig. 7.2 shows the major types of pattern bonds.
The estimator must determine the quantity of brick and block required separately
for each of the various pattern bonds and wall types.

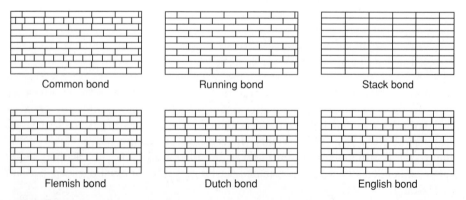

Common bond          Running bond          Stack bond

Flemish bond          Dutch bond          English bond

**FIGURE 7.2**
Common brick pattern bonds.

# TAKEOFF OF BRICK
# AND CONCRETE BLOCK

Clay brick is available in a variety of shapes, textures, sizes, and colors. Figure 7.3 shows some of the various types and sizes of bricks, and Fig. 7.4 shows how they can be placed in a wall.

It is fortunate that an architect's design usually specifies only one to three different types of brick on a single project. However, the local material supplier should be contacted to check the material cost of the various types of bricks.

The type of brick can affect the cost of labor. Brick that is dark in color often is hard and brittle. As a result, these bricks will have a tendency to chip. Closer inspection by the mason will be required when they are installed in the wall, thus lowering the productivity rate. A lower productivity rate will result if a variety of colors, textures, or sizes are used on the same project because the mason will need to make sure that the correct unit is being used.

Concrete block is also manufactured in a variety of sizes, shapes, face textures, types of aggregate, and colors. The common nominal face dimensions of a concrete block are 8 inches high by 16 inches long. A concrete block is available in widths of 4, 6, 8, 10, or 12 inches. The actual dimensions are $\frac{3}{8}$ inch less on all sides. A $\frac{3}{8}$ inch mortar joint is used to give a module dimension of 8 and 16 inches. The various shapes and sizes are shown in Fig. 7.5.

The drawings and specifications could require the use of heavy aggregate, light aggregate, and/or a special color additive in concrete block. The light

Modular brick

| Unit type | Nominal dimensions (inches) | | |
|---|---|---|---|
| | H | D | L |
| Modular | $2\frac{2}{3}$ | 4 | 8 |
| Engineer | $3\frac{1}{5}$ | 4 | 8 |
| Economy | 4 | 4 | 8 |
| Double | $5\frac{1}{3}$ | 4 | 8 |
| Roman | 2 | 4 | 12 |
| Norman | $2\frac{2}{3}$ | 4 | 12 |
| Norwegian | $3\frac{1}{5}$ | 4 | 12 |
| Utility | 4 | 4 | 12 |
| Triple | $5\frac{1}{3}$ | 4 | 12 |
| Scr brick | $2\frac{2}{3}$ | 6 | 12 |

**FIGURE 7.3**
Types and sizes of brick.

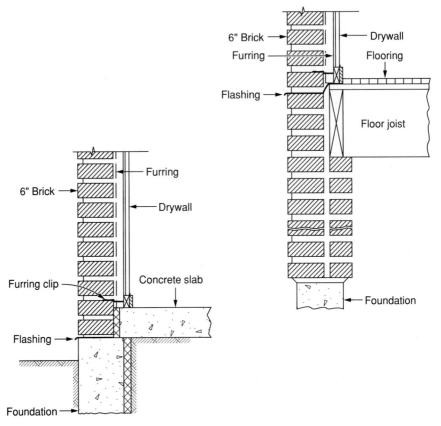

**FIGURE 7.4**
Brick placement in walls.

aggregate block can weigh as much as 30% less, which allows for increased field productivity. The color additive increases the cost of the material. The estimator will need to check with the local supplier on the cost of color additives and the cost difference between heavy and light block.

The estimator needs to keep all of the various sizes, shapes, textures, and colors separate in the quantity survey because of material cost differences. The estimator also needs to separate the quantity survey by the location of the units in the building. For example, the cost of labor and equipment to place the brick on the first floor will be considerably less than that on the fourth floor of a multistory building. The extent of the breakdown of the quantity survey due to the location in the building will vary depending on company policy and the complexity of the project. The following is a list of possible items in a breakdown due to the effect of different material, labor, and equipment costs. These require different takeoff categories. Remember: if it is different, keep it separate!

Different size of brick and block
Different color of brick and block

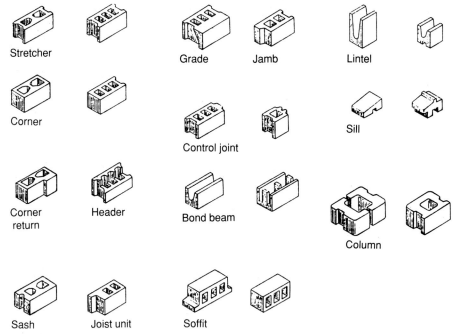

**FIGURE 7.5**
Types of concrete block.

Special shape of brick and block
Different texture of brick and block
Different pattern bonds on the same project
Different wall types on the same project
    Single-wythe walls
    Veneer walls
    Multiwythe walls
    Composite walls
Brick laid as rowlocks
Brick laid as soldiers
Brick laid as headers
Brick laid as sailors
Brick laid as pavers
Brick used in chimneys
Masonry walls below or at ground level
Masonry walls above ground level
Exterior load-bearing walls
Interior partitions
Short or long walls

After the breakdown of the estimate is determined, the estimator must accurately determine the number of bricks and blocks in each category of the project. The counting of brick and block is accomplished by either the square footage method or the coursing method. Either method can be used on a project; they have similar degrees of accuracy.

## Square Foot Method

The square foot method is accomplished by multiplying the area of the wall in square feet by the number of bricks or blocks in one square foot. The estimator should use the centerline method (see Chapter 3) when determining the square footage of wall. The number of masonry units per square foot varies depending on the size of the unit, width of the mortar joint, and pattern bond. The plans and specifications need to be checked to determine these requirements. For standard brick laid in running bond with a $\frac{3}{8}''$ mortar joint most estimators use seven bricks in each square foot of wall and 1.25 blocks per square foot in the same type of wall. This is determined by dividing the face size of the unit plus one mortar joint on the horizontal and one on the vertical into the number of square inches in one square foot and rounding up to account for waste:

Quantity of brick per square foot of wall service

$$= \frac{12'' \times 12''}{[8'' + \frac{3}{8}''(\text{mortar joint})] \times [2\frac{1}{4}'' + \frac{3}{8}''(\text{mortar joint})]}$$

$$= 6.54 \text{ bricks per sf} + \text{waste} = 7 \text{ bricks per sf}$$

The quantity of block per square foot of wall is determined as follows:

$$\frac{12'' \times 12''}{[15\frac{3}{8}'' + \frac{3}{8}''(\text{mortar joint})] \times [7\frac{5}{8}'' + \frac{3}{8}''(\text{mortar joint})]}$$

$$= 1.125 \text{ blocks per sf} + \text{waste} = 1.25 \text{ blocks per sf}$$

A brick wall measuring 568 square feet, of which 44 square feet are windows, is laid up in running bond. The number of bricks required is:

$$(568 - 44) \text{ sf} \times 7 \text{ bricks/sf} = 3654 \text{ bricks}$$

The easiest way to calculate the number of bricks for a different pattern bond is to determine the percentage of the wall area that is taken up by stretchers and headers. For example, a "common bond" pattern has every sixth course as a row of headers. Therefore, one-sixth of the wall surface is headers. The number of header brick in one square foot is calculated by the same method as the stretcher, except the face of the header is used. Figure 7.6 shows the number of bricks required per square foot of wall, without waste, for different bond patterns and mortar joints of various widths. For example, a 522-square-foot wall that is laid in common bond requires

$$(522 \text{ sf} \times \tfrac{5}{6} \times 7) \text{ bricks/sf} + (522 \text{ sf} \times \tfrac{1}{6} \times 14) \text{ bricks/sf} = 4263 \text{ bricks}$$

| Unit type | Units per square foot | | | | |
|---|---|---|---|---|---|
| | Any standard size | Joint size | | | |
| | | $\frac{1"}{4}$ | $\frac{3"}{8}$ | $\frac{1"}{2}$ | $\frac{5"}{8}$ |
| Brick: | | | | | |
| Modular | 6.750 | | | | |
| Engineer | 5.625 | | | | |
| Economy | 4.500 | | | | |
| Double | 3.375 | | | | |
| Roman | 6.000 | | | | |
| Norman | 4.500 | | | | |
| Norwegian | 3.750 | | | | |
| Utility | 3.000 | | | | |
| Triple | 2.250 | | | | |
| Scr brick | 4.500 | | | | |
| Standard | $(2\frac{1}{4} \times 3\frac{3}{4} \times 8)$ | 6.98 | 6.55 | 6.16 | 5.81 |
| CMU: (face dimensions in inches) | | | | | |
| $8 \times 12$ | 1.500 | | | | |
| $4 \times 16$ | 2.250 | | | | |
| $8 \times 16$ | 1.125 | | | | |

Note 1:
   Quantities above are for bond patterns without headers.
Note 2:
   Percentages to be added for various brick bond patterns:
   Common—header course every 5th course ........................................ 20.00%
   Common—header course every 6th course ..................................... 16.67%
   Common—header course every 7th course ..................................... 14.33%
   English/English cross—full headers every 6th course ...................... 16.67%
   Dutch/Dutch cross—full headers every 6th course ........................... 16.67%
   Flemish —full headers every 5th course ........................................... 6.67%
   Flemish —full headers every 6th course ........................................... 5.67%
   Double headers—alternating with stretcher every 5th course ........... 10.00%
   Double headers—alternating with stretcher every 6th course ........... 8.33%
Note 3:
   Note that the values for modular bricks will not vary with joint size, as the
   differences in joint thickness are compensated for by smaller actual dimensions
   of the brick.

**FIGURE 7.6**
Brick requirements per square foot.

## Coursing Method

To determine the number of blocks or bricks in a building using the coursing method, a worksheet similar to the one shown in Fig. 7.7 should be used. This method requires that the estimator divide the height of the wall by the height of one brick or block plus a mortar joint. This gives the number of courses high. If a fraction of a course results, the estimator should round up to the next whole

MASONRY WORKSHEET

| COMPUTED BY: | KB |
| CHECKED BY: | RL |

PROJECT: Haywood Crossing
ARCHITECT: Greenwood Brothers

DATE: 12-1
PAGE: 1 OF 1
INDEX NO: 064

| REF | DESCRIPTION | LENGTH | HEIGHT | AREA | UNITS | MODULES LENGTH | MODULES HEIGHT | EXTENSION 8"CMU | EXTENSION | EXTENSION | EXTENSION | EXTENSION | EXTENSION |
|---|---|---|---|---|---|---|---|---|---|---|---|---|---|
|  | 8"x16" CMU | 215 | 10 | 2150 | SF | 162 | 15 | 2430 |  |  |  |  |  |
|  |  |  |  |  |  |  |  |  |  |  |  |  |  |

| TOTAL FROM PREVIOUS PAGE: | 0 |
| TOTALS: | 2430 |

**FIGURE 7.7**
Coursing worksheet.

number. The estimator then needs to divide the length of the wall by the length of one block or brick plus a mortar joint. This gives the number of masonry units in one course. If a fraction results, round up to the next whole number. By multiplying the number of courses high by the number of units in one course, the estimator can determine the number of bricks or blocks in the wall.

When using the coursing method, the rounding up of the fractions will account for most of the waste due to walls not being designed in module lengths and heights. However, 2 to 5 percent should be added for other waste and breakage. In both the square foot method and coursing method the waste should be increased if it is anticipated that an unusual number of cuts are required.

Figure 7.7 is an example of the coursing method using a masonry worksheet for a wall that is 215 feet long by 10 feet high using an 8-inch-wide concrete block with a $\frac{3}{8}$-inch mortar joint.

File MASONRY.WQ1 (MASONRY.WKI) is a template that can be used for calculating the quantity of masonry units. Figure 7.8 shows one of the four screens of this menu-driven template. The template calculations are based on the coursing method. It will round up to the next whole number if the height or the length of the wall is not designed to the brick or block module dimensions.

## TAKING OFF ACCESSORIES AND MORTAR

### Ties, Anchors, and Inserts Takeoff

The installation of brick or block requires the mason to install items that are embedded in the masonry work. Figure 7.9 shows some of the common inserts and anchors used in masonry construction. These items are used to make connections between two or more building materials. The wall tie can be used to tie an inner wythe of masonry to an outer wythe, or tie brick veneer to a stud wall. Other inserts provide for the connection of stone to masonry; a steel plate embedment can provide for the connection of a steel joist to the wall. The estimator will need to count the number of embedments. The specifications should be checked for the type and spacing requirements.

To determine the number of ties required per square foot of wall, divide 144 square inches per square foot by the spacing of the ties. If the tie spacing is 16 inches horizontally and 24 inches vertically the ties required per square foot is 144 in.$^2$/(16 in. $\times$ 24 in.) = 0.375 ties per square foot. The 0.375 is then multiplied by the total square footage of wall to determine the total number of ties. Approximately 10 percent should be added for waste and extra ties required for control joints, wall intersections, and vertical supports. For example:

$$2784 \text{ sf of wall} \times 0.375 \text{ ties/sf} = 1044 \text{ ties}$$
$$1044 \text{ ties} \times 1.06 = 1107 \text{ total ties required}$$

### Horizontal Masonry Reinforcing Takeoff

Figure 7.10 shows the various types of horizontal masonry reinforcement. The purpose of the reinforcing is to minimize shrinkage, temperature, and settlement

MASONRY TAKEOFF

| CODE | TYPE OF UNIT |
|---|---|
| 1 | 8" BLOCK |
| 2 | FACE BRICK |
| 3 | LINTEL BLK |
| 4 | FIRE BRICK |
| 5 | 8 SPLIT BLK |
| 6 | |

| | |
|---|---|
| ALT I | Information |
| ALT P | Project Data |
| ALT Q | Quantity Takeoff |
| ALT S | Subtotals |

| Enter "Y" = yes or "N" = no for SUBTOTAL | LOCATION | SIZE CODE | PANEL SIZE IN FEET LENGTH | HT. | EXTRA WASTE IN % | CODE 1 TOTAL 8" BLOCK | CODE 2 TOTAL FACE BRICK | CODE 3 TOTAL LINTEL BLK | CODE 4 TOTAL FIRE BRICK | CODE 5 TOTAL 8 SPLIT BLK | CODE 6 TOTAL 0 |
|---|---|---|---|---|---|---|---|---|---|---|---|
| N | WEST END | 1 | 32 | 10 | | 381 | | | | | |
| N | COL. LINE 2 | 5 | 32 | 10 | | | | | | 761 | |
| Y | BELOW GRADE | | | | | | | | | | |
| N | EAST END | 2 | 22 | 12 | | | 1652 | | | | |
| N | WEST END | 2 | 32 | 10 | | | 2003 | | | | |
| Y | BRK @ ENDS | | | | | | | | | | |
| N | FIRST FLOOR | 3 | 123 | 2 | | | | 293 | | | |
| N | 2ND FLOOR | 3 | 2 | 12 | | | | 30 | | | |
| Y | LINTELS | | | | 5.00% | | | | | | |
| N | | | | | | | | | | | |
| N | | | | | | | | | | | |
| N | | | | | | | | | | | |
| N | | | | | | | | | | | |
| N | | | | | | | | | | | |
| N | | | | | | | | | | | |

**FIGURE 7.8**

Computer screen showing a masonry worksheet.

186

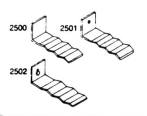

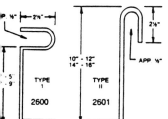

### Veneer anchors

16 ga. or 14 ga., mill galvanized or hot dipped. Widths are $1\frac{1}{4}"$. Lengths are $3\frac{1}{2}"$ with 2" bends.

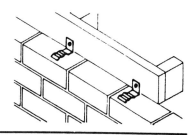

### Column flange tie

Finish in hot dipped or mill galvanized steel. Wire meets ASTM A-82 in $\frac{3}{16}"$* or $\frac{1}{4}"$ diameter.

* $\frac{3}{16}"$ available in Class I or Class III Coating.

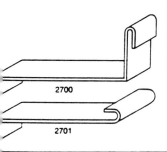

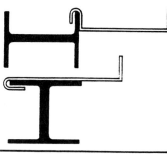

### Column flange strap anchor

16 ga. and $\frac{1}{8}"$ thick. 1" or 2" widths. Plain, hot dipped, or mill galvanized.

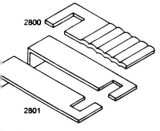

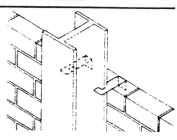

### Column or beam anchors

$\frac{1}{8}"$ thick × 2" wide × 7" long. Plain, Hot Dipped, or Mill Galvanized. Flange slot is $\frac{5}{8}"$ wide × 1" deep, located 1" from end.

**FIGURE 7.9**

Masonry inserts and anchors (Courtesy of Masonry Reinforcing Corporation of America d/b/a WIREBOND).

**187**

2-Wire Systems

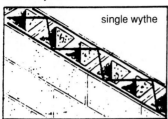

single wythe

3-Wire Systems

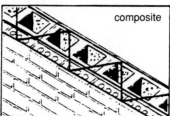

composite

4-Wire Systems

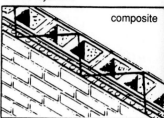

composite

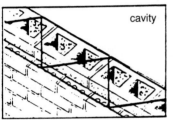

cavity

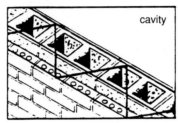

cavity

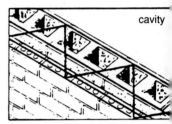

cavity

**FIGURE 7.10**
Horizontal masonry reinforcement (Courtesy of Masonry Reinforcing Corporation of America d/b/a WIREBOND).

cracks in the wall, and provide shear transfer to the steel. After the drawings and specifications are checked as to the type and spacing, the estimator must calculate the linear footage required for each type.

## Deformed Bar Reinforcing Takeoff

The design of some walls may require the use of bar reinforcing. The estimator will need to calculate the total length of each bar type and convert this to the total number of pounds required. See Chapter 6 for the weight of the various sizes of reinforcing bars. The drawings may require the reinforcing bar to be placed horizontally and/or vertically (see Fig. 7.11).

## Taking Off Grout

The block cores are often filled with grout. The grouting is usually done as the wall is going up to ensure that no voids occur. This is called low-lift grouting, and is performed every four feet of wall height. The following shows the quantity of grout required for various block sizes:

| Block Size | Coverage for 1 cf of grout |
| --- | --- |
| 6″ block, 2 or 3 core | 5.25 sf |
| 8″ block, 2 or 3 core | 3.63 sf |
| 12″ block, 2 or 3 core | 2.00 sf |

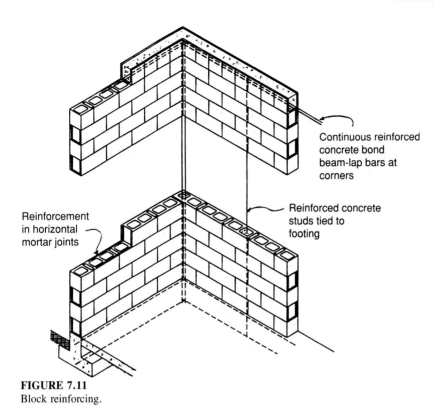

Continuous reinforced
concrete bond
beam-lap bars at
corners

Reinforced concrete
studs tied to
footing

Reinforcement
in horizontal
mortar joints

**FIGURE 7.11**
Block reinforcing.

The estimator will need to have a separate line in the estimate for the grout fill. The reinforcing and grouting of the walls will require a lower productivity rate for the masons. The estimator should account for this and adjust the rate for walls that are heavily reinforced.

## Control Joint Takeoff

The design will often require one or more control joints to be placed in the walls (Fig. 7.12). A control joint completely cuts the wall from the bottom to the top to allow for expansion and contraction. The specification will require that the joint be filled with caulk, neoprene and molded rubber, or metal. The estimator will need to calculate the linear feet of joint. Extra labor will be required because the units in alternate courses have to be cut or half-size units used to make a straight vertical line.

## Flashing Takeoff

Flashing that is built into the masonry walls is usually installed by the mason. Flashing is available in a wide variety of materials. The specifications should be checked carefully. Several locations may require flashing material. It may be required over windows and doors, at the sills and copings, at the intersection

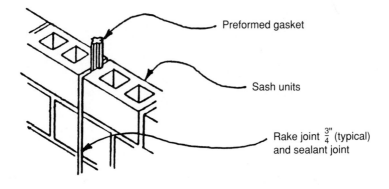

Preformed gasket

Sash units

Rake joint $\frac{3}{4}"$ (typical)
and sealant joint

**Flush wall control joint**

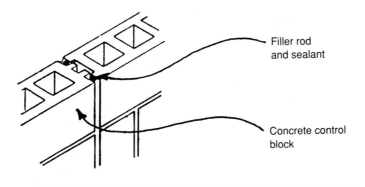

Filler rod
and sealant

Concrete control
block

**Control joint block**

**FIGURE 7.12**
Vertical control joint.

of the roof and wall, and at the base of the wall. The flashing material may be purchased under the masonry division; however, it is usually purchased under the thermal and moisture protection division (division 7) and supplied to the masons for installation. The estimator will need to calculate the lineal or square footage of flashing required by type of material to determine the total cost.

## Lintels, Sills, and Copings Takeoff

Lintels, sills, and copings can be made of a variety of materials, and are set by the masons. Lintels are above a wall opening, sills are below a wall opening, and copings are at the top of a masonry wall (see Fig. 7.13). Depending on the material used, the estimator will need to determine the lineal feet of precast concrete, number of steel angles, or number of masonry units required to make the lintel, sill, or coping. These items should be listed separately on the estimate.

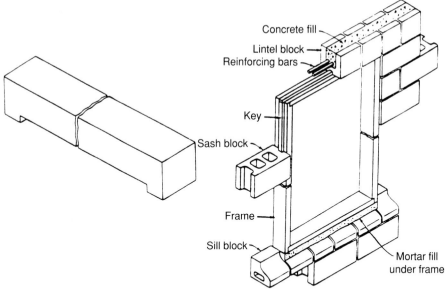

**FIGURE 7.13**
Masonry lintels.

## Mortar Takeoff

Mortar is available in the ASTM types of M, S, N, and O. The specifications indicate the type to be used. The amount of mortar and sand required depends on the type of masonry unit, size of the unit, size of the mortar joint, and number of wythes. The mortar is measured in number of cubic feet or number of bags of premixed mortar. Figure 7.14 shows the amount of mortar and sand required for various sizes and types of masonry units.

Colored mortar is often required. A pigment is added to the mortar mix, and sometimes a different sand may be required. The specifications will indicate if a colored mortar is required on the project. The local supplier should be consulted for this added cost.

## Sample Panels

A sample panel is often required to show the brick mortar color, pattern bond, and mortar joint type. The estimator should include a separate line item in the estimate showing the cost of a sample panel, which are very expensive per brick or block. Usually, they are made before the masonry is laid in the building.

## Insulation Takeoff

Insulation is often required in the spaces of cavity-type masonry walls and in the cores of concrete blocks. The type of insulation is specified either in the masonry

| Unit type | Cu. ft. of mortar per 1000 Units | | |
|---|---|---|---|
| | Joint size | | |
| | $\frac{1}{4}$" | $\frac{3}{8}$" | $\frac{1}{2}$" |
| **Brick:** | | | |
| Modular | 5.65 | 8.10 | 10.30 |
| Engineer | 5.94 | 8.52 | 10.84 |
| Economy | — | 9.15 | 11.65 |
| Double | — | 10.19 | 12.87 |
| Roman | — | 10.72 | 13.67 |
| Norman | 7.82 | 11.24 | 14.35 |
| Norwegian | 8.11 | 11.66 | 14.89 |
| Utility | 8.54 | 12.29 | 15.70 |
| Triple | — | 13.34 | 17.05 |
| Scr brick | — | 17.45 | 22.55 |
| $2\frac{1}{4} \times 3\frac{3}{4} \times 8$ brick | 5.70 | 8.80 | 11.70 |
| **Cmu:** | (Nominal dimensions — H × D × L) | | |
| 8 × 4 × 12 | 40.00 | | |
| 8 × 6 × 12 | 43.33 | | |
| 8 × 8 × 12 | 46.67 | | |
| 8 × 10 × 12 | 50.00 | | |
| 8 × 12 × 12 | 53.33 | | |
| 4 × 4 × 16 | 40.00 | | |
| 4 × 6 × 16 | 42.22 | | |
| 4 × 8 × 16 | 44.44 | | |
| 8 × 4 × 16 | 44.44 | | |
| 8 × 6 × 16 | 44.44 | | |
| 8 × 8 × 16 | 53.33 | | |
| 8 × 10 × 16 | 57.78 | | |
| 8 × 12 × 16 | 62.22 | | |

Note 1:
   No waste factor included in the above amounts for brick.
Note 2:
   A waste factor has been included for CMU.
Note 3:
   Factors to adjust for additional mortar required for bond
   patterns with headers can be found in Figure 7.6.

**FIGURE 7.14**
Mortar and sand quantities.

section or the thermal and moisture protection division of the specifications. If the insulation is a board product, the estimator will need to calculate the total square footage required. If the insulation is a granular product such as vermiculite, the estimator will need to calculate the cubic feet of insulation required. The volume required to fill the cores of concrete block is the same as the volume required to fill the cores with grout. Fill insulation is normally sold in 4-cubic-foot bags.

## Cleaning Takeoff

All exposed masonry must be cleaned to remove excess mortar. A variety of methods may be specified for the cleaning process. The specifications may require clear water, soap and water, acid solution, wire brush, or sandblasting. The estimator should determine the total square footage of wall that is required to be cleaned. Note that interior walls require both surfaces of the wall to be cleaned.

## LABOR REQUIREMENTS

After the estimator has determined the quantity of masonry units in each of the various categories of size, texture, types of walls, bond pattern, and so on, the expected productivity of the masons and the size of the masonry crew must be determined. The productivity of a mason is usually measured by the number of units a mason can lay in one day. This is not an easy calculation because of the many variables that can affect productivity. The estimator will need to examine all factors that may influence the productivity of the crew and make adjustments in the number of units a mason can lay in one day. Chapter 4 shows how general factors can affect the productivity of a labor crew; the estimator should also consider the following specific factors:

- Are both sides of the wall tooled? If the mason is required to tool both sides, it will take more time.
- What are the horizontal and vertical distances that the masonry units must be moved? This will affect the number of laborers required in the crew and determine whether a forklift or other piece of equipment is necessary.
- Are the walls long and straight, or do they have jogs in them? The mason will not be able to lay as many units per day in a short wall that has several jogs.
- What is the bond pattern? More complicated patterns require more time to lay.
- Is there an excessive number of openings? An opening requires the cutting of the masonry units, thus lowering the productivity rate.
- How extensive is the scaffolding requirement? The scaffold will have to be erected and removed. This may require additional laborers in the crew.
- Do local collective bargaining agreements restrict such things as total number of units that can be laid by each mason in one day? Do the agreements require a certain size crew?
- Are there multiple textures, colors, or sizes of brick on the same project? This could slow the productivity of the mason.
- Is there an excessive number of embedments in the wall? The mason must install all of the embedments, thus lowering the number of masonry units that the mason can install in one day.

| Number of units per day per mason | 3 masons 1 laborer | 2 masons 1 laborer | 5 masons 3 laborers | 5 masons 3 laborers $\frac{1}{3}$ operator | 3 masons 2 laborers | 5 masons 3 laborers $\frac{1}{2}$ foreman | 4 masons 3 laborers | 7 masons 1 foreman 4 laborers $\frac{1}{2}$ operator |
|---|---|---|---|---|---|---|---|---|
| 60 | .1778 | .2000 | .2133 | .2221 | .2222 | .2267 | .2333 | .2381 |
| 70 | .1523 | .1714 | .1829 | .1904 | .1904 | .1943 | .2000 | .2041 |
| 80 | .1333 | .1500 | .1600 | .1766 | .1667 | .1700 | .1750 | .1786 |
| 85 | .1254 | .1412 | .1506 | .1568 | .1568 | .1600 | .1647 | .1681 |
| 90 | .1184 | .1333 | .1422 | .1480 | .1481 | .1511 | .1556 | .1587 |
| 100 | .1067 | .1200 | .1280 | .1332 | .1333 | .1360 | .1400 | .1429 |
| 110 | .0970 | .1091 | .1164 | .1211 | .1212 | .1236 | .1273 | .1299 |
| 120 | .0889 | .1000 | .1067 | .1110 | .1111 | .1133 | .1167 | .1190 |
| 125 | .0853 | .0960 | .1024 | .1066 | .1067 | .1088 | .1120 | .1143 |
| 130 | .0820 | .0923 | .0985 | .1025 | .1025 | .1046 | .1077 | .1099 |
| 140 | .0761 | .0857 | .0914 | .0952 | .0952 | .0971 | .1000 | .1020 |
| 150 | .0711 | .0800 | .0853 | .0888 | .0889 | .0907 | .0933 | .0952 |
| 160 | .0667 | .0750 | .0800 | .0833 | .0833 | .0850 | .0875 | .0893 |
| 170 | .0627 | .0706 | .0753 | .0784 | .0784 | .0800 | .0824 | .0840 |
| 180 | .0592 | .0667 | .0711 | .0740 | .0741 | .0755 | .0778 | .0794 |
| 190 | .0561 | .0632 | .0674 | .0701 | .0702 | .0716 | .0737 | .0752 |
| 200 | .0533 | .0600 | .0640 | .0666 | .0667 | .0680 | .0700 | .0714 |
| 225 | .0474 | .0533 | .0569 | .0593 | .0593 | .0604 | .0622 | .0634 |
| 250 | .0427 | .0480 | .0512 | .0533 | .0533 | .0544 | .0560 | .0571 |
| 300 | .0356 | .0400 | .0427 | .0444 | .0444 | .0453 | .0467 | .0476 |
| 325 | .0328 | .0369 | .0394 | .0410 | .0410 | .0418 | .0431 | .0439 |
| 350 | .0305 | .0343 | .0366 | .0381 | .0381 | .0388 | .0400 | .0408 |
| 375 | .0284 | .0320 | .0341 | .0356 | .0356 | .0362 | .0373 | .0380 |
| 400 | .0267 | .0300 | .0320 | .0333 | .0333 | .0340 | .0350 | .0357 |
| 425 | .0251 | .0282 | .0301 | .0314 | .0314 | .0320 | .0329 | .0336 |
| 450 | .0237 | .0267 | .0284 | .0296 | .0296 | .0302 | .0311 | .0317 |
| 475 | .0225 | .0253 | .0269 | .0281 | .0281 | .0286 | .0295 | .0300 |
| 500 | .0213 | .0240 | .0256 | .0267 | .0267 | .0272 | .0280 | .0285 |
| 525 | .0203 | .0229 | .0244 | .0254 | .0254 | .0259 | .0267 | .0272 |
| 550 | .0194 | .0218 | .0233 | .0242 | .0242 | .0247 | .0255 | .0259 |
| 575 | .0186 | .0209 | .0223 | .0232 | .0232 | .0236 | .0243 | .0248 |
| 600 | .0178 | .0200 | .0213 | .0222 | .0222 | .0226 | .0233 | .0238 |
| 650 | .0164 | .0185 | .0197 | .0205 | .0205 | .0209 | .0215 | .0219 |
| 700 | .0152 | .0171 | .0183 | .0190 | .0190 | .0194 | .0200 | .0204 |
| 725 | .0147 | .0166 | .0177 | .0184 | .0184 | .0187 | .0193 | .0197 |
| 750 | .0142 | .0160 | .0171 | .0177 | .0178 | .0181 | .0187 | .0190 |
| 800 | .0133 | .0150 | .0160 | .0166 | .0166 | .0170 | .0175 | .0178 |
| 825 | .0129 | .0145 | .0155 | .0161 | .0161 | .0164 | .0169 | .0173 |
| 850 | .0125 | .0141 | .0150 | .0156 | .0156 | .0160 | .0164 | .0168 |
| 875 | .0122 | .0137 | .0146 | .0152 | .0152 | .0155 | .0160 | .0163 |
| 900 | .0119 | .0133 | .0142 | .0148 | .0148 | .0151 | .0156 | .0158 |

**FIGURE 7.15**
Worker hours.

| 5 masons<br>3 laborers<br>$\frac{1}{2}$ foreman<br>$\frac{1}{2}$ operator | 5 masons<br>3 laborers<br>1 operator | 12 masons<br>1 foreman<br>8 laborers<br>1 operator | 8 masons<br>1 foreman<br>5 laborers<br>1 operator | 5 masons<br>1 foreman<br>3 laborers<br>$\frac{1}{2}$ operator | 5 masons<br>1 foreman<br>3 laborers<br>$\frac{2}{3}$ operator | 5 masons<br>1 foreman<br>3 laborers<br>$\frac{3}{4}$ operator | 1 mason<br>1 laborer | 3 masons<br>2 laborers<br>1 operator |
|---|---|---|---|---|---|---|---|---|
| .2400 | .2400 | .2444 | .2500 | .2533 | .2576 | .2600 | .2667 | .2667 |
| .2057 | .2057 | .2095 | .2143 | .2171 | .2208 | .2229 | .2286 | .2286 |
| .1800 | .1800 | .1833 | .1875 | .1900 | .1932 | .1950 | .2000 | .2000 |
| .1694 | .1694 | .1725 | .1765 | .1788 | .1818 | .1835 | .1882 | .1882 |
| .1600 | .1600 | .1630 | .1667 | .1689 | .1717 | .1733 | .1778 | .1778 |
| .1440 | .1440 | .1467 | .1500 | .1520 | .1545 | .1560 | .1600 | .1600 |
| .1309 | .1309 | .1333 | .1364 | .1392 | .1405 | .1418 | .1455 | .1455 |
| .1200 | .1200 | .1222 | .1250 | .1267 | .1288 | .1300 | .1333 | .1333 |
| .1152 | .1152 | .1173 | .1200 | .1216 | .1236 | .1248 | .1280 | .1280 |
| .1108 | .1107 | .1128 | .1154 | .1169 | .1189 | .1200 | .1231 | .1231 |
| .1029 | .1028 | .1048 | .1071 | .1086 | .1104 | .1114 | .1143 | .1143 |
| .0960 | .0960 | .0977 | .1000 | .1013 | .1030 | .1040 | .1067 | .1067 |
| .0900 | .0900 | .0917 | .0937 | .0950 | .0966 | .0975 | .1000 | .1000 |
| .0847 | .0847 | .0863 | .0882 | .0894 | .0909 | .0918 | .0941 | .0941 |
| .0800 | .0800 | .0815 | .0833 | .0844 | .0859 | .0867 | .0889 | .0889 |
| .0758 | .0757 | .0772 | .0789 | .0800 | .0813 | .0821 | .0842 | .0842 |
| .0720 | .0720 | .0733 | .0750 | .0760 | .0773 | .0780 | .0800 | .0800 |
| .0640 | .0640 | .0652 | .0667 | .0675 | .0686 | .0693 | .0711 | .0711 |
| .0576 | .0576 | .0587 | .0600 | .0608 | .0618 | .0624 | .0640 | .0640 |
| .0480 | .0480 | .0489 | .0500 | .0506 | .0515 | .0520 | .0533 | .0533 |
| .0443 | .0443 | .0451 | .0462 | .0467 | .0475 | .0480 | .0492 | .0492 |
| .0411 | .0411 | .0419 | .0429 | .0434 | .0441 | .0446 | .0457 | .0457 |
| .0384 | .0384 | .0391 | .0400 | .0405 | .0412 | .0416 | .0427 | .0427 |
| .0360 | .0360 | .0367 | .0375 | .0380 | .0386 | .0390 | .0400 | .0400 |
| .0338 | .0339 | .0345 | .0353 | .0357 | .0363 | .0367 | .0376 | .0376 |
| .0320 | .0320 | .0326 | .0333 | .0337 | .0343 | .0347 | .0356 | .0356 |
| .0303 | .0303 | .0309 | .0316 | .0320 | .0325 | .0328 | .0337 | .0337 |
| .0288 | .0288 | .0293 | .0300 | .0304 | .0309 | .0312 | .0320 | .0320 |
| .0274 | .0274 | .0279 | .0286 | .0289 | .0294 | .0297 | .0305 | .0305 |
| .0261 | .0262 | .0267 | .0273 | .0276 | .0281 | .0284 | .0291 | .0291 |
| .0250 | .0250 | .0255 | .0261 | .0268 | .0268 | .0271 | .0278 | .0278 |
| .0240 | .0240 | .0244 | .0250 | .0253 | .0257 | .0260 | .0267 | .0267 |
| .0221 | .0222 | .0226 | .0231 | .0233 | .0237 | .0240 | .0246 | .0246 |
| .0205 | .0206 | .0210 | .0214 | .0217 | .0220 | .0223 | .0229 | .0229 |
| .0198 | .0199 | .0202 | .0207 | .0209 | .0213 | .0215 | .0221 | .0221 |
| .0192 | .0192 | .0195 | .0200 | .0202 | .0206 | .0208 | .0213 | .0213 |
| .0180 | .0180 | .0183 | .0351 | .0190 | .0193 | .0195 | .0200 | .0200 |
| .0174 | .0174 | .0177 | .0181 | .0184 | .0187 | .0189 | .0193 | .0193 |
| .0169 | .0169 | .0173 | .0176 | .0178 | .0181 | .0183 | .0188 | .0188 |
| .0164 | .0165 | .0168 | .0171 | .0173 | .0176 | .0178 | .0183 | .0183 |
| .0160 | .0160 | .0163 | .0167 | .0168 | .0171 | .0173 | .0178 | .0178 |

**FIGURE 7.15** (*continued*)

The most difficult decision of the estimator is the expected production rate of the masons and the number of people in the crew. This decision is made by considering the above factors; studying the production records of similar projects; consulting with others in the construction firm such as the masonry supervisor, general superintendent, and other estimators; studying the plans and specifications; determining the time of year that the masonry will be installed; and checking with material suppliers. When other bond patterns, short walls, and other factors are encountered, the production rate will need to be lowered or increased as necessary. Depending on such factors as labor availability and working conditions, the crew size may also have to be varied. It is the responsibility of the estimator to consider all of the factors and make a decision on the production rate and crew size for the project being estimated. After the production rate and crew size are determined, the number of labor hours per unit is calculated. Chapter 4 has additional information on labor hour calculations.

As an example, a typical small commercial project such as a bank facility is being estimated. A previous similar project used a crew of 5 masons and 3 laborers. The average production rate on that project was 800 bricks a day and 150 eight-inch blocks per day per mason. The estimator has decided to use a crew of 5 masons and 3 laborers with a production rate of 850 bricks per day and 140 eight-inch blocks per day per mason for the running bond units. The worker hours per brick is

$$\frac{8 \text{ workers} \times 8 \text{ hours}}{5 \text{ masons} \times 850 \text{ bricks/mason}} = 0.0151 \text{ worker hours per brick}$$

The worker hours per block is

$$\frac{8 \text{ workers} \times 8 \text{ hours}}{5 \text{ masons} \times 140 \text{ blocks/mason}} = 0.0914 \text{ worker hours per block}$$

Figure 7.15 shows the worker hours per unit for various crew sizes and different production rates of the masons. By using this table the estimator can match the crew with the production rate of the mason to determine the worker hours per unit. If a crew size or production rate is needed that is not on the table, the estimator will need to calculate the worker hours per unit. File WORK_HR.WQ1 (WORK_HR.WK1) on the disk can be used to determine the worker hours per unit for any combination of crew size and production rate. Figure 7.16 shows the screen for this template.

After the worker hours per unit is determined the labor cost estimate can be calculated. The worker hours per unit is multiplied by the number of masonry units to determine the total number of worker hours. The total worker hours is then multiplied by the average wage rate of the crew members. The result is the cost of the labor to place the masonry units. The total crew hours can be calculated by dividing the total worker hours by the total number of people in the crew. Multiplying the crew hours by the total wage rate of the crew will also result in the total cost of the labor. For example:

```
                MASONRY PRODUCTIVITY

ENTER NUMBER OF WORK HOURS PER DAY =   8
    ENTER PRODUCTION OF ONE MASON =   500
                              ENTER
          CREW               NUMBER
          MEMBERS            OF PEOPLE
          ===============   ==========

          MASON                 3
          MASON N.W.F.           1
            (NON-WORKING
            FORMAN)
          MASON W.F.             0
            (WORKING
            FORMAN)
          LABOR                 6
          OPERATOR             0.5

    AVERAGE WORKER HOURS PER UNIT = 0.0560
```

**FIGURE 7.16**
Template screen.

### Given

3578 eight-inch concrete blocks laid in a running bond

Crew size $=$ 5 masons and 3 laborers

Each mason should place 140 units per day

Mason wage rate $=$ \$15.75 per hour

Laborer wage rate $=$ \$12.00 per hour

### Solution

$$\frac{8 \text{ workers} \times 8 \text{ hours per day}}{5 \text{ masons} \times 140 \text{ units per day/mason}} = 0.0914 \text{ worker hours per unit}$$

0.0914 × 3578 units = 327 worker hours × \$14.34 average wage rate = \$4689.

Each construction company should develop standards and policies that will govern what is included in a labor productivity measurement. A crew of 5 masons and 3 laborers with a productivity of 750 bricks per day per mason may or may not include the time required to set the wall ties on a brick veneer project or place the horizontal reinforcing. This will depend on the standard that is set by the construction company. If the productivity of the masons and the crew size does not include the cost for setting the accessories, additional money should be included in the estimate to cover these costs. In most companies, the mixing of the mortar and placing of the horizontal reinforcing is usually included in the productivity figures of placing the masonry units. The other accessories (bar reinforcing, flashing, lintels, etc.) usually require additional labor costs.

If the data is available from the company's historical records, the labor cost for placing accessories can be calculated in terms of worker hours or as a unit price. The unit price method requires that the estimator multiply the number of units by the unit cost for placing one unit. For example:

$$550 \text{ pounds of reinforcing} \times \$0.35 \text{ per pound} = \$193$$

## MATERIAL COST

Most of the material estimate in masonry is calculated from unit prices. The pricing of the material in masonry requires that the estimator contact the local suppliers for the unit cost of the various items. Chapter 4 should be reviewed for precautions when checking material prices from local suppliers.

It is common for the owner to include in the specifications a unit cash allowance for the purchase of the face brick. The estimator will need to use this amount for calculating the material cost of the brick. This will allow the owner and architect to determine the exact type of brick desired at a later date. After the unit price of the material is determined from either the local suppliers or an allowance, the unit price is multiplied by the total number of units to determine the total material cost. For example:

*Given*

> 378 10-inch concrete blocks
>
> Material cost of 10 inch concrete block = $1.15

*Solution*

$$378 \text{ blocks} \times \$1.15 \text{ per block} = \$435$$

## Climate Considerations

Masonry should not be laid when the temperature is 40° F and falling or below 32° F without taking precautions. The precautions can include heating the water, heating the sand, and building temporary enclosures. The masonry should be protected from freezing for at least forty-eight hours after it is laid. If it is expected that the masonry will be laid in cold weather, the estimator will need to include any cost for heating the water and sand, building temporary enclosures, providing temporary heat in the enclosure, and removing the temporary enclosure. As the masonry is being laid, temporary covers should be provided to protect any walls that are not completed. Temporary covers should also be provided for the stored mortar and concrete block. The cost for the temporary cover is not great, but the estimator should include it in the estimate.

Wind can also damage masonry walls that are under construction. The cost of providing temporary bracing is minimal and should be included in the estimate if it is expected that the walls will be exposed to a wind hazard.

## TOOLS AND EQUIPMENT COSTS

The tools and equipment required in masonry construction include mason's hand tools, mortar boards, mortar boxes, a mortar mixer, hoes, shovels, wheelbarrows, and pails. Some projects may also require scaffolding, power hoists, and forklifts.

The estimator should include a line item in the estimate for the tools and mortar mixer. A cost per day should be calculated and then multiplied by the expected time to complete all of the masonry. Other equipment cost depends on the type of equipment and the amount of time it is needed. The duration required is the number of crew hours that has been calculated in the labor cost to complete the task. The cost is determined by multiplying the crew hours by the cost per hour for the equipment.

As in all components of the estimate, the estimator should do a complete analysis on the cost of ownership versus the rental cost of the equipment. Chapter 4 includes a complete discussion of this process.

The square footage of wall requiring scaffolding should be calculated. There are many types of scaffolding. The project requirements and site conditions should be studied to determine the most effective and efficient type. To determine the scaffolding cost, the square footage of wall requiring it is multiplied by the cost per square foot for the type of scaffold used. Also, the estimator will have to decide the number of times that the scaffolding will have to be moved. The number of moves should be considered when determining the number of laborers that will have to be included in the masonry crew.

## SUBCONTRACTORS

Many general contractors subcontract the masonry work to a masonry contractor. Chapter 4 gives information on the methodology of subcontracting and the precautions the estimator should take.

Even if the decision is made to subcontract the masonry, the estimator should still prepare an estimate for it. Sometimes the proposal from the subcontractor is for material and labor; other times it may only be for labor.

The estimator should have a clear understanding of the subcontractor's scope of work. The following questions should be asked of the subcontractor.

Is the scope of work clearly understood?

Is caulking included?

Is the labor required for setting lintels, flashing, reinforcing bar, and other embedded items included, and is the material cost included in the bid?

Is the hoisting equipment or forklift included in the bid?

Is the scaffolding included in the bid?

## TAKING OFF AND PRICING
## MASONRY WORK

Figures 7.17 and 7.18 contain examples of a masonry takeoff worksheet and summary sheet, respectively. This is only part of the masonry estimate for a commercial project.

**MASONRY WORKSHEET**

COMPUTED BY: KB  
CHECKED BY: RL  
PROJECT: Captain Warehouse  
ARCHITECT: Starland Design  
DATE: 12-3  
PAGE: 1 OF 1  
INDEX NO: 065

| REF. | DESCRIPTION | LENGTH | HEIGHT | AREA | UNITS | MODULES LENGTH | MODULES HEIGHT | 6"cmu EXTENSION | 8"cmu EXTENSION | 12"cmu EXTENSION | 4"cmu EXTENSION |
|---|---|---|---|---|---|---|---|---|---|---|---|
| 5-2 | 6"x16" Cmu | 516 | 10 | 5160 | SF | 388 | 15 | 5820 | | | |
| 5-2 | 8"x16" Cmu | 1282 | 10 | 12,820 | SF | 964 | 15 | | 14,460 | | |
| 5-2 | 12"x16" Cmu | 389 | 10 | 3890 | SF | 293 | 15 | | | 4395 | |
| 5-2 | Glass Blok 4"x4" | 210 | 10 | 2100 | SF | 634 | 30 | | | | 19,200 |
| | | | | | | | | | | | |
| | Waste +3% | | | | | | | 175 | 434 | 132 | 576 |
| | | | | | | | | | | | |
| **TOTAL FROM PREVIOUS PAGE:** | | | | | | | | 0 | 0 | 0 | 0 |
| **TOTALS:** | | | | | | | | 5995 | 14894 | 4527 | 19776 |

**FIGURE 7.17**
Masonry worksheet.

| COMPUTED BY: KB | | | | | | | | | | | | | | | DATE: 12-4 |
| CHECKED BY: RL | | | | | | | | | | | | | | | PAGE: 1 OF 1 |
| PROJECT: Captain Warehouse | | | | | | | | | | | | | | | INDEX NO: 092 |
| ARCHITECT: Starland Design | | | | | | | | | | | | | | | |

| | | QUANTITY | | MATERIAL COST | | LABOR COST | | | | | | | EQUIPMENT COST | | SUB. OR OTHER | TOTAL COST |
|---|---|---|---|---|---|---|---|---|---|---|---|---|---|---|---|---|
| REF | DESCRIPTION | TOTAL | UN. | UNIT COST | MATERIAL SUBTOTAL | DAILY PROD. OF CREW | CREW MAKE-UP | MAN-HOUR PER UNIT | TOTAL MAN HOURS | TOTAL CREW HOURS | AVG. WAGE RATE | LABOR SUBTOTAL | RATE PER HOUR | EQUIP. SUBTOTAL | SUB. OR OTHER | TOTAL COST |
| 65 | 6" CMU | 5995 | EA | 0.76 | 4557 | 220 | 8/5 | .058 | 348 | 70 | 16.00 | 5568 | 2.00 | 140 | 0 | 10265 |
| 65 | 8" CMU | 14874 | EA | 0.89 | 13256 | 200 | 8/5 | .044 | 953 | 191 | 16.00 | 15252 | 2.00 | 382 | 0 | 28890 |
| 65 | 12" CMU | 4527 | EA | 1.05 | 4754 | 180 | 8/5 | .071 | 322 | 65 | 16.00 | 5143 | 2.00 | 130 | 0 | 10027 |
| 65 | 4"x4" Glass Blk | 19776 | EA | 1.25 | 24720 | 150 | 8/5 | .085 | 1681 | 336 | 16.00 | 26896 | 2.00 | 672 | 0 | 52288 |
| | TOTAL FROM PREVIOUS PAGE: | | | | 0 | | | | | | | 0 | | 0 | 0 | 0 |
| | TOTAL: | | | | 47,887 | | | | | | | 52859 | | 1324 | | 101,470 |

FIGURE 7.18
Masonry summary sheet.

## MASONRY REMINDER LIST

A reminder list for masonry is shown below. The reminder list shows the units of measure for the various major components of the masonry division, other estimating-related considerations, and the items that should be checked when subcontracting out the masonry work.

**Masonry reminder list**

| Quantity takeoff | |
|---|---|
| **Item** | **Unit of measure** |
| Normal weight concrete block | ea |
| Heavy weight concrete block | ea |
| Solid block | ea |
| Hollow block | ea |
| Decorative block | ea |
| Concrete brick | ea |
| Special block | ea |
| Brick | ea |
| Special texture brick | ea |
| Special color brick | ea |
| Special shape brick | ea |
| Fire brick | ea |
| Structural clay tile | ea |
| Structural glazed tile | ea |
| Glass block | ea |
| Stone masonry | sf/tn |
| Mortar | bag/cf |
| Mortar color | bag |
| Motar admixtures | bag/cf |
| Sand | ton/cy |
| Lime | cf/lb |
| Horizontal reinforcement | lf by size |
| Bar reinforcing | ton/lb |
| Cavity wall insulation | sf |
| Core insulation | cf/bag/sf |
| Sound insulation | sf |
| Tuck pointing | sf |
| Wall ties | ea |
| Control joint | lf |
| Anchors | ea |
| Misc. inserts | ea |
| Fireplace inserts | ea |
| Bolts | ea |
| Dowels | ea |
| Reglets | lf |
| Precast concrete lintels | ea |
| Steel lintels | ea/lb |
| Sills | ea |
| Coping | ea/lf |
| Weep holes | ea |

## Masonry reminder list (*continued*)

| | |
|---|---|
| Cleaning | sf |
| Sealer and protective coatings | sf |
| Scaffolding | sf/square |
| Mixer | ls |
| Small tools | ls |
| Protective cover | ls |
| Rough hardware | ls |
| Sample panel | ea |
| Grouting of columns | ea/cf |
| Grout door frames | ea/cf |
| Backplastering (parging) | sf/cf |

### Other considerations that can affect costs

Pattern bond
Type of wall
Paving
Small cut-up walls or large uninterrupted walls
Angling walls
Height of walls
Quality of masonry units
Hoisting equipment
Weather protection
Special cutting of masonry units
Distance units must be moved vertically and horizontally
Composite wall type
Load-bearing and non-load-bearing walls
Type of joint
Mechanical and electrical embedments
Weight and size of masonry unit
Installation of hollow metal door frames
ASTM regulations
Sales tax on materials

### Specialty contractor bid to general contractor

Brick panelization
  Connections
  Hoisting
  Product delivery
  Shop drawings
  Engineering
All masonry subcontracted
  Reinforcing included?
  Insulation included?
  Thru-wall flashing included?
Minority-owned business
Documented total quality management program
Safety performance record
Union or merit shop contractor
Performance and payment bonds
Certificate of insurance
Cleanup

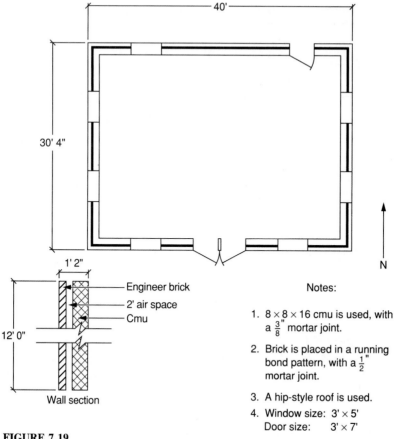

Notes:

1. $8 \times 8 \times 16$ cmu is used, with a $\frac{3}{8}$" mortar joint.

2. Brick is placed in a running bond pattern, with a $\frac{1}{2}$" mortar joint.

3. A hip-style roof is used.

4. Window size:  $3' \times 5'$
   Door size:    $3' \times 7'$

**FIGURE 7.19**
Masonry drawing.

## STUDENT EXERCISES

**7.1.** Determine the number of face bricks and blocks required for the drawing shown in Fig. 7.19.

**7.2.** Develop a spreadsheet that will calculate the amount of horizontal reinforcing.

   Entered information
      Vertical spacing of reinforcing
      Size of reinforcing
      Length of wall
   Output
      Total linear feet of horizontal reinforcing by size and type of reinforcing

**7.3.** Using the drawings and specifications provided by the instructor, do a takeoff and price for the masonry division.

# CHAPTER
# 8

## METALS

This chapter covers the major items in division 5, steel and plastics, of the Uniform Construction Index. These items include structural steel framing, plates and rods, connections, joists, light-gauge metal, and miscellaneous items.

The intent of this chapter is to (1) provide sufficient background so that the estimator understands the major items in division 5; (2) establish a basis for estimating structural-steel-related items associated with general construction; and (3) provide an introduction to the specialized area of structural steel construction. The methodology used to estimate structural steel items also applies to aluminum framing and connections and many of the other more specialized items in division 5.

Structural steel can be a large part of the estimate for some types of buildings. The typical steel components found in these buildings include girders, beams, joists, columns, decking, and various other load-supporting members. One will also find bracing, plates, and connections in steel frame buildings. Figure 8.1 shows various steel-related items.

The required level of precision of the estimate depends on who is developing it and what it will be used for. A lot of detail is required if the estimate is being prepared by the contractor who will be installing the material. On the other hand, if the estimate is being developed by another party (e.g., the general contractor or construction manager) for the purpose of checking or evaluating the steel erector's bid, a less detailed estimate (e.g., based solely on the quantity of tons to be placed) can be developed.

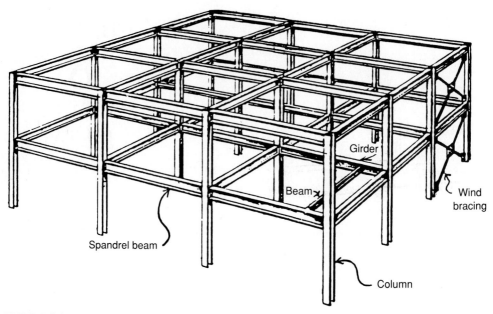

**FIGURE 8.1**
Three-dimensional illustration of structural steel.

## TAKING OFF STRUCTURAL STEEL ITEMS

Taking off structural steel work includes the following categories:

1. Structural steel members
2. Steel plates and rods
3. Connections
4. Joists
5. Decking
6. Miscellaneous and Ornamental

### Structural Steel Members

Structural steel members include commercially available sections. Some of these are nothing more than single sections of preformed material such as angles, channels, and I-shaped members (i.e., wide flange); others are made up of various preformed sections to produce such members as deep girders, joists, and trusses.

From time to time the estimator may find that a structural steel component, because of its size, may have to be fabricated on-site. In this case, the component is assembled using commercially available sections along with auxiliary metal, such as plates. Examples include a deep building girder or special architectural framing section.

Structural steel is usually taken off and priced in units of weight because it is purchased for a price per weight quantity. Some components, however (such as light sections or special prefabricated items), are purchased and thus taken off by the linear foot.

Available shapes and sizes of commercially available sections are published by steel fabricators; most are listed in the *American Institute of Steel Construction Manual*. Within these listings one can find the weight per linear foot for each type of section along with other physical properties, such as cross-sectional dimensions. Figure 8.2 shows some of the more common types of commercially available sections.

Since major structural steel components are usually taken off by total weight in pounds or tons, the estimator's task is to determine the total length of each member and multiply by the unit weight (pounds per foot). For example:

Find the total weight of a W10 × 35 which is 12′ 6″ long.

Total weight $= 12.5$ ft $\times 35$ lb/ft $= 437.5$ lb or $0.22$ tons

When determining the length of a member, the estimator should be as exact as possible. However, at times exact lengths may be available only from shop drawings that are produced by the fabricator after the original estimate is developed. In this case the estimator has only the construction drawings, which include framing plans, elevations, and sections. In this case, lengths can be obtained using column line and row dimensions for horizontal members such as beams and

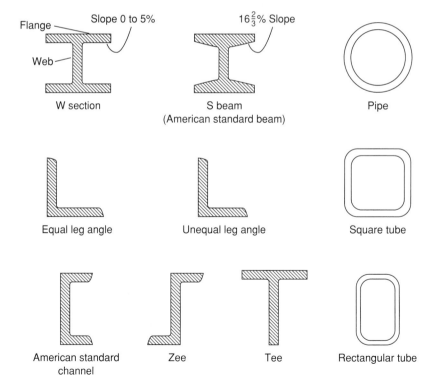

**FIGURE 8.2**
Examples of steel sections.

joists. For column lengths, refer to the plans and/or elevations. In some cases, such as for diagonal bracing, the estimator will have to calculate the length of the member using information from the drawings and right-triangle mathematical relationships.

Items prefabricated off-site, such as roof trusses, are usually purchased by lump sum. However, the general contractor should know how many of each type of member are required and the total weight of each type for installation purposes.

The more exact the structural steel takeoff, the less waste one adds in the material takeoff. Since framing members are ordered and fabricated to the exact length, no waste is added to the takeoff.

When taking off structural steel items, it is recommended that the estimator begin with the horizontal members using the framing plans. The members are taken off by type (grade of steel), size (manufacturer's designation), and length for each floor. The takeoff itself is accomplished by searching for and taking off members in order of standard size. For example, one would scan the drawings and locate each wide flange section, each channel section, and so forth. It is usual for any one standard section to have various lengths. Each length takes up one line on the worksheet. Once all members of the same size are listed, the estimator can calculate the total length and convert this to weight using the unit weight of the member. This process continues for each floor until all the structural members have been taken off. A specially designed takeoff sheet, as shown in Fig. 8.3, can be used.

For any one size section, the total weight (if it appears on more than one floor) can be obtained by summing the weights from each of the entries for each floor. This can be documented on the general worksheet in a summary section for structural steel (see Fig. 8.4 for an example).

In the case of vertical steel members (columns), the estimator will need to refer to the framing plans to determine member size and the elevation drawings to determine member length. Some sets of drawings have column schedules to help the estimator. The schedule will list each column and its length. The take-off and documentation of columns is done exactly the same as for horizontal members.

For diagonal members, the estimator must perform some intermediate cal-culations to obtain the total weight (see Fig. 8.5). For horizontal and vertical members, this information should be appropriately documented on the worksheet, as shown in Fig. 8.6.

## Steel Plates and Rods

The next part of the structural steel estimate is the takeoff of steel plates and rods. Plates connect other steel members together, or they can be used as individual components, such as bearing and base plates. Rods are sometimes used for bracing members. For plates and rods, the estimator can take one of two approaches to the takeoff.

WORKSHEET-B-

| COMPUTED BY: | KB | | PROJECT: | Clemson Apartment Complex | | | DATE: | 11-26 |
|---|---|---|---|---|---|---|---|---|
| CHECKED BY: | (signature) | | ARCHITECT: | Jones + Jones A/H | | | PAGE: | 1 OF 1 |
| | | | | | | | INDEX NO. | 206 |

| REF. | DESCRIPTION | SIZE: W12x22 | | | SIZE: W14x30 | | | SIZE: W14x26 | | | SIZE: W16x31 | | | SIZE: | | |
|---|---|---|---|---|---|---|---|---|---|---|---|---|---|---|---|---|
| | | NO. | LENGTH | TOTAL | NO. | LENGTH | TOTAL | NO. | LENGTH | TOTAL | NO. | LENGTH | TOTAL | NO. | LENGTH | TOTAL |
| 5-1 | Beams (2nd Floor) | 12 | 14 | 168 | | | | | | | | | | | | |
| | '' | 4 | 18 | 72 | | | | | | | | | | | | |
| | '' | 4 | 10 | 40 | | | | | | | | | | | | |
| 5-1 | Columns (2nd Floor) | | | | 12 | 10 | 120 | | | | | | | | | |
| 5-1 | Beams (1st Floor) | | | | | | | 12 | 14 | 168 | | | | | | |
| | '' | | | | | | | 4 | 18 | 72 | | | | | | |
| | '' | | | | | | | 4 | 10 | 40 | | | | | | |
| 5-1 | Columns (1st Floor) | | | | | | | | | | 12 | 10 | 120 | | | |
| | Subtotal | | | 280 | | | 120 | | | 280 | | | 120 | | | |
| | Conversion: | | 22/ft | | | 30/ft | | | 26/ft | | | 31/ft | | | | |
| | TOTALS FROM PREVIOUS PAGE: | | | 0 | | | 0 | | | 0 | | | 0 | | | |
| | TOTALS | | 16 | 6160 | | 16 | 3600 | | 16 | 7280 | | 16 | 3720 | | | |

FIGURE 8.3
Example worksheet for structural steel.

209

WORKSHEET: A

| COMPUTED BY: | KB |
| CHECKED BY: | PL |

| PROJECT: | Clemson Apartment Complex |
| ARCHITECT: | Jones, #1A |

| DATE: | 11-26 |
| PAGE: | 1 OF 1 |
| INDEX NO: | 207 |

| REF. | DESCRIPTION | QUAN. | DIMENSIONS | | | SUBTOTAL | | TOTAL | | REMARKS |
|---|---|---|---|---|---|---|---|---|---|---|
| | | | LENGTH | WIDTH | HEIGHT | QUAN. | UN. | QUAN. | UN. | |
| S-1 | W12X19 Beams (3rd) | 16 | 22 | | | 352 | LF | | | |
| | '' | 6 | 18 | | | 108 | LF | | | |
| S-1 | W12X19 Columns (3rd) | 24 | 10 | | | 240 | LF | | | |
| S-1 | W12X19 Beams | 8 | 12 | | | 96 | LF | | | |
| | '' | 4 | 12 | | | 48 | LF | | | |
| | Subtotal | | | | | 844 | LF | 8 | TON | (1916/LF) |
| | TOTAL FROM PREVIOUS PAGE: | | | | | 0 | | 0 | | |
| | TOTAL: | | | | | 844 | LF | 8 | TON | |

**FIGURE 8.4**
Obtaining total steel weight.

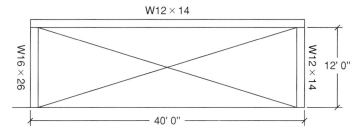

Given: Cross bracing of member weight 8 lb/ft
Length of bracing = L = $\sqrt{(40')^2 + (12')^2}$ = 47.77 ft
Weight of bracing = 2 × 47.77 ft × 8.0 lb/ft = 764.32 lb

**FIGURE 8.5**
Determining weight of diagonal members.

The first approach involves taking off the plate or rod as a separate item by type and size and then calculating the weight knowing the unit weight of the material (for steel it is 490 lb/cf). For example:

Determine the total weight of five 10″× 14″ × $\frac{3}{4}$″ plates.

$$\text{Total weight} = 5 \times \frac{10'' \times 14'' \times 0.75''}{1728 \text{ in.}^3/\text{cf}} \times 490 \text{ lb/cf} = 148.88 \text{ lb}$$

This information is documented on the worksheet shown in Fig. 8.7. It is usually more efficient to take off the steel plates in the same order as the members they support.

The second approach is to take off the plates and/or rods as part of the major structural steel components. The reason behind this method is that there is a direct relationship between the number of steel plates that are required for a given weight of steel members. In other words, the total weight of the steel plates is a known percentage of the total weight of structural steel members. One can obtain the percentage or a range of percentages from past experience. A typical range is 5 percent to 10 percent; the example in Fig. 8.8 uses 10 percent.

## Connections

Connections for structural steel members are welded, bolted, or both. From a structural design standpoint there are two major types of connections: type I (called a simple connection), which is designed to take only shear forces, and type II (referred to as a semirigid or rigid connection), which is used when the connection has to resist shear and moment forces. Figure 8.9 provides examples of each. The estimator should refer to the structural drawings to determine the types that exist on a project.

As in the case of steel plates and bars, the estimator has two choices in taking off connections. First, each type can be counted and documented, from which a total number of connectors can be determined. This will work for bolts. For welds, the estimator will have to take off the length of each type and size

COMPUTED BY: KB
CHECKED BY: RL

PROJECT: Clemson Apartment Complex
ARCHITECT: Jones & Jones, AIA

DATE: 1-26
PAGE: 1 OF 1
INDEX NO. 209

| REP. | DESCRIPTION | SIZE: 1 3/4" Tube | | | SIZE: W12X14 | | | SIZE: W16X26 | | | SIZE: | | | SIZE: | | |
|---|---|---|---|---|---|---|---|---|---|---|---|---|---|---|---|---|
| | | NO. | LENGTH | TOTAL | NO. | LENGTH | TOTAL | NO. | LENGTH | TOTAL | NO. | LENGTH | TOTAL | NO. | LENGTH | TOTAL |
| 5-1 | Cross Bracing | 2 | 4ft.16 | 84 | | | | | | | | | | | | |
| 5-1 | Beam | | | | 1 | 40 | 40 | | | | | | | | | |
| 5-1 | Columns | | | | | | | 2 | 12 | 24 | | | | | | |
| | Subtotal | | | 84 | | | 40 | | | 24 | | | | | | |
| | Conversion | | | 3.65#/F | | | 14#/F | | | 26#/F | | | | | | |
| | TOTALS FROM PREVIOUS PAGE: | | | 0 | | | 0 | | | 0 | | | | | | |
| | TOTALS: | | | 307 LB | | | 560 LB | | | 624 LB | | | | | | |

**FIGURE 8.6**
Worksheet for obtaining the total weight of structural steel members.

WORKSHEET A

| COMPUTED BY: | DB | PROJECT: | CENTRAL WAREHOUSE | | DATE: | 1-26 |
| CHECKED BY: | RL | ARCHITECT: | JONES - JONES, A/A | | PAGE: 1 OF 1 | |
| | | | | | INDEX NO: | |

| REF | DESCRIPTION | QUAN | DIMENSIONS | | | SUBTOTAL | | TOTAL | | REMARKS |
| | | | LENGTH | WIDTH | HEIGHT | QUAN | UN | QUAN | UN | |
| S-2 | 3/4" BASE PLATE | 6 | 1.62 | 1.17 | 0.06 | .6823 | CF | | | BAY 1 |
| S-2 | " | 6 | 1.62 | 1.17 | 0.06 | .6823 | CF | | | BAY 2 |
| S-2 | " | 8 | 2.17 | 1.17 | 0.06 | 1.219 | CF | | | BAY 3 |
| S-2 | " | 8 | 2.17 | 1.17 | 0.06 | 1.219 | CF | | | BAY 4 |
| | SUBTOTAL | | | | | 3.803 | CF | | | |
| | TOTAL | | | | | | | 1864 | LB | WT/CF = 490 LB |
| TOTAL FROM PREVIOUS PAGE: | | | | | | 0 | CF | 0 | | |
| TOTAL: | | | | | | 3.803 | CF | 1864 | LB | |

**FIGURE 8.7**
Worksheet for determining total weight of a steel plate.

**WORKSHEET - A**

COMPUTED BY: KB
CHECKED BY: RL
PROJECT: Post Office
ARCHITECT: Jones + Jones, AIA
DATE: 11-26
PAGE: 1 OF 1
INDEX NO: 262

| REF. | DESCRIPTION | QUAN. | DIMENSIONS | | | SUBTOTAL | | TOTAL | | REMARKS |
|---|---|---|---|---|---|---|---|---|---|---|
| | | | LENGTH | WIDTH | HEIGHT | QUAN. | UN. | QUAN. | UN. | |
| 5-1 | W16X26 Columns | 12 | 10 | | | 120 | LF | 3130 | LB | (26 lb/LF) |
| 5-1 | W6X12 Beams | 12 | 14 | | | 168 | LF | 2016 | LB | (12 lb/LF) |
| 5-1 | W8X18 Beams | 6 | 40 | | | 240 | LF | 4320 | LB | (18 lb/LF) |
| | Subtotal | | | | | | | 9456 | LB | |
| 5-1 | Plates | | | | | | | 946 | LB | 10% Allowance |
| | Total | | | | | | | 10,402 | LB | |
| | TOTAL FROM PREVIOUS PAGE: | | | | | | | 0 | | |
| | TOTAL: | | | | | | | 10,402 | LB | |

**FIGURE 8.8**
Worksheet using steel plates as a percentage of total weight.

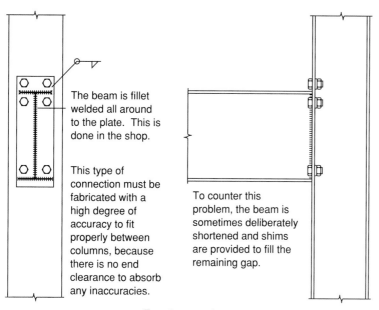

The beam is fillet welded all around to the plate. This is done in the shop.

This type of connection must be fabricated with a high degree of accuracy to fit properly between columns, because there is no end clearance to absorb any inaccuracies.

To counter this problem, the beam is sometimes deliberately shortened and shims are provided to fill the remaining gap.

Type I connections

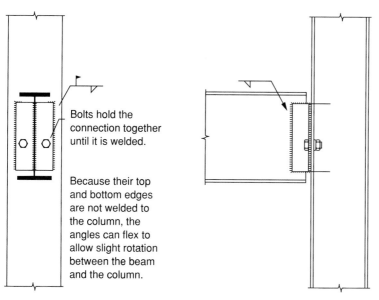

Bolts hold the connection together until it is welded.

Because their top and bottom edges are not welded to the column, the angles can flex to allow slight rotation between the beam and the column.

Type II connections

**FIGURE 8.9**
Structural steel connections. (Adapted from *Fundamentals of Building Construction: Materials and Methods, 2/e.* by Edward Allen. ©1990 John Wiley & Sons, Inc. Reprinted by permission of John Wiley & Sons, Inc.)

WORKSHEET-A.

| | | | | | | |
|---|---|---|---|---|---|---|
| COMPUTED BY: | KB | PROJECT: | Clemson Apartment Complex | | DATE: | 11-26 |
| CHECKED BY: | RL | ARCHITECT: | Jones + Jones, AIA | | PAGE: 1 OF 1 | |
| | | | | | INDEX NO: | 271 |

| REF. | DESCRIPTION | QUAN. | DIMENSIONS | | | SUBTOTAL | | TOTAL | | REMARKS |
|---|---|---|---|---|---|---|---|---|---|---|
| | | | LENGTH | WIDTH | HEIGHT | QUAN. | UN. | QUAN. | UN. | |
| S-3 | 5/8" Fillet weld | 136 | 0.75 | | | | | 102 | LF | |
| S-3 | 1/2" Fillet weld | 216 | 0.83 | | | 180 | LF | | | |
| | " | 160 | 0.75 | | | 120 | LF | | | |
| | Subtotal | | | | | | | 300 | LF | |
| S-3 | 5/8" A325 Bolts | 860 | | | | | | 860 | EA | |
| S-3 | 5/8" A325 Bolts | 400 | | | | | | 400 | EA | |
| S-3 | 3/4" A325 Bolts | 540 | | | | | | 540 | EA | |
| | | | | | | | | | | |
| TOTAL FROM PREVIOUS PAGE: | | | | | | 0 | | 0 | | |
| TOTAL: | | | | | | 0 | | 0 | | |

**FIGURE 8.10**
Steel connections worksheet.

216

of weld for each connection and then determine the total length of each type and size weld. These methods are time-consuming and require complete information on the drawings, so general contractors seldom use them. An example of how one would take off and document this procedure for bolts and welds is shown in Fig. 8.10.

The other method of taking off connections is to include them in the estimate of the structural steel itself. For plates, this is based on the relationship between the weight of the steel that needs to be put into place and the number of connections and related work required. A range of acceptable percentages is 3 percent to 6 percent. (see Fig. 8.11).

Figure 8.12 contains a framing plan, column and bearing plate schedule, and information about connections. Figure 8.13 shows the worksheet documenting the takeoff.

## Taking Off Steel Joists, Decking, Light-Gauge Metal, and Miscellaneous Items

Steel joists (sometimes called open web joists) are prefabricated lightweight trusses. The six basic series are J, H, LJ, LH, DLJ, and DLH. The first two types are used for relatively short spans; the second two for medium to long spans; the last two for very long spans. For any one type and size joist, the maximum length it can span and its physical properties can be found in a publication available from the Steel Joist Institute, or consult a local supplier.

Unlike many of the other steel framing components, the weight per foot of joist section is not given in its designation. For instance, a 12 H 4 joist is approximately 12″ deep and has web members constructed of no. 4 steel rods. The weight per foot must be obtained from the manufacturer, supplier, or Steel Joist Institute publication. Refer to Fig. 8.14 for an example of a table of general information for LH and DLH series joists.

Steel joists are purchased by weight. Therefore, in developing the estimate, first multiply the total linear feet of each joist type by the respective weight per foot to obtain the total weight. Besides the joists themselves, the estimator must also consider various accessories such as bridging, extensions, anchors, and other items needed to install the joists and the materials that may be fastened to them. These items are all taken off by type, size, and number required. Connections are taken off the same way as for steel framing members (discussed earlier in this chapter).

Steel decking is used for roof and floor coverings. A wide variety of shapes, sizes, thicknesses (gauges), and accessories are available. Figure 8.15 shows some typical types of steel decking. The drawings and specifications provide the estimator with the information necessary to perform the takeoff. Steel decking is purchased by the square. There are 100 square feet in one square. To obtain the total number of squares, the estimator should calculate the total area in square feet to be covered by the decking, add a percentage for laps and waste, and divide by 100. The amount to be added for laps depends on the type of decking and method of installation. The manufacturer or supplier can provide this information.

WORKSHEET -A-

COMPUTED BY: KB | PROJECT: Clemson Apartment Complex | DATE: 11-26

CHECKED BY: RL | ARCHITECT: Jones + Jones, AIA | PAGE: 1 OF 1

INDEX NO:

| REF. | DESCRIPTION | QUAN. | DIMENSIONS LENGTH | WIDTH | HEIGHT | SUBTOTAL QUAN. | UN. | TOTAL QUAN. | UN. | REMARKS |
|---|---|---|---|---|---|---|---|---|---|---|
| S-2 | Structural Steel | | | | | 160 | TONS | | | |
| | Connections | | | | | 8 | TONS | | | 5% Allowance |
| | Total | | | | | | | 168 | TONS | |
| TOTAL FROM PREVIOUS PAGE: | | | | | | 0 | | 0 | | |
| TOTAL: | | | | | | 0 | | 168 | TONS | |

**FIGURE 8.11**
Steel connections by percentage.

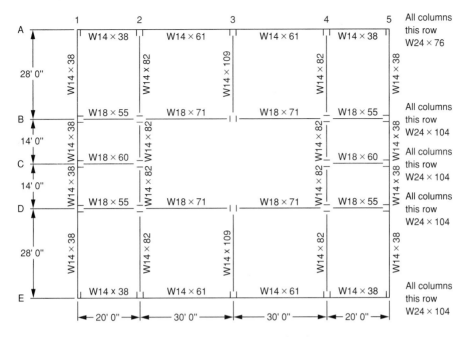

Note: All columns are 10' 0" in length

| Column Schedule | | |
|---|---|---|
| Column | A-1 thru A-5 | B-1 thru E-5 |
| Column size | W24 × 76 | W24 × 104 |
| Btm. of base plate elev. | 698.00" | 698.00" |
| Base plate size | 3/4" x 26" × 12" | 7/8" x 26" × 15" |
| Anchor bolts | 4-7/8" ϕ × 16" | 4-1" ϕ × 18" |
| Top of column elevation | 708.00" | 708.00" |

**FIGURE 8.12**
Structural steel drawing.

It may also be contained in the technical specifications for the specific project. A 3 percent to 5 percent waste factor is sufficient.

Light-gauge metal members are available in a variety of sections. Components include studs, joists, and others. They are used in combination with other framing systems for interior load- and nonload-bearing partitions, exterior curtain walls, fire separation walls, parapets, trusses, and suspended ceilings. Figure 8.16 shows some typical types of light-gauge sections.

Light-gauge metal members are taken off similar to structural steel. The general contractor usually obtains a price from a subcontractor, who works with a supplier or fabricator.

COMPUTED BY: KB
CHECKED BY: RL

PROJECT: Oconee Office Towers
ARCHITECT: Jones + Jones, AIA

DATE: 11-36
PAGE: 1 OF 1
INDEX NO.: 292

| REF. | DESCRIPTION | SIZE: W24X76 NO. | LENGTH | TOTAL | SIZE: W24X104 NO. | LENGTH | TOTAL | SIZE: W14X38 NO. | LENGTH | TOTAL | SIZE: W14X61 NO. | LENGTH | TOTAL | SIZE: W14X82 NO. | LENGTH | TOTAL |
|---|---|---|---|---|---|---|---|---|---|---|---|---|---|---|---|---|
| S-2 | Columns | 5 | 10 | 50 | | | | | | | | | | | | |
| S-2 | Columns | | | | 19 | 10 | 190 | | | | | | | | | |
| S-3 | Beams | | | | | | | 4 | 20 | 80 | | | | | | |
| | | | | | | | | 4 | 28 | 112 | | | | | | |
| | | | | | | | | 4 | 14 | 56 | | | | | | |
| S-3 | Beams | | | | | | | | | | 4 | 30 | 120 | | | |
| S-3 | Beams | | | | | | | | | | | | | 4 | 28 | 110 |
| | | | | | | | | | | | | | | 4 | 14 | 56 |
| | Subtotal | | | 50 | | | 190 | | | 248 | | | 120 | | | 166 |
| | Conversion | | | 76#/ft | | | 104#/ft | | | 38/ft | | | 61/ft | | | 82#/ft |
| TOTALS FROM PREVIOUS PAGE: | | | 0 | | | 0 | | | 0 | | | 0 | | | 0 | |
| TOTALS: | | 3800 | LB | | 19760 | LB | | 9424 | LB | | 7320 | LB | | 13612 | LB | |

**FIGURE 8.13**
Structural steel worksheet.

**HIGH STRENGTH**

**ECONOMICAL**

**DESIGN**—Vulcraft LH & DLH Series long-span steel joists are designed in accordance with the specifications of the Steel Joist Institute.

**ROOF SPANS TO 144' 0**

**FLOOR SPANS TO 120' 0**

**PAINT**—Vulcraft joists receive a shop-coat of rust inhibitive primer whose performance characteristics conform to those of the Steel Joist Institute specification 102.4.

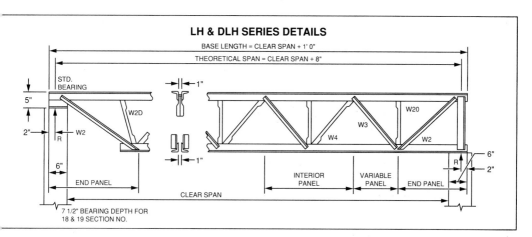

### LH & DLH SERIES DETAILS

### LH & DLH TABLE
#### MINIMUM BEARING LENGTHS

| Joist Type | On Masonry | On Concrete | On Steel |
|---|---|---|---|
| LH 02 thru 17<br>DLH 10 thru 19 | 6"* | 6"* | 4" |

#### MINIMUM BEARING PLATE WIDTHS

| | | |
|---|---|---|
| LH 02 thru LH 12<br>DLH 10 thru DLH 12 | 9"* | 9"* |
| LH 13 thru LH 17<br>DLH 13 thru DLH 19 | 12"* | 12"* |

*See Sect. 104.4 on page 43.

### BRIDGING SPACING

| Section No.* | Min. Bolt Diameter** | Maximum Spacing of Lines of Bridging |
|---|---|---|
| LH 02 to 09, incl. | 3/8" | 11' 0" |
| DLH 10 | 3/8" | 14' 0" |
| LH 10 to 14, incl. | 3/8" | 16' 0" |
| DLH 11 to 14, incl. | 3/8" | 16' 0" |
| LH 15 to 17, incl. | 1/2" | 21' 0" |
| DLH 15 to 17, incl. | 1/2" | 21' 0" |
| DLH 18 to 19, incl. | 5/8" | 26' 0" |

*Last two digits of joint designation shown in load table.
**Size required due to requirements as indicated for bolted or bridging connections in Section 104.5 (e). Minimum A307 Bolt required for connection.

### JOIST SPACING FOR BRIDGING ANGLE SIZE
#### DIAGONAL BRIDGING CHART
##### BRIDGING ANGLE SIZE

| DEPTH | L1×1×1/64 | L1 1/4×1 1/4×1/64 | L1 1/2×1 1/2×1/64 | L1 3/4×1 3/4×1/8 | L2×2×1/8 |
|---|---|---|---|---|---|
| 18 | 6' 5" | 8' 2" | 9' 10" | 11' 6" | |
| 20 | 6' 5" | 8' 1" | 9' 10" | 11' 6" | |
| 24 | 6' 4" | 8' 1" | 9' 9" | 11' 5" | |
| 28 | 6' 2" | 8' 0" | 9' 8" | 11' 5" | |
| 32 | 6' 1" | 7' 10" | 9' 7" | 11' 4" | 13' 0" |
| 36 | | 7' 9" | 9' 6" | 11' 3" | 12' 11" |
| 40 | | 7' 7" | 9' 5" | 11' 2" | 12' 10" |
| 44 | | 7' 5" | 9' 3" | 11' 0" | 12' 9" |
| 48 | | 7' 3" | 9' 1" | 10' 11" | 12' 8" |
| 52 | | | 9' 0" | 10' 9" | 12' 7" |
| 56 | | | 8' 10" | 10' 8" | 12' 5" |
| 60 | | | 8' 7" | 10' 6" | 12' 4" |
| 64 | | | 8' 5" | 10' 4" | 12' 2" |
| 68 | | | 8' 2" | 10' 2" | 12' 0" |
| 72 | | | 8' 0" | 10' 0" | 11' 10" |

#### †HORIZONTAL BRIDGING CHART
##### BRIDGING ANGLE SIZE

| DEPTH | L1×1×1/64 | L1 1/4×1 1/4×1/64 | L1 1/2×1 1/2×1/64 | L1 3/4×1 3/4×1/8 | L2×2×1/8 |
|---|---|---|---|---|---|
| ALL DEPTHS | 5' 0" | 6' 3" | 7' 6" | 8' 9" | 10' 0" |

†See specification section 104.5 for the proper use of horizontal bridging.

**FIGURE 8.14**

Physical properties of open web joists. (Courtesy of Vulcraft Division Nucor Corporation.)

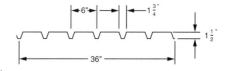

SECTION PROPERTIES                           Fy = 33 ksi

| Type No. | Design Thickness | Weight (Lb/Ft.²) Painted | Galv. | I In⁴/Ft | Sp In³/Ft | Sn In³/Ft |
|---|---|---|---|---|---|---|
| 1.5F 22 | 0.0295 | 1.63 | 1.73 | 0.120 | 0.111 | 0.120 |
| 1.5F 21 | 0.0329 | 1.82 | 1.92 | 0.136 | 0.126 | 0.135 |
| 1.5F 20 | 0.0358 | 1.99 | 2.09 | 0.150 | 0.139 | 0.147 |
| 1.5F 19 | 0.0418 | 2.32 | 2.42 | 0.180 | 0.165 | 0.172 |
| 1.5F 18 | 0.0474 | 2.64 | 2.74 | 0.206 | 0.189 | 0.194 |

Type F (intermediate rib) deck is designed to provide the most economical combination of structural load carrying capacity and insulation materials. The rib openings permit fast and easy installation, and the nestable design eliminates the need for die-set ends. 1" rigid insulation is recommended for Type F deck.

VERTICAL LOADS TYPE 1.5F

| Span Condition | Type No. | Max. Span SDI Const. Load Stress (26.6 KSI) | Δ = L/240 | 4-0 | 4-6 | 5-0 | 5-6 | 6-0 | 6-6 | 7-0 | 7-6 | 8-0 | 8-6 | 9-0 | 9-6 | 10-0 | 10-6 | 11-0 |
|---|---|---|---|---|---|---|---|---|---|---|---|---|---|---|---|---|---|---|
| | 1.5F22 | 4' 11 | 4' 9 | 92 | 73 | 59 | 49 | 41 | 35 | 30 | 26 | 23 | 20 | | | | | |
| | 1.5F21 | 5' 7 | 5' 1 | 105 | 83 | 67 | 56 | 47 | 40 | 34 | 30 | 26 | 23 | 21 | | | | |
| ONE | 1.5F20 | 6' 2 | 5' 5 | 116 | 92 | 74 | 61 | 51 | 44 | 38 | 32 | 28 | 25 | 23 | 21 | | | |
| | 1.5F19 | 7' 3 | 5' 11 | 137 | 109 | 88 | 73 | 61 | 51 | 43 | 37 | 32 | 28 | 26 | 23 | 21 | 20 | |
| | 1.5F18 | 8' 4 | 6' 5 | 157 | 124 | 101 | 83 | 70 | 59 | 49 | 42 | 36 | 32 | 28 | 26 | 23 | 22 | 20 |
| | 1.5F22 | 6' 0 | 5' 10 | 100 | 79 | 64 | 53 | 44 | 38 | 33 | 28 | 25 | 22 | 20 | | | | |
| | 1.5F21 | 6' 10 | 6' 2 | 112 | 89 | 72 | 60 | 50 | 43 | 37 | 32 | 28 | 25 | 22 | 20 | | | |
| TWO | 1.5F20 | 7' 6 | 6' 6 | 122 | 97 | 78 | 65 | 54 | 46 | 40 | 35 | 31 | 27 | 24 | 22 | 20 | | |
| | 1.5F19 | 8' 11 | 7' 1 | 143 | 113 | 92 | 76 | 64 | 54 | 47 | 41 | 36 | 32 | 28 | 25 | 23 | 21 | 19 |
| | 1.5F18 | 10' 3 | 7' 7 | 162 | 128 | 103 | 86 | 72 | 61 | 53 | 46 | 40 | 36 | 32 | 29 | 26 | 23 | 21 |
| | 1.5F22 | 6' 0 | 5' 10 | 125 | 99 | 80 | 66 | 56 | 47 | 41 | 36 | 31 | 28 | 25 | 22 | 20 | | |
| THREE | 1.5F21 | 6' 10 | 6' 2 | 141 | 111 | 90 | 74 | 62 | 53 | 46 | 40 | 35 | 31 | 28 | 25 | 22 | 20 | |
| OR | 1.5F20 | 7' 6 | 6' 6 | 153 | 121 | 98 | 81 | 68 | 58 | 50 | 44 | 38 | 34 | 30 | 27 | 24 | 22 | 20 |
| MORE | 1.5F19 | 8' 11 | 7' 1 | 179 | 142 | 115 | 95 | 80 | 68 | 59 | 51 | 45 | 40 | 35 | 32 | 29 | 26 | 24 |
| | 1.5F18 | 10' 3 | 7' 7 | 202 | 160 | 129 | 107 | 90 | 77 | 66 | 57 | 51 | 45 | 40 | 36 | 32 | 29 | 27 |

Allowable Total (Dead + Live) Uniform Load (Lbs./Sq. Ft.) — Span (Ft.-In.)

**FIGURE 8.15**
Steel decking. (Courtesy of Vulcraft Division Nucor Corporation.)

Miscellaneous, ornamental, and other items in division 5 are also taken off by item type in the units used to purchase it. (The metals reminder list at the end of this chapter presents units of takeoff for all the major items in division 5.) Figure 8.17 is an example of a worksheet showing the takeoff of some of the metal items discussed in this section.

## PRICING OF STRUCTURAL STEEL

Structural steel is priced in the same units in which it is taken off. However, this causes some problems when considering the labor and equipment required to install the components. Material cost depends on weight, area, or length of the member, but the cost of labor and equipment depends more on the number of members to be placed. For instance, about twice the labor effort is required to install two columns as compared to one column, even if they are different sizes. Therefore, to obtain the labor and equipment costs one needs to know the amount of time it will take to install a certain quantity of material. This cost is usually provided to the general contractor as a total lump-sum price from the fabricator or as a unit price per ton, unit of length, or square.

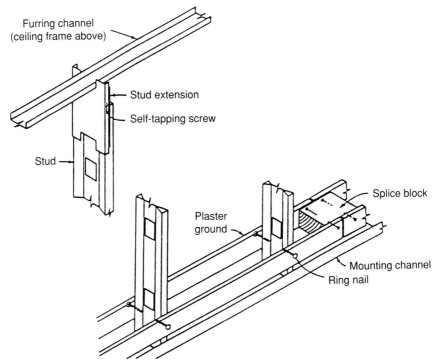

Furring channel
(ceiling frame above)

Stud extension

Self-tapping screw

Stud

Splice block

Plaster
ground

Mounting channel
Ring nail

**FIGURE 8.16**
Light-gauge metal sections.

## Material

The price of the material is available from steel manufacturers and fabricators. The contractor is usually quoted a lump-sum price for all the structural steel, decking, and joists per drawings and specifications. On occasion, a standard price per ton (or square or linear foot) is quoted, with various extras added, such as shop painting, high-quality steel, or number of different size members. Other costs to be considered are those for the development of shop drawings, shop fabrication, mill and shop reports, and specified field inspections.

## Labor

The labor effort to install the steel items may involve many different steps and procedures. First, the steel members may have to be off-loaded. This task is usually the contractor's responsibility. Once the steel is off-loaded it is set in storage and inventoried or placed into its final position, plumbed, and secured or tightened. Finally, all detail work must be performed. All of these steps affect productivity.

The estimator needs to know the following information to obtain the total labor cost:

| COMPUTED BY: KB | PROJECT: Oconne Office Towers | | | | | | | | DATE: 11-26 |
| CHECKED BY: RL | ARCHITECT: Jones + Jones, AIA | | | | | | | | PAGE: 1 OF 1 |
| | | | | | | | | | INDEX NO: 298 |

| REF. | DESCRIPTION | QUAN. | DIMENSIONS | | | SUBTOTAL | | | TOTAL | | REMARKS |
| | | | LENGTH | WIDTH | HEIGHT | QUAN. | UN. | | QUAN. | UN. | |
| S-1 | Open-Web Joists | 64 | 50 | | | 3200 | LF | | 16 | TON | 10 LB/LF |
| S-1 | Metal Decking | 1 | 168 | 50 | | | | | 8400 | SF | |
| S-2 | Alum Pipe Railing | 1 | 112 | | | | | | 112 | LF | |
| S-3 | Cast Iron Trench Cover | 1 | 364 | | | | | | 364 | LF | |
| | | | | | | | | | | | |
| | | | | | | | | | | | |
| | | | | | | | | | | | |
| | | | | | | | | | | | |
| | | | | | | | | | | | |
| | | | | | | | | | | | |
| | | | | | | | | | | | |
| | | | | | | | | | | | |
| | | | | | | | | | | | |
| | | | | | | | | | | | |
| | | | | | | | | | | | |
| | | | | | | | | | | | |
| | | | | | | | | | | | |
| | | | | | | | | | | | |
| | | | | | | | | | | | |
| | | | | | | | | | | | |
| TOTAL FROM PREVIOUS PAGE: | | | | | | 0 | | | 0 | | |
| TOTAL: | | | | | | 0 | | | 0 | | |

**FIGURE 8.17**
Worksheet for miscellaneous steel items.

1. Makeup of the crew
2. Wage rates of the various crew members
3. Productivity of the crew

The most difficult aspect of estimating the cost of labor is determining crew size and productivity. This information usually comes from historical data.

The wage rates depend on the trade classification of the various crew members and the rates paid to each. An example of calculating the labor cost is shown in Fig. 8.18.

## Equipment

The cost for equipment depends on the type and size of the equipment and the number of hours it will be used. The type and size is determined by the contractor and is based on the weight to be lifted, the distance to be moved (both horizontally and vertically), and availability of the equipment. The equipment is either owned by the contractor, rented, or leased. The number of hours the equipment is needed depends on its productivity. This is related to labor productivity and comes from the company's historical records. The estimator should not forget to consider related equipment costs such as transportation, mobilization, and demobilization.

## Summary of Pricing
## Structural Steel

The pricing is documented on a standard summary sheet, shown in Fig. 8.19, and is based on production rates shown in Fig. 8.18 and quantities shown in Fig. 8.13 and Fig. 8.17.

---

Takeoff indicates 40 tons of steel must be placed.

| Labor requirements | Hourly wage |
|---|---|
| 2 Iron workers | $17.00 |
| 1 Helper | $10.50 |
| 1 Supervisor | $21.00 |
| 1 Welder | $16.00 |

Crew productivity: 5 tons/8 hour day

$$\text{Total time} = \frac{40 \text{ tons}}{5 \text{ tons/day}} = 8 \text{ days or 64 hours}$$

Total hourly crew cost:
$(2 \times \$17) + \$10.50 + \$21.00 + \$16.00 = \$81.50/\text{hr}$
Total labor cost:
$\$81.50/\text{hr} \times 64 \text{ hrs} = \$5,216.00$

**FIGURE 8.18**
Labor cost determination.

SUMMARY SHEET

COMPUTED BY: KB
CHECKED BY: RL
PROJECT: Oconee Office Towers
ARCHITECT: Jones + Jones, A/A
DATE: 5-26
PAGE: 1 OF 1
INDEX NO: 299

| REF | DESCRIPTION | QUANTITY | | MATERIAL COST | | DAILY PROD. OF CREW | CREW MAKE-UP | MAN-HOUR PER UNIT | TOTAL MAN HOURS | TOTAL CREW HOURS | AVG. WAGE RATE | LABOR SUBTOTAL | RATE PER HOUR | EQUIP. SUBTOTAL | SUB OR OTHER | TOTAL COST |
|-----|-------------|---------|-----|---------------|-----|------|------|------|------|------|------|------|------|------|------|------|
| | | TOTAL | UN. | UNIT COST | MATERIAL SUBTOTAL | | | | | | | | | | | |
| 299 | Struc. Steel | 27 | TONS | 890 | 23,993 | 5 | 5 | 8 | 216 | 44 | 16.30 | 3521 | 58 | 2552 | 0 | 30066 |
| 298 | Open Web Joists | 16 | TONS | 750 | 12,000 | 12 | 8 | 5.33 | 86 | 11 | 15.75 | 1344 | 130 | 1387 | 0 | 14731 |
| 298 | Metal Deck | 8400 | SF | 2.95 | 24,780 | 1350 | 4 | .024 | 120 | 50 | 18 | 3584 | | 0 | 0 | 28364 |
| 298 | Pipe Railing | 112 | LF | 40 | 4480 | 15 | 1 | .533 | 60 | 60 | 17 | 1015 | | 0 | 0 | 5495 |
| 298 | Trench Cover | 364 | LF | 35 | 12,594 | 20 | 1 | .46 | 146 | 146 | 17 | 2475 | | 0 | 0 | 15069 |
| | TOTAL FROM PREVIOUS PAGE: | | | | 0 | | | | | | | 0 | | 0 | 0 | 0 |
| | TOTAL: | | | | 77,847 | | | | | | | 11939 | | 3939 | | 93725 |

FIGURE 8.19
Summary sheet.

226

When developing the estimate, the estimator needs to consider not only the direct costs of the materials, labor, and equipment but also factors which affect these costs. To help facilitate this process, the reminder list shown below should be used. On occasion a speciality contractor may quote a price for the installation of the steel. The general contractor will need to analyze the bid to make sure that everything has been included. The reminder list could be used for this purpose.

## Metals reminder list

| Quantity takeoff | |
|---|---|
| **Item** | **Unit of measure** |
| Structural metals | |
| Aluminum | lb |
| Canopy framing | lb |
| Columns | lf set/lb/ea/sf face/ton |
| Light-gauge framing | lb |
| Preengineered steel buildings | sf flr/lf/ea/opng/sf |
| Space frame | sf |
| Stressed skin | sf |
| Structural steel | ton/lb/ea/sf |
| Vibration pads | bf/sf/kip |
| Welding rods | lb |
| Welding | hr/ton/lf |
| Metal joists and deck | |
| Bulb tee | sf/lb |
| Light-gauge joists | lf/lb |
| Metal decking | sf |
| Open web joists | ton/ea |
| Misc. and ornamental metals | |
| Aluminum | lb |
| Area wall | ea |
| Bumper rails | lf |
| Checkered plate | lb/sf |
| Construction castings | ea/lb |
| Corner guards | lf/ea |
| Crane rail | lb |
| Curb edging | lf |
| Decorative covering | sf |
| Door frames | ea |
| Door protection | lf |
| Fire escape | lb/lf/ea/flight |
| Floor grating, aluminum | sf/lf |
| Floor grating, planks | lf |
| Floor grating, steel | sf/lb/lf |
| Grating frame | lf/ea |
| Ladder | vlf |

## Metals reminder list (*continued*)

| | |
|---|---|
| Lamp posts | ea |
| Lead | cwt |
| Lintels | lb |
| Manhole covers | ea |
| Pipe support | lb |
| Railings, all types | lf |
| Rolling grille supports | lf |
| Solar screens | sf |
| Stair | riser/sf/vlf |
| Stair treads | ea |
| Toilet partition supports | stall |
| Trench cover | lf |
| Weathervane | ea |
| Window guards | sf/opng |
| Wire | mlf/clf/csf |
| Wire rope | lf |
| Expansion control and fasteners | |
| Drilling | ea |
| Expansion control | lb |
| Expansion joint assemblies | lf |
| Expansion shields | ea/c |
| Hollow wall anchors | c |
| Lag screws | c |
| Machine screws | c |
| Machinery anchors | ea |
| Nails | lb |
| Rivets | c |
| Sheet metal screws | c |
| Studs | ea/c/m |
| Timber connectors | ea/inch/truss |
| Toggle bolts | ea |
| Track | cwt |
| Wedge bolts | ea |
| Welded studs | ea |
| Wood screws | c |

### Other considerations that can affect cost

Shop coat of paint
Specialty coatings
Time required to fabricate steel
Steel delivery time
Large number of pieces relative to the total weight
Special equipment requirements
Cost of freight
Cost of shop drawings and other required submittals
Buy American regulations
Metals that are included in the supplier's bid but are not in the metals
 division of the specifications
Metals that are not included in the supplier's bid but are in the metals
 division of the specifications
Sales tax on material

## Metals reminder list (*continued*)

### Specialty contractor bid to general contractor

Time required for installation
Items supplied but not installed
Items installed but not supplied
Unloading of steel delivered to the project
Field touch-up paint
All necessary equipment to install the steel
Minority-owned business
Union or merit shop contractor
Performance and payment bonds
Safety performance record
Documented total quality management program
Cleanup

## STUDENT EXERCISES

**8.1.** Perform a quantity takeoff of the structural steel columns and beams of the one-story building in Figure 8.20.

**8.2.** Using the information from Exercise 8.1, compute the cost of erecting the structural steel beams and columns. The daily productivity is as follows. Columns—3 tons per

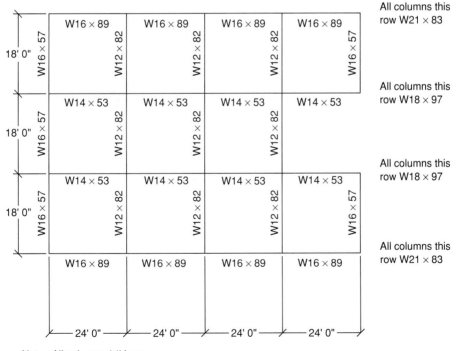

Note: All columns 14' long.

**FIGURE 8.20**
Structural steel drawing.

day; beams—6.5 tons per day. Four iron workers with an average wage of $21.50 per hour make up the crew for both the beams and columns. A crane will be required for the duration of the job at the rate of $125.00 per day. The crane operator's wage is included in the rental price.

**8.3.** Determine the cost of installing the metal roof deck for the project shown in Fig. 8.20 if the productivity of four iron workers is 1200 sf per day with an average wage rate of $19.30 per hour.

**8.4.** Determine the cost to install 126 tons of structural steel given the following information:

Material cost: $560/ton

4 iron workers: $20.82/hr

2 helpers: $14.15/hr

1 supervisor: $25.63/hr

1 welder: $18.95/hr

Crew productivity: 8 tons/day

1 crane@ $110/day

1 Welding Machine: $30/hr

Crew works eight-hour days

**8.5.** Using the drawings and specifications provided by the instructor, do a takeoff of the structural steel and miscellaneous steel.

# CHAPTER

# 9

# CARPENTRY

This chapter covers many of the major items in division 6 of the Uniform Construction Index. These include floor, ceiling, roof and wall wood framing, wood subflooring, sheathing and decking, fasteners, and interior and exterior finish carpentry items.

The purpose of this chapter is to (1) establish a basis for estimating carpentry items associated with general construction; (2) provide enough background information so that the estimator understands the major items in division 9; and (3) provide an introduction to the specialized area of carpentry construction.

There are two major categories of carpentry: rough and finish. Rough carpentry work includes wall, floor, ceiling, roof, and related members (such as bridging). Most rough framing includes the structural members for wood-framed buildings. Figure 9.1 illustrates many of the rough carpentry components found in western platform framing.

Finish carpentry includes trim and moldings, cabinets, paneling, and related miscellaneous items. Figure 9.2 shows some of the more common types of finish carpentry components.

The amount of carpentry work on a project varies depending on the type of building. For instance, commercial and industrial buildings usually have relatively little carpentry work; residential buildings have a lot. Most buildings, however, have some carpentry work.

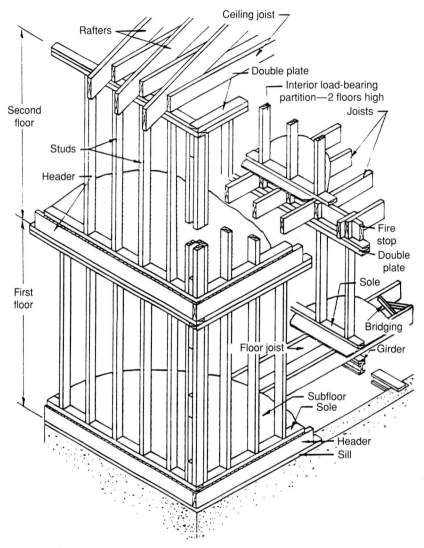

**FIGURE 9.1**
Rough framing components.

Framing and some of the other types of carpentry items are taken off in units of board foot measure. One board foot measure is a wood member 1 inch thick by 12 inches wide by 1 foot long. To convert any size and length of lumber to board feet, determine the product of the cross-sectional dimensions, divide by 12, and multiply by the length. For example, the board foot measure for a 2″ × 12″ board that is 10 feet long would be

$$\frac{2 \times 12}{12} \times 10 = 20 \text{ bfm}$$

If one had 10 of these pieces of lumber, then the total board feet would be

$$20 \text{ bfm} \times 10 = 200 \text{ bfm}$$

Other carpentry items are taken off by the square foot, linear foot, or individual unit. Refer to the reminder list at the end of this chapter for the unit of takeoff for the various items in division 6.

The estimator will need to determine how each size and type of rough or finish carpentry item is categorized and sold by the supplier. For instance, most framing lumber is sold in even foot lengths; finish flooring material may be available only in random lengths. On the other hand, plywood is available in standard panel sizes. In addition, the estimator must keep the various grades of lumber separate if there is significant cost difference.

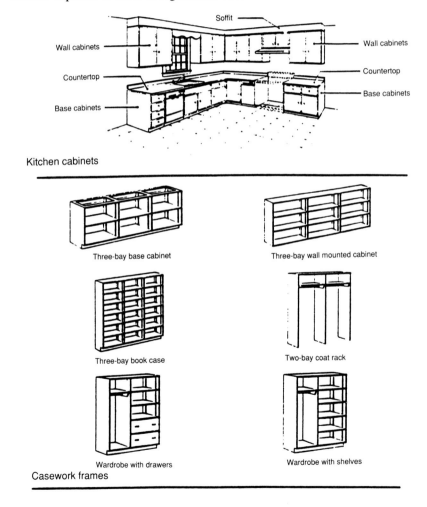

Kitchen cabinets

Three-bay base cabinet

Three-bay wall mounted cabinet

Three-bay book case

Two-bay coat rack

Wardrobe with drawers

Wardrobe with shelves

Casework frames

**FIGURE 9.2**
Finish carpentry items.

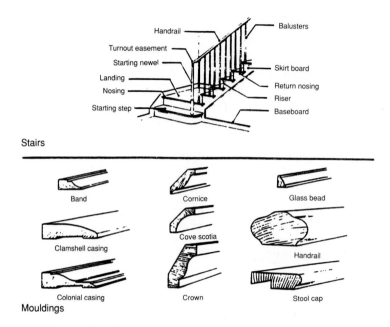

Stairs

Mouldings

**FIGURE 9.2** (*continued*)

## TAKING OFF ROUGH CARPENTRY

Rough carpentry members are taken off by grade, cross-sectional dimension, length, and number of pieces of a specific length. Once this information is obtained, the estimator then performs the necessary calculations to derive the board foot measure, area, or linear foot measure.

Waste may be added to the resulting quantity. Waste depends on the care taken by the workers and the dimensions of the building and its various components. The estimator should be careful not to add too much. When considering waste, first determine what lengths of lumber are available from the supplier. In some cases, the waste will occur automatically when even foot lengths (e.g., 8 ft, 10 ft) must be ordered but the actual length shown on the drawings is shorter. On the other hand, some lumber comes in random lengths; in this case, little waste will be added. Typically, waste can range from as little as 3 percent to 15 percent for framing members to 10 percent to 30 percent for boarding and sheathing.

Specifically, there are two ways to take off rough carpentry framing members. The first is for the estimator to count each member (stud, joist, rafter, etc.) separately, group them by common grade, size, and length, and convert to board foot measure. This method is especially appropriate for specialized framing systems or subsystems.

The second method, which is less time consuming, takes advantage of the fact that most rough carpentry items repeat themselves at a standard spacing. For example, floor joists may be spaced at 24″ on center; wall studs may be spaced at 16″ on center. It should be noted that even in a framing system utilizing a common spacing, one can always find exceptions or breaks in the sequence, such as the addition of extra members to frame an opening. In this case the estimator would determine the number of members based on the common spacing and then add the additional members.

An example of determining the number of 8′ 0″ studs spaced 16″ on center for a wall 24′ 0″ long is as follows:

$$\text{No. of } 8' \ 0'' \text{ studs} = \frac{24 \text{ ft} \times 12 \text{ in./ft}}{16} = 18 + 1 = 19 \text{ studs}$$

If the wall contains openings, the estimator must add extra studs for jambs and possibly sills. It is important that care be taken to make sure all members are taken off. The typical wood frame building is composed of various sizes and lengths of members.

Be thorough and systematic when going through the drawings. Identifying members by purpose and location is one method that the estimator can use. For example, all 2″ × 8″ joists located on the second floor framing plan might be taken off first, followed by the first floor framing. After taking off all the floor framing, take off the wall framing, and so on.

## Floor and Ceiling Framing

The composition of floor and ceiling framing can be found on framing plans or other drawings. These drawings provide the estimator with information about the size and spacing of the various members. To determine the length of each member, refer to the drawing dimensions and then round off to the standard length of the material. All members of the same size, grade, and length should be recorded on the same line of the worksheet for any one level of the building's framing system.

Most framing systems use the same member many times. When this is the case, the estimator can get the quantity by dividing the dimension over which the members occur (that is, the dimension perpendicular to the members) by the standard spacing and adding 1, as was illustrated for studs.

Additional framing members (such as extra joists, headers, and trimmers) can usually be found in the floor and ceiling system. They are taken off individually by size and recorded by use on the worksheets. Their lengths are determined the same as for other wood-framing members.

Another member found in the floor and ceiling framing system is bridging. These are diagonal or horizontal members that provide rigidity to the framing. The estimator must find the number of pieces of bridging along with their lengths. The number of pieces can be determined by knowing the number of spaces between structural members, the number of rows of bridging, and whether the bridging is a single piece of lumber or occurs in pairs between any two framing members.

For instance, if the floor system in the previous example had two rows of bridging and they occurred in pairs, then the total amount of bridges would be

$$2 \text{ rows} \times 2 \text{ pieces per pair} \times 10 \text{ spaces} = 40 \text{ pieces}$$

To find the length of one piece of diagonal bracing, one would use the right-triangle relationship. For the $2'' \times 10''$ at $24''$ on center, the length of one piece of bridging would be determined as shown below.

The clear space between joists is $24'' - 1.5'' = 22.5''$:

$$L = \sqrt{(22.5'')^2 + (9.5'')^2} = 24.43'' \quad \text{or} \quad 25''$$

If the bridging is horizontal, the length will be $22.5''$.

Once the length of one piece of bridging or one bridging member is known and its size read off the drawing, the total board foot measure can be calculated as follows:

$$40 \text{ pieces} \times 25'' \text{ per piece} = 1000'' \quad \text{or} \quad 83.33 \text{ feet}$$

For $1'' \times 3''$ bridging, the total board feet needed is

$$\frac{1'' \times 3''}{12} \times 83.33 \text{ ft} = 20.84 \text{ bfm}$$

This information is then recorded in the appropriate spaces on the worksheet.

## Subflooring, Sheathing, and Decking

Subflooring is used to support the finish flooring material. It is installed directly onto the floor framing members. Sheathing, on the other hand, is applied to exterior wall and roof surfaces. It is also applied directly to the framing members. The subflooring and sheathing are usually secured by nails; sometimes adhesives are also used.

When taking off subflooring and sheathing material, the estimator will first need to determine the type of material being specified. Materials such as plywood, hardboard, and waffleboard are typically used for sheathing and subflooring. The unit of takeoff will be square feet or the quantity of panels. If it is square feet, all the estimator has to do is obtain the area over which the material occurs and subtract the area of large openings such as garage doors and storefronts. Smaller openings are rarely deducted. If the material is purchased in panels, all the estimator has to do is divide the total square footage by the area of one panel and round to the next whole panel. One may want to add some waste to the square foot figure before determining the number of panels based on standard sizes and the amount of area deducted for openings. Waste will range from 3 percent to 5 percent.

Within the subflooring/sheathing category, the estimator may have to determine the amount of decking required. Decking is comprised of framing members such as $2'' \times 6''$. They are installed with the larger dimension horizontally and placed at right angles to the supporting structural members (joists) with a small space between each to allow for drainage of water. To determine the total number of members, the estimator will need to know the width over which the boards will be installed and the amount of space between them. Then, knowing the length of the decking from the drawing, the estimator can calculate the total board foot measure, keeping in mind that even foot lengths will be ordered (see Fig. 9.3).

If the sheathing is being installed on a sloped roof, the estimator will have to determine the square footage required based on the horizontal area to be covered by the roof and its slope. When determining the horizontal projection, do not forget the area covered by the cornice projection. Figure 9.4 shows an example of calculating the square footage of sheathing required for a sloping roof with overhang.

Instead of using right-triangle relationships to determine the sloped length, conversion tables are available to simplify calculations. The information in Fig. 9.5 can be used to convert horizontal areas to sloping areas.

For the example shown in Fig. 9.4, the table in Fig. 9.5 can be used to obtain the square footage of sheathing as follows:

$$1.118 \times 20 \times 32 = 715.52 \text{ or } 716 \text{ sf}$$

## Wall Framing

Framing for the wall includes plates (top and bottom or sill), studs, headers, and other miscellaneous members such as braces and ribbons. Because exterior walls

---

The second floor of a building has floor dimensions of $20' \times 40'$ with an opening of $12' \times 4'$ for stairs. The subflooring members are $1'' \times 6''$ nominal supplied in $8'$ lengths. These members are installed at right angles to the supporting members. Determine the amount of lumber required both in number of boards and board feet.

First, calculate the total floor area:
  $(20' \times 40') - (12' \times 4') = 752$ sf

Next, calculate the area of one piece of subflooring:
  $8' \times 5.5'' \times 1'/12'' = 3.667$ sf/piece
  (Note that actual dimensions are used)

Divide the floor area by the area of one piece of subflooring:
  $(752)/(3.667) = 205$ pieces

Add 5 percent for waste:
  $205 \times 0.05 = 10.25$
  Therefore, use 10 pieces for waste.

Total pieces of subflooring required:
  $205 + 10 = 215$ pieces

To convert one piece to board feet:
  $[(1'' \times 6'')/12] \times 8' = 4$ bf/piece
  Note that nominal dimensions are used to calculate board feet.

Total board feet required:
  4 bf/piece $\times$ 215 pieces $= 860$ bf

---

**FIGURE 9.3**
Quantity of decking.

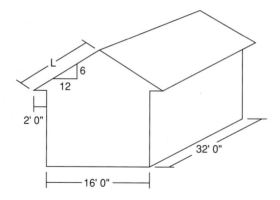

Horizontal projection = 8 ft + 2 ft = 10 ft

Based on 6" rise to 12" run, total rise = 5' 0"

Therefore L = $\sqrt{(5')^2 + (10')^2}$ = 11.18'

Area = 11.18 × 32 × 2 = 715.52 or 716 sf

If purchasing 4' × 8' sheets of plywood sheathing then:

Total number of sheets = 716/32 = 22.38 or 23 sheets with no waste

**FIGURE 9.4**
Sheathing example for sloped roof.

may be framed differently from interior walls, it is a good idea to keep their takeoff separate. The size of wall-framing members can be obtained from the drawings and their grade of lumber from the specifications.

Wall plates may be purchased in any available length. However, because of the various lengths of plates required, it is common practice to order them in random lengths. Beginning with the outside walls, determine the total number of feet required from the dimensions on the drawings and record this on the worksheet. If the drawing calls for a single bottom plate and a double top plate, the linear footage of the wall is multiplied by 3 to get the total length needed. A small waste factor is then added.

To find the total length of plates required for interior walls, the total linear feet of walls must first be determined. Since there are a relatively large number of interior walls running in different directions in most wood-frame buildings, it is recommended to list all wall lengths from top to bottom of the floor plan. To obtain the total length of plates, follow the same procedure as for exterior walls. (Don't forget to deduct for openings.)

The length of studs will vary with the finished ceiling height and the number of plates. The estimator will need to refer to the drawings to obtain this information. Keep in mind that studs come in even lengths. An exception to this may be a precut stud for a specific ceiling height.

The number of studs required is determined in the same manner as for floor-framing members. To allow for additional studs required for corner pieces, two

| Rise | Run | Pitch | Percentage factor | Rise | Run | Pitch | Percentage factor |
|------|-----|-------|-------------------|------|-----|-------|-------------------|
| 2 | 12 | 1/12 | 1.014 | 16 | 12 | 2/3 | 1.667 |
| 3 | 12 | 1/8 | 1.032 | 17 | 12 | 17/24 | 1.734 |
| 4 | 12 | 1/6 | 1.054 | 18 | 12 | 3/4 | 1.803 |
| 5 | 12 | 5/24 | 1.082 | 19 | 12 | 19/24 | 1.873 |
| 6 | 12 | 1/8 | 1.118 | 20 | 12 | 5/6 | 1.942 |
| 7 | 12 | 7/24 | 1.158 | 21 | 12 | 7/8 | 2.016 |
| 8 | 12 | 1/3 | 1.202 | 22 | 12 | 11/12 | 2.088 |
| 9 | 12 | 3/8 | 1.25 | 23 | 12 | 23/24 | 2.162 |
| 10 | 12 | 5/12 | 1.302 | 24 | 12 | 1 | 2.236 |
| 11 | 12 | 11/24 | 1.357 | 25 | 12 | 25/24 | 2.311 |
| 12 | 12 | 1/2 | 1.414 | 26 | 12 | 13/12 | 2.387 |
| 13 | 12 | 13/24 | 1.474 | 27 | 12 | 9/8 | 2.463 |
| 14 | 12 | 7/12 | 1.537 | 28 | 12 | 7/6 | 2.538 |
| 15 | 12 | 5/8 | 1.601 | 29 | 12 | 29/24 | 2.615 |

**FIGURE 9.5**
Slope conversion table.

studs are added for each outside corner. In addition, two studs must be added for backing at each intersecting partition, and to allow for door and window openings. Calculating studding in this manner will allow for all door and window headers and blocking. The exception to this is for relatively large openings where larger lumber is required for the headers. The estimator should refer to the drawings to determine the size and length of special headers.

Some estimators prefer a simplified method for finding the number of studs when the spacing is 16″ on center. The procedure is to allow one stud for each linear foot of wall. In this procedure, a sufficient number of studs for backing, corner posts, openings, and blocking is included.

For buildings with gable roofs it will be necessary to order material for gable end studs. Because the gable ends are triangular in shape, one-half the plate length is used as the basis for determining the number of studs required for each gable end. The plate length is divided by the stud spacing, and 1 is added to get the number of studs. The length of the studs may be obtained from the drawing dimensions and rounded to the next even foot. One piece of stud material will make a long and a short gable stud. This helps to account for the fact that only one-half of the plate length is used.

Many times, especially for commercial and industrial buildings, required wood members are not shown on the drawings. An example is wood nailers. In this case, the estimator will need to determine how and where the members will be installed. If the estimator doesn't know, the appropriate person should be contacted for the information. The size and grade of lumber can be obtained from the technical specifications and/or drawings.

## Roof Framing

The size and spacing of rafters can be found on the roof framing plan and/or wall section. The number of rafters is determined in the same manner as for floor joists. The length of lumber required can be found by determining the rise and run of the rafter and calculating its length by using the right-triangle relation, as shown in Fig. 9.6. An alternative approach would be to multiply the factor from Fig. 9.6 for the slope of the roof (1.032) by the horizontal projection of 13 feet.

Hip roofs require hip rafters in addition to common and jack rafters. The length of the rafter member required may be found mathematically by determining the diagonal of the total rise and run, similar to the example shown in Fig. 9.6. Hip rafters run into the building at a forty-five-degree angle in plan view. Therefore, the run of the hip rafter is the diagonal distance of the common rafter run. This must be determined when calculating the diagonal of total rise and total run to get the rafter length. If there is a cornice projection, its rise and run must be included in the calculations.

The number of hip rafters required for a rectangular or square building is four. However, if the building has a number of wings or offsets, the number of hip rafters required can be obtained from the drawings. Besides hip rafters, valley rafters may be required. The number and location are found on the drawings, and the length is determined in the same manner as for hip rafters.

Jack rafters are nothing more than common rafters that have been cut to fit against a hip or valley rafter. For a plain hip roof, the amount of material required for jack rafters is determined by assuming that the building has a

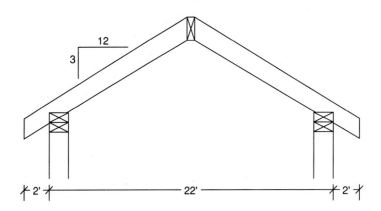

The rafter run is 13'. The rafter rise is determined as follows:

$$\left(\tfrac{3}{12}\right) \times (13') = 3.25'$$

The length of the rafter is calculated as follows:

$$\sqrt{(3.25')^2 \times (13')^2} \;=\; \sqrt{10.56 \text{ sf} + 169 \text{ sf}} \;=\; 13.40'$$

Therefore, use 14' rafter lengths.

**FIGURE 9.6**
Determining rafter length.

gable roof and that all the rafters are common rafters. Knowing this, the number of rafters can be determined as for common rafters. When determining the amount of rafter material, the length of the building must include the width of the cornice projection (overhang) on each end. On complicated hip and intersecting roofs, a sketch should be drawn to determine the amount of material required for each triangular section.

The amount of material needed for ridge boards is determined by finding the total linear footage of ridge and then listing the material in convenient lengths. Many roofs have collar beams. The number and length of these members can be obtained from the drawings. This information, along with the length, is recorded on the worksheet.

## Fasteners

The major fastener used in wood construction is nails. However, adhesives, staples, and possibly even wood screws can be specified. When using nails, the type and size depend on what is being fastened. The amount of nails required is based on the quantity of lumber involved. The estimator can calculate the type, size, and quantity of nails (or other fasteners) using the information in the technical specifications and the past experience of the company. Tables such as the one shown in Fig. 9.7 can also be used.

Figure 9.8 shows a typical wood-framing plan and wall section. Figure 9.9 is the worksheet showing the results of the quantity takeoff of the framing from Fig. 9.8.

**The following table gives the number of wire nails in pounds for the various kinds of lumber per 1,000 ft., board measure. It includes allowance for waste.**

| Material | Size & type of nail | Pounds of nails required |
|---|---|---|
| Bevel or lap siding, 1/2x4 | 6d Coated | 15 lb |
| Bevel or lap siding, 1/2x6 | 6d Coated | 10 lb |
| Drop siding, 1x6 | 8d Common | 25 lb |
| 3/8" hardwood flooring | 4d Common | 16 lb |
| Subflooring, 1x4 | 8d Casing | 17 lb |
| Subflooring, 1x6 | 8d Casing | 18 lb |
| Sheathing boards, 1x6 | 8d Common | 25 lb |
| Sheathing boards, 1x8 | 8d Common | 20 lb |
| Sheathing boards, 1x10 | 8d Common | 15 lb |
| Sheathing boards, 1x12 | 8d Common | 12.5 lb |
| Studs, 2x4 | 16d Common | 10 lb |
| Joist, 2x6 | 16d Common | 7 lb |
| Joist, 2x8 | 16d Common | 5 lb |
| Joist, 2x10 | 16d Common | 4 lb |
| Joist, 2x12 | 16d Common | 3.5 lb |

**FIGURE 9.7**
Nails required for rough carpentry.

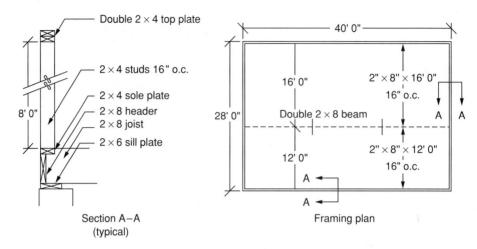

Section A–A
(typical)

Framing plan

Take off the following:

1. Sill plate
2. Joists and header
3. Sole plate
4. Top plate
5. Studs

For estimating purposes, assume the following for rough openings:

2 doors @ 3' 0" wide × 6' 0" high
2 windows @ 4' 0" wide × 3' 0" high
2 windows @ 2' 6" wide × 3' 0" high

**FIGURE 9.8**
Wood-frame building.

## FINISH CARPENTRY TAKEOFF

Finish carpentry is more varied than rough carpentry. Therefore, it is more difficult to develop a specific takeoff methodology. Furthermore, most finish carpentry items are priced individually. For example, wood paneling is priced per square foot or panel of a certain size, whereas trim is priced per linear foot in specific lengths.

Because of the great variance of finish carpentry items, it is critical that the estimator develop an effective and efficient takeoff strategy. Each different type and size (and grade, if appropriate) of item is recorded separately on the worksheet.

### Exterior Finish Carpentry

Exterior finish carpentry includes cornice work and trim (see Fig. 9.10). Some of the items included under exterior trim are corner boards, water tables, rake boards, fascia boards, frieze boards, and crown and bed moldings. The unit of

COMPUTED BY: KB  
CHECKED BY: RL  

PROJECT: Smith Lake House  
ARCHITECT: Jones + Jones, AIA  

DATE: 12-6  
PAGE: 1 OF 1  
INDEX NO. 122

| REF. | DESCRIPTION | SIZE: 2"x4" NO. | LENGTH | TOTAL | SIZE: 2"x6" NO. | LENGTH | TOTAL | SIZE: 2"x8" NO. | LENGTH | TOTAL | SIZE: NO. | LENGTH | TOTAL | SIZE: NO. | LENGTH | TOTAL |
|------|-------------|----|--------|-------|----|--------|-------|----|--------|-------|----|--------|-------|----|--------|-------|
| A-2 | Top + Sole Plates | 26 | 16 | 416 | | | | | | | | | | | | |
| A-2 | Studs | 102 | 8 | 816 | | | | | | | | | | | | |
| | Corners | 8 | 8 | 64 | | | | | | | | | | | | |
| | Jambs | 16 | 8 | 128 | | | | | | | | | | | | |
| A-2 | Sill Plate | | | | 9 | 16 | 144 | | | | | | | | | |
| A-2 | Joists | | | | | | | 31 | 12 | 372 | | | | | | |
| | | | | | | | | 31 | 16 | 496 | | | | | | |
| A-3 | Beam | | | | | | | 5 | 16 | 80 | | | | | | |
| | | | | | | | | 9 | 16 | 144 | | | | | | |
| | Sub total | | | 1424 | | | 144 | | | 1092 | | | | | | |
| | Conversion: (LF ⇒ BF) | | | 0.67 | | | 1.0 | | | 1.33 | | | | | | |
| | TOTALS FROM PREVIOUS PAGE: | | | 0 | | | 0 | | | 0 | | | | | | |
| | TOTALS: | | | 950 BF | | | 144 BF | | | 1453 BF | | | 0 BF | | | |

**FIGURE 9.9**  
Worksheet.

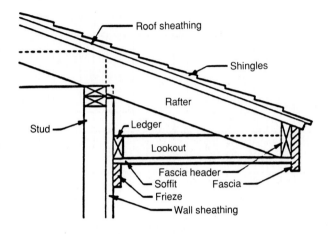

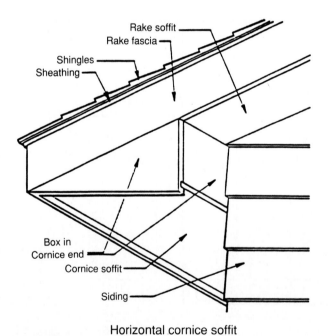

Horizontal cornice soffit

**FIGURE 9.10**
Exterior finish carpentry.

measure for trim is linear foot. Each member of trim and cornice is listed on the worksheet along with the size, type of material, and length needed in each location. After the quantity takeoff is completed, it can be summarized.

Exterior wood paneling can be obtained in panels of plywood or some other type of material. To estimate the amount of paneling required, the area (in square feet) to be covered must be determined as described earlier in this chapter for sheathing.

## Interior Finish Carpentry

Interior carpentry is essentially trim and other related items such as shelving, closet poles, and thresholds. The trim itself includes all the millwork in the form of casings, stops, baseboard, base, shoe, and other types of moldings.

A number of different approaches may be taken to prepare an estimate for interior carpentry items. The first is to list each room and then list all the trim materials needed in that room. A second method is to list a trim item and then indicate the amount needed in each area. A third method is to combine the first two.

Base trim is listed in linear feet. When taking off base trim, the perimeter of the room is taken, without regard for door openings. The pattern, kind of material, and size of the various base-trim pieces are listed, along with the total length of each. Trim for windows, doors, and other locations is taken off in linear feet by specific type.

Shelving is taken off and listed by the thickness, width, length, and kind of material of each piece needed. Cabinets are taken off by the linear foot by specific type. Other items of interior finish carpentry are listed by quantity, size, and location for each type.

## Fasteners

Nails are the most common fastener. However, adhesives and other fasteners can also be used. Fasteners are estimated for finish carpentry in the same manner as for rough carpentry. Refer to Fig. 9.11 for an example of the nail requirement for some finish carpentry items.

**The following table gives the number of wire nails in pounds for the various kinds of lumber per 1,000 ft., board measure. It includes allowance for waste.**

| Material | Size and kind of nail | Pounds of nails required |
|---|---|---|
| Interior trim, 5/8″ thick | 6d finish | 7 lb |
| Interior trim, 3/4″ thick | 8d finish | 14 lb |
| 5/8″ trim nailed to jamb | 4d | 3 lb |
| 1″ × 2″ furring or bridging | 6d common | 15 lb |
| 1″ × 1″ grounds | 6d common | 30 lb |

**FIGURE 9.11**
Finish carpentry nail requirements.

The den of a new home has floor plan dimensions of 12' × 15'. A typical wall section is shown below. The kitchen of this home has floor plan dimensions of 9' × 12'. A typical wall section through the cabinets is shown below. The cabinets run the entire length of the north and east walls.

Take off the following:

1. Base cabinets
2. Wall cabinets
3. Cabinet shelving
4. Wainscot paneling
5. Cap molding
6. Base
7. Shoe mold

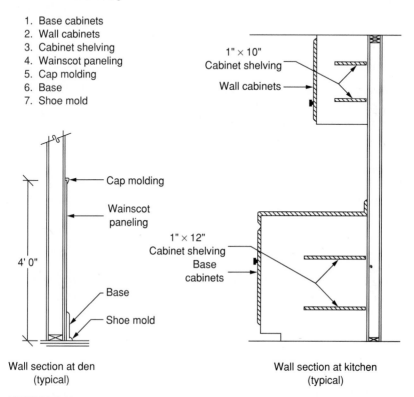

Wall section at den
(typical)

Wall section at kitchen
(typical)

**FIGURE 9.12**
Finish carpentry drawing.

An example of a finish carpentry application is shown in Fig. 9.12. The takeoff of the finish carpentry is shown in Fig. 9.13.

## PRICING ROUGH AND FINISH CARPENTRY WORK

Installing carpentry members involves one or more of the following tasks: measuring, cutting, and fastening. The actual work to be performed depends on the specific carpentry item. The estimator must make this determination and ensure that the item is priced correctly.

### Material Cost

The material cost is obtained from a local supplier. It is important to use the same units for which the supplier quotes the price on the summary sheet (from

**FINISH CARPENTRY**

| | | |
|---|---|---|
| COMPUTED BY: DB | PROJECT: SMITH LAKE HOUSE | WORKSHEET -A- |
| CHECKED BY: RL | ARCHITECT: JONES + JONES, AIA | |

DATE: Z-7  
PAGE: 1 OF 1  
INDEX NO: 116

| REF | DESCRIPTION | QUAN. | DIMENSIONS LENGTH | DIMENSIONS WIDTH | DIMENSIONS HEIGHT | SUBTOTAL QUAN. | UN. | TOTAL QUAN. | UN. | REMARKS |
|---|---|---|---|---|---|---|---|---|---|---|
| A-6 | BASE MOLD | 5 | 16 | | | | | 80 | LF | Room 2 |
| A-6 | " | 6 | 12 | | | | | 72 | LF | Room 3 |
| A-6 | " | 4 | 16 | | | | | 64 | LF | Room 4 |
| A-6 | " | 12 | 12 | | | | | 144 | LF | Room 6 |
| A-6 | " | 10 | 16 | | | | | 160 | LF | Room 7 |
| | TOTAL | | | | | | | 520 | LF | |
| A-6 | SHOE MOLD | 5 | 16 | | | | | 80 | LF | Room 2 |
| A-6 | " | 6 | 12 | | | | | 72 | LF | Room 3 |
| A-6 | " | 4 | 16 | | | | | 64 | LF | Room 4 |
| A-6 | " | 12 | 12 | | | | | 144 | LF | Room 6 |
| A-6 | " | 10 | 16 | | | | | 160 | LF | Room 7 |
| | TOTAL | | | | | | | 520 | LF | |
| A-8 | BASE CABINETS | | 8 | | | | | 8 | LF | Room 8 |
| A-8 | BASE CABINETS | | 10 | | | | | 10 | LF | Room 9 |
| A-10 | BASE CABINETS | | 21 | | | | | 21 | LF | Room 10 |
| A-10 | WALL CABINETS | | 18 | | | | | 18 | LF | Room 10 |
| | | | | | | | | 41 | LF | |
| TOTAL FROM PREVIOUS PAGE: | | | | | | | | | | |
| TOTAL: | | | | | | | | | | |

**FIGURE 9.13**
Finish carpentry takeoff.

the worksheet). Lumber items such as framing material are usually priced by the board foot; finish (millwork) items are priced either by length or by a lump sum. The general contractor will most often obtain a lump-sum price, which includes the fasteners.

## Labor Cost

The labor cost depends on the size, length, and quantity of the lumber to be installed, the makeup of the crew performing the work (i.e., the number of carpenters and laborers), the wage scale for the crew members, and how much work the crew can do in a unit of time (such as an hour or day). If the work consists of the fabrication of stud walls, few members need to be cut. Therefore, a large number of board feet of lumber can be placed per hour. On the other hand, some work entails more measuring and cutting, resulting in a lower crew productivity.

It should be noted that labor productivity factors for finish carpentry activities are more difficult to obtain. Each project and each type of finish carpentry item should be looked at differently and company historical productivity factors used in developing the estimate.

## Equipment/Tools Cost

Equipment needed for carpentry work may include sawhorses, workbenches, large and small power tools, extension cords, router templates, jigs, ladders, and scaffolding. The costs for these and other items can be obtained from company historical records and placed on the summary sheet. The costs of smaller types of equipment and tools may be placed under job overhead.

Figure 9.14 shows the pricing on a summary sheet for a portion of the rough and finish carpentry takeoffs from Fig. 9.9 and Fig. 9.13.

## ESTIMATING OTHER DIVISION SIX ITEMS

As noted at the beginning of this chapter, there are other items besides rough and finish carpentry in this division. The takeoff and pricing of these is accomplished by recording for each specific type of member or unit its location and size along with the quantity of each. All of this information can be obtained from the drawing.

The takeoff should be in the units in which the item is to be purchased (see Fig. 9.15). The estimator should check with the supplier to be sure the units being used are correct.

As for other items in this division, the total estimated cost is derived by adding the material, labor, and equipment costs. These are all documented on the summary sheet. Refer to Fig. 9.15 and Fig. 9.16 for examples of a worksheet and summary sheet containing some of the other items in division 6.

When developing the estimate for division 6 items, the estimator needs to consider not only the direct costs of the materials, labor, and equipment but also factors that may affect these costs (such as subcontracting the work). To aid in facilitating this process, the reminder list noted below should be used.

## Wood reminder list

### Quantity takeoff

| Item | Unit of measure |
| --- | --- |
| Framing Lumber | bfm |
| Flooring | sf |
| Sheathing | bfm/sf |
| Hardboard | sf |
| Shingles | sq/bundle |
| Siding | sf |
| Stair stringers | bfm |
| Furring and grounds | lf |
| Trusses | ea |
| Laminated timbers | ea |
| Trim and moldings | lf |
| Cabinets | ea/lf |
| Beams and columns | lf |
| Cupolas | ea |
| Counter tops | lf |
| Paneling | sf |
| Pegboard | sf |
| Shelving | lf |
| Stairs | ea/lf |
| Fireplace mantel | ea |

### Other considerations that can affect cost

Casework specified in division 10?
Custom-made millwork or prefabricated
Special equipment requirements
Disposal of shipping cartons
Grade of lumber
Design that is not in the modular size of lumber
Cost of shop drawings and other submittals
Sales tax on materials

### Specialty contractors bid to general contractor

Receiving and unloading of material
Equipment required for installation
Minority-owned business
Cleanup
Union or merit shop contractor
Performance and payment bonds
Safety performance record
Documented total quality management program

SUMMARY SHEET

COMPUTED BY: KB  
CHECKED BY: RL  
PROJECT: Smith Lake House  
ARCHITECT: Jones + Jones, AIA  
DATE: 12-8  
PAGE: 1 OF 1  
INDEX NO: 142

| REF. | DESCRIPTION | QUANTITY TOTAL | UN. | MATERIAL COST UNIT COST | MATERIAL SUBTOTAL | DAILY PROD. OF CREW | CREW MAKE-UP | MAN-HOUR PER UNIT | TOTAL MAN HOURS | TOTAL CREW HOURS | AVG. WAGE RATE | LABOR SUBTOTAL | RATE PER HOUR | EQUIP. SUBTOTAL | SUB. OR OTHER | TOTAL COST |
|---|---|---|---|---|---|---|---|---|---|---|---|---|---|---|---|---|
| 116 | Rough Framing | 2609 | BF | 0.37 | 956 | 1230 | 2 | .013 | 34 | 17 | 12.00 | 407 | | 0 | 0 | 1372 |
| 116 | Wainscot | 7 | EA | 28.8 | 202 | 52 | 2 | .031 | 3 | 1 | 12.00 | 26 | | 0 | 0 | 228 |
| 116 | Cap molding | 64 | LF | 0.1 | 6 | 270 | 1 | .030 | 2 | 2 | 12.00 | 23 | | 0 | 0 | 29 |
| 116 | Wood Base | 64 | LF | 0.12 | 8 | 200 | 1 | .04 | 3 | 3 | 12.00 | 31 | | 0 | 0 | 39 |
| 116 | Shoe Mold | 64 | LF | 0.11 | 7 | 240 | 1 | .033 | 3 | 3 | 12.00 | 26 | | 0 | 0 | 33 |
| 116 | Shelving 1x6" | 48 | LF | 1.22 | 59 | 180 | 2 | 0.089 | 5 | 2 | 10.75 | 46 | | 0 | 0 | 105 |
| 116 | Shelving 1"x12" | 48 | LF | 1.50 | 72 | 170 | 2 | .094 | 5 | 3 | 10.75 | 49 | | 0 | 0 | 121 |
| 116 | Base Cab. | 21 | LF | 95 | 1995 | 25 | 2 | 0.645 | 14 | 7 | 14.00 | 190 | | 0 | 0 | 1885 |
| 116 | Wall Cab. | 21 | LF | 40 | 846 | 68 | 2 | .235 | 5 | 3 | 14.00 | 69 | | 0 | 0 | 909 |

TOTAL FROM PREVIOUS PAGE:  
TOTAL:

**FIGURE 9.14**  
Rough and finish carpentry summary sheet.

WORKSHEET -A-

| | | | | | | | | | | | | DATE: 12-4 |
|---|---|---|---|---|---|---|---|---|---|---|---|---|
| COMPUTED BY: DB | | | PROJECT: SMITH LAKE HOUSE | | | | | | | | | PAGE: 1 OF 1 |
| CHECKED BY: RL | | | ARCHITECT: JONES + JONES, AIA | | | | | | | | | INDEX NO: 156 |

| REF | DESCRIPTION | QUAN. | DIMENSIONS | | | SUBTOTAL | | TOTAL | | REMARKS |
|---|---|---|---|---|---|---|---|---|---|---|
| | | | LENGTH | WIDTH | HEIGHT | QUAN. | UN. | QUAN. | UN. | |
| A-4 | OAK STAIR TREADS | 12 | | | | | | 12 | EA | MAIN S'CASE |
| A-4 | " | 10 | | | | | | 10 | EA | LOFT |
| | TOTAL | | | | | | | 22 | EA | |
| | | | | | | | | | | |
| A-4 | PINE RISERS | 12 | 3 | | | | | 36 | LF | MAIN |
| A-4 | " | 10 | 3 | | | | | 30 | LF | LOFT |
| | TOTAL | | | | | | | 66 | LF | |
| | | | | | | | | | | |
| A-6 | EXTERIOR SHUTTERS | 6 | | | | | | 6 | PR | E ELEV |
| A-6 | " | 4 | | | | | | 4 | PR | W ELEV |
| A-7 | " | 4 | | | | | | 4 | PR | N ELEV |
| A-7 | " | 8 | | | | | | 8 | PR | S ELEV |
| | TOTAL | | | | | | | 22 | PR | |

TOTAL FROM PREVIOUS PAGE

TOTAL

**FIGURE 9.15**
Worksheet.

251

SUMMARY SHEET

COMPUTED BY:    PROJECT:    DATE:
CHECKED BY:    ARCHITECT:    PAGE:   OF    INDEX NO:

| REF | DESCRIPTION | QUANTITY TOTAL | UN. | MATERIAL COST UNIT COST | MATERIAL SUBTOTAL | DAILY PROD. OF CREW | CREW MAKE-UP | MAN-HOUR PER UNIT | TOTAL MAN HOURS | TOTAL CREW HOURS | AVG. WAGE RATE | LABOR SUBTOTAL | RATE PER HOUR | EQUIP. SUBTOTAL | SUB. OR OTHER | TOTAL COST |
|---|---|---|---|---|---|---|---|---|---|---|---|---|---|---|---|---|
| 156 | 4'x4'Beams | 224 | LF | 1.7 | 381 | 180 | 2 | .089 | 20 | 10 | 10.75 | 214 | | 0 | 0 | 595 |
| 156 | Oak treads | 12 | EA | 17.25 | 207 | 18 | 1 | 0.44 | 6 | 6 | 12.00 | 67 | | 0 | 0 | 271 |
| 156 | Pine risers | 36 | LF | 1.20 | 43 | 66 | 1 | 0.021 | 5 | 5 | 12.00 | 52 | | 0 | 0 | 95 |
| 156 | Shutters | 4 | PR | 31.00 | 124 | 10 | 1 | 0.8 | 4 | 4 | 12.00 | 38 | | 0 | 0 | 162 |
| 156 | Pl. Counter | 21 | LF | 10.00 | 210 | 30 | 1 | .267 | 6 | 6 | 12.00 | 67 | | 0 | 0 | 277 |
| 156 | Ex. Soffits | 156 | SF | 0.50 | 78 | 400 | 2 | .038 | 6 | 3 | 10.75 | 64 | | 0 | 0 | 142 |
| TOTAL FROM PREVIOUS PAGE: | | | | | 0 | | | | | | | 0 | | 0 | 0 | 0 |
| TOTAL: | | | | | 1043 | | | | | | | 499 | | 0 | 0 | 1543 |

**FIGURE 9.16**
Summary sheet.

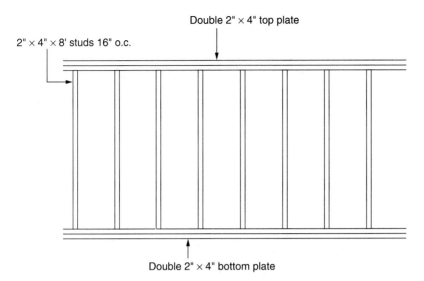

Double 2" × 4" top plate

2" × 4" × 8' studs 16" o.c.

Double 2" × 4" bottom plate

Note:  The wall is 60' in length.

**FIGURE 9.17**
Takeoff exercise.

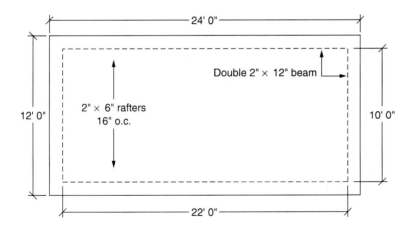

24' 0"

Double 2" × 12" beam

2" × 6" rafters
16" o.c.

12' 0"

10' 0"

22' 0"

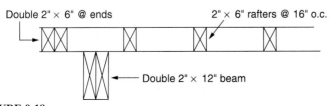

Double 2" × 6" @ ends

2" × 6" rafters @ 16" o.c.

Double 2" × 12" beam

**FIGURE 9.18**
Rough framing takeoff detail.

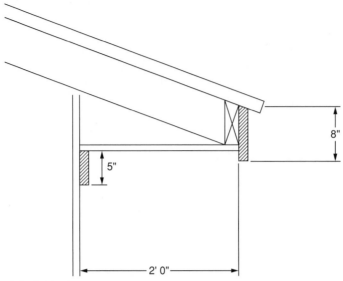

**FIGURE 9.19**
Wood trim detail.

## STUDENT EXERCISES

**9.1.** Convert the following into a total amount of lumber in board foot measure.

$$14-2'' \times 4'' \times 12 \text{ ft}$$
$$10-2'' \times 8'' \times 10 \text{ ft}$$
$$8-1'' \times 6'' \times 12 \text{ ft}$$
$$65-2'' \times 4'' \times \phantom{0}8 \text{ ft}$$
$$22-1'' \times 4'' \times \phantom{0}8 \text{ ft}$$

**9.2.** Determine the total board feet of material required for the wall in Fig. 9.17.

**9.3.** What is the cost of constructing the roof framing project in Fig. 9.18 if the daily (eight-hour day) crew productivity is 1000 bfm and the crew is made up of three carpenters earning $20.00/hr each?

**9.4.** What is the cost of installing the soffit, frieze, and fascia for 60′ 0″ of detail given in Figure 9.19? Assume a daily crew productivity of 200 f for the frieze and fascia and 16 size per day for the soffit. The crew consists of 2 carpenters with an average wage of $18.00/hour. The crew works 8-hour days.

**9.5.** Using the drawings, specifications, and estimating information provided by the instructor, do a takeoff and price the rough and finish carpentry items on the project.

# CHAPTER
# 10

# MISCELLANEOUS AND SPECIALTY WORK

The intent of this chapter is to (1) provide sufficient background so that the estimator understands the general items in the various divisions; (2) establish a basis for estimating the various materials covered; and (3) provide an introduction to the specialized areas for those interested in the respective construction specialty area. Most of the materials contained in the divisions covered in this chapter are installed by specialty contractors or subcontractors. The items discussed in this chapter are contained in CSI divisions 7 through 14, inclusive. This chapter covers some of the major items in each division.

Because the work is to be performed by qualified contractors who are experienced with the respective material and/or system, they will develop the detailed estimate and provide a price to the general contractor for inclusion in the total project estimate. The general contractor, however, must be able to analyze the various subcontractor bids to ensure that they all include the same scope of work (see Chapter 4).

At times the general contractor may wish to evaluate the bids against his or her own estimate. In this case, the general contractor will not prepare a detailed estimate but will usually determine the quantity of each type of item and apply a unit price that includes the material and installation costs. This chapter contains lists that indicate the most common units of measure used to take off the various items.

Whatever the level of involvement by the general contractor in the estimating of specialty items, he or she must be aware of the work items covered in CSI divisions 7 through 14, inclusive. This chapter presents an overview of these divisions and discusses the important items that the general contractor needs when assessing subcontractor bids.

## THERMAL AND MOISTURE PROTECTION

Some of the items in this division are installed by the general contractor; others are furnished and installed by specialty contractors. The general contractor often installs shingles, some roof accessories, and caulking. For most of the items in this division, the quantities are taken off in square feet for the specific type of item. However, some items, such as flashing and caulking, may be taken off in linear feet. Figure 10.1 is a list of items contained in division 7 along with their units of takeoff.

| | | |
|---|---|---|
| 7.0 | Waterproofing | |
| | 05 Bentonite | sf/bag |
| | 10 Bituminous coating | sf/gal |
| | 15 Building paper | csf |
| | 20 Caulking and sealants | gal/clf/lf/ea |
| | 25 Cement parging | sf |
| | 40 Elastomeric waterproofing | sf/clf/gal |
| | 50 Membrane waterproofing | sf/sq |
| | 55 Metallic | sf |
| | 65 Pitch | ton/gal |
| | 66 Rubber coating | sf |
| | 70 Silicone or stearate | sf |
| 7.2 | Insulation | |
| | 15 Clips | c |
| | 25 Masonry insulation | sf/cf |
| | 30 Perimeter insulation | sf |
| | 35 Poured insulation | cf |
| | 40 Reflective | csf |
| | 50 Roof deck | sf/bf |
| | 70 Sprayed | ea |
| | 80 Wall insulation | sf |
| | 85 Wall or ceiling insulation non-rigid | sf/lf/bf |
| 7.3 | Shingles | |
| | 05 Aluminum shingles | sf/lf |
| | 07 Aluminum tiles | sq |
| | 15 Asphalt | sq/lf |
| | 20 Clay tile | sq |
| | 25 Concrete tile | sq |
| | 30 Porcelain enamel | sq |
| | 35 Slate | sq |
| | 40 Steel | sq |
| | 42 Stl. tile | sq/lf |
| | 45 Wood | sq |
| 7.4 | Roofing and siding | |
| | 03 Aluminum roofing | sf/lf |
| | 06 Aluminum siding | sf/m/lf/vlf |

**FIGURE 10.1**
Division 7: thermal and moisture protection.

| | | |
|---|---|---|
| 12 | Asphalt | sq/gal/ton |
| 13 | Asphalt panels | sf/lf |
| 15 | Built up | sq/total/bag |
| 18 | Cants | lf |
| 27 | Elastomeric roofing | sf |
| 30 | Epoxy panels | sf |
| 35 | Felt | sq |
| 36 | Fiberglass | sf |
| 40 | Integrated | sf |
| 42 | Metal facing panels | sf |
| 45 | Protected metal | sf |
| 57 | Steel roofing | sf/lf |
| 60 | Steel siding | sf |
| 69 | Vinyl siding | sf/lf |
| 72 | Walkway | sf |
| 7.6 | Sheet metal work | |
| 05 | Copper roofing | sq |
| 10 | Downspouts | lf/ea |
| 12 | Drip edge | lf |
| 13 | Elbows | ea |
| 15 | Expansion joint | lf/ea |
| 20 | Fascia | sf |
| 25 | Flashing | sf/gal/sy |
| 30 | Gravel stop | lf |
| 33 | Gutters | lf/ea |
| 36 | Gutter guard | lf |
| 39 | Lead roofing | sq |
| 42 | Louvers | ea/sf/lf |
| 45 | Mansard | sf/lf |
| 51 | Reglet | lf |
| 54 | Soffit | sf |
| 57 | Stainless steel roofing | sf |
| 60 | Termite shields | lf |
| 63 | Zinc | sq |
| 7.8 | Roof accessories | |
| 10 | Ceiling catches | ea |
| 20 | Roof hatches | ea |
| 30 | Roof vents | ea |
| 40 | Skylight | sf/ea |
| 50 | Skyroofs | sf/hor/sf |
| 55 | Smoke hatches | ea |
| 90 | Ventilators | ea |

**FIGURE 10.1** (*continued*)

## Taking Off Insulation

Thermal insulation is often used in walls, ceilings, floors, and roofs. Insulation can also be used for sound control. The general contractor often subcontracts the insulation for a project. The roofing contractor usually includes the insulation on the roof deck, and the drywall/plaster subcontractor often includes the insulation in the walls. The general contractor must install perimeter insulation at the floor slab. The estimator for the general contractor should calculate the basic quantities of insulation materials for each type so that he or she can evaluate the subcontract bids and make certain that all insulation is included in the bid.

Insulation is available in different forms, including batts, blankets, loose, and rigid boards. Batts and blankets are available in different widths and thicknesses, and come with different types of backings or with no backing. Rigid boards are available in different thicknesses and sizes and can be ordered with different backings. Also, different types of materials are used to manufacture insulation. The estimator should include a separate line in the estimate for each of the various types of insulation. To calculate the total amount needed, the estimator must know what form of insulation is required and the coverage of one unit.

If loose insulation is specified, such as for ceilings, the estimator will need to determine the total volume required. If purchasing loose insulation in bags, the estimator will have to know the volume of one bag and then calculate the number of bags from the total volume required. Check with the supplier on the quantity each bag can hold. Most suppliers have four-cubic-foot bags available.

## Taking Off Roof Shingles and Tiles

The general contractor often installs roofing shingles on small commercial or residential projects. Shingles are available in many types of materials, including asphalt, fiberglass, clay, aluminum, steel, vinyl, and wood. Most types are also available in different styles, sizes, and exposures. The estimator must refer to the drawings and specifications to determine this information.

Shingles are taken off by the square (one square is equal to 100 square feet). Asphalt shingles are packaged in bundles. The estimator should consult with the material supplier to determine the coverage in squares of one bundle for a specific type and size of shingle. In addition, the amount of shingle that will be exposed (known as *exposure*) will affect the number of bundles per square.

In determining the area to be covered by asphalt shingles, allow one extra course of shingles at the eaves, which must always be doubled. Hips and ridges are taken off by the linear foot and are considered to be $1'0''$ wide to calculate the square footage of shingles required in these regions. Five to 8 percent waste is typically used for asphalt shingles. From 2 to 3 pounds of $\frac{7}{8}''$ to $1\frac{3}{4}''$ galvanized, large-headed nails are used to secure one square of asphalt shingles.

Shingles are usually placed over an underlayment of roofing felt. The felt is specified by the type of material and weight per square (e.g., 15 lb). The felt should have a minimum top lap of $2''$ and end lap of $4''$. Therefore, to determine the square footage of felt required, multiply the roof area by a 5 percent to 8 percent lap and waste factor. The same estimating procedure is used for fiberglass shingles.

Wood shakes and shingles are also taken off by the square. Since these can also be used for building sidings, one will need to deduct for relatively large openings, such as for windows and doors. A double starter course on roofs is usually required; in some constructions, roofing felt is also needed. In addition, extra material is needed to cover hips and ridges.

Wood shakes and shingles come in bundles. The estimator will need to consult with the material supplier to determine the square foot coverage of one bundle. Other information needed to develop an estimate includes how the material will be placed (single or double coursing) and the exposure. This data is available from the drawings and specifications.

Nails used to secure wood shakes and shingles are corrosion resistant and are $1\frac{3}{4}''$ to $2''$ long. The quantity needed is from 2 to 4 pounds per square. A waste factor of 5 percent is sufficient.

Slate shingles are taken off by the amount required to cover a square following the manufacturer's exposure recommendations. To this amount the estimator adds one square foot per foot length of hips and ridges. Slate shingles are fastened with copper nails ($1\frac{1}{4}''$ to $1\frac{1}{2}''$ long). Roofing felt is also required. Waste on slate shingles will vary from 8 percent to 20 percent depending on the shape, number of irregularities, and care in installation.

Roofing tile is taken off similar to the other types of shingles. However, one also needs to take off the linear feet of special pieces and shapes required for ridges, hips, terminals, and other special applications. Roofing felt may also be required; in some cases, furring strips may be needed. A 5 percent waste factor is sufficient for roofing tile.

The following is an example of the takeoff of wood and asphalt shingles:

Find the bundles of wood shingles required to side the house and the bundles of asphalt shingles for the roof of the building shown in Fig. 10.2 given the following information:

- Wood shingles: For the given shingle length and exposure, one bundle will cover 20 sf. One bundle has 50 lf of shingles in it. Use a waste factor of 5 percent.

- Asphalt shingles: For the given exposure, three-bundle squares will be purchased. One bundle contains 88 lf of shingles. Use a waste factor of 5 percent.

- Total wall area to receive wood shingles: $9' \times [2(40') + 2(28)] = 1224$ sf. Deduct openings of doors — $2 \times 3' \times 7' = 42$ sf; windows — $3' \times 2.5' + 5(3' \times 5') = 82.5$ sf. Total net area to receive wood shingles: $1224$ sf $-$ $(42$ sf $+ 82.5$ sf$) = 1099.5$ sf. Including a 5 percent waste factor, the area is $1.05 \times 1099.5$ sf $= 1155$ sf.

- Number of bundles for side walls: $1155$ sf$/20$ sf $= 57.75$, or 58 bundles. The addition for a starter course $= 136$ lf$/50$ lf $= 2.72$, or 3 bundles. Total bundles of wood shingles required: 61.

- The area of the roof is $42' \times 30' = 1260$ sf horizontal projection. For the rise over run of 6 in 12, the factor to convert to actual area is 1.118 (see Fig. 9.6). Therefore, the actual area $= 1.118 \times 1260 = 1409$ sf. Add 5% for waste and the area $= 1.05 \times 1409 = 1480$ sf, or 14.80 squares.

- Number of bundles $= 14.8 \times 3 = 44.40$ bundles. The length of the starter course $= 2 \times 42' = 84'$. The length of the ridge $= 42'0''$. Number of extra bundles required for the starter course and ridge: $(84' + 42')/88$ lf $= 1.44$ bundles. Therefore, the total number of bundles required is 45.84, or 46 bundles.

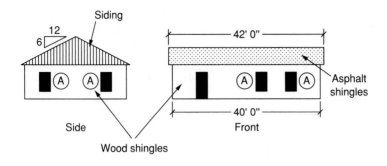

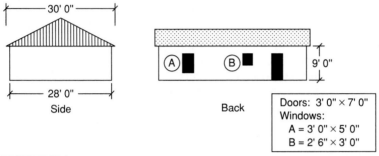

**FIGURE 10.2**
Elevations of building.

## Taking Off Built-Up, Single-Ply, and Sheet Roofing

There are many other types, sizes, and styles of roofing. Most of these are furnished and installed by a specialty subcontractor, who submits a bid to the general contractor. This section examines some of these other major types of roofing.

Built-up roofing consists of layers of overlapping roof felt with each layer set in a mopping of hot tar or asphalt. This type of roofing is usually specified by the number of thicknesses of felt. For instance, a five-ply roof has six coats of asphalt and five plies of felt. A single-ply roof—often referred to as EPDM (ethylene propylene diene monomer)—consists of one sheet of plastic or resin base that is used for the roofing membrane. The estimator must refer to the drawings and specifications to determine the type and configuration of the built-up roof or single-ply roof. The subcontractor's detailed estimate includes calculating the amounts of each component of the system. For example, relative to a built-up roof, the estimator will determine the number of squares of felt, the number of pounds of aggregate, the required accessories, and so on.

The roofing can also be made of metal. Metal roofing materials consist of steel, copper, lead, and terne. Each is available in different styles, sizes, and projections. The takeoff is performed similar to other roof coverings in that the total square footage to be covered is determined, taking into consideration laps and seams. From this, one can calculate the number of squares and/or the number of panels of a predetermined size required.

## Taking Off Flashing

Flashing is used to keep water from penetrating the building. It is available in many different types of materials and forms. Depending on the type of flashing specified, it is taken off by the piece, linear footage with the width stated, or square foot. The gauge of the material will also be stated in the estimate. The estimator will need to refer to the specifications and drawings to determine the location, type, and size of flashing required.

## Taking Off Roof Trim and Other Components

Other items such as gravel stops, fascia, coping, ridge strips, gutters, downspouts, and soffits are taken off by the linear foot by type and size. Special pieces such as elbows and ends are estimated by the number of pieces of each type required. It should be noted that some flashing and other items may be included in the bid of the roofing contractor and some may not. In some cases, such as for masonry, the flashing may be supplied by the general contractor and installed by the specialty contractor.

## Taking Off Sealants and Caulking

Some sealants and caulking are purchased by the gallon and some in preformed strips. In the first case, the estimator will need to know the conversion factor of linear feet to one gallon. In the second case, the estimator will determine the total linear feet of material needed from the drawings. The coverage for sealants depends on the porosity of the surface and the type of material specified as a sealant. The chart in Fig. 10.3 can be used to convert the linear footage of caulked joints to gallons. The general contractor may or may not perform this work. Some specialty caulking will be done by subcontractors, such as glazing contractors and masonry contractors.

| Caulking bead dimensions | Linear feet/gallon |
|---|---|
| 1/4″ × 1/2″ | 154 |
| 1/2″ × 1/2″ | 77 |
| 3/8″ × 3/4″ | 68 |
| 1/2″ × 1″ | 38 |
| 3/4″ × 3/4″ | 34 |
| 3/4″ × 1″ | 26 |
| 1″ × 1″ | 19 |

**FIGURE 10.3**
Caulking conversion table.

## WINDOWS AND DOORS

Division 8 includes windows, doors, glazing, hardware, and special curtain walls. Figure 10.4 is a list of the various items contained in this division along with the units of measure for takeoff.

From the standpoint of the general contractor, most of the items contained in this division are taken off by the unit and categorized by type and size. Therefore, the calculation is nothing more than counting the number of each type and size unit. For example, many general contractors install all of the doors, door frames, finish hardware, and preglazed windows on the project. The doors and windows are counted and classified by size and type.

| | |
|---|---|
| 8.1 Metal doors | |
|     10 Hollow metal | ea/sf |
|     20 Hollow metal doors & frames | ea/pr/above/opng |
|     30 Aluminum frames | opng |
|     40 Aluminum doors & frames | ea/pr/leaf/opng |
| 8.2 Wood and plastic doors | |
|     10 Wood frames | ea |
|     20 Wood doors & frames, commercial | ea/pr |
|     30 Wood doors & frames, residential | ea/pr/opng/sf |
| 8.3 Special doors | |
|     06 Cold storage | ea/sf/opng |
|     09 Counter doors | opng |
|     12 Darkroom doors | opng |
|     13 Double acting | pr |
|     15 Floor, commercial | opng |
|     18 Floor, industrial | opng |
|     21 Floor, industrial | opng |
|     24 Glass swing | opng |
|     27 Hanger doors | sf |
|     30 Jalousie | opng |
|     33 Kennel | opng |
|     39 Overhead, commercial | ea |
|     42 Overhead, residential | ea/total |
|     45 Rolling service doors | ea/sf/opng/lf |
|     51 Roll up grill | sf/opng |
|     54 Shock absorbing | opng |
|     57 Sliding | sf |
|     60 Swing | ea/pr |
|     63 Telescoping | sf |
|     66 Tin clad | opng |
|     69 Vault front | opng/ea |
|     78 Vertical lift | sf |
| 8.4 Entrances and storefronts | |
|     10 Balanced doors | ea |
|     20 Revolving doors | opng |
|     25 Sliding entrance | opng |
|     30 Sliding panel | opng |

**FIGURE 10.4**
Division 8: windows and doors.

|  |  |
|---|---|
| 35 Stainless steel | opng |
| 40 Storefront systems | sf |
| 60 Swing doors | opng |
| 8.5 Metal windows | |
| 10 Aluminum sash | sf/lf |
| 20 Aluminum windows | ea |
| 30 Jalousies | ea |
| 50 Screens | sf |
| 60 Steel sash | sf/lf |
| 70 Steel windows | ea |
| 8.6 Wood windows | |
| 30 Wood sash | ea/lf |
| 45 Wood screens | sf |
| 60 Wood windows | opng/ea |
| 8.7 Finish hardware and specialities | |
| 01 Average percent | door/pr |
| 05 Automatic openers | ea/pr/opng |
| 10 Auto operators | opng/lf/ea |
| 12 Bumper plates | lf/ea |
| 15 Door closer | ea/opng |
| 20 Doorstops | ea |
| 25 Floor checks | ea |
| 32 Hinges | pr/ea |
| 35 Kick plate | ea |
| 40 Lockset | ea/ttl |
| 45 Panic device | ea/pr |
| 50 Push-pull | ea |
| 60 Threshold | ea |
| 70 Weatherstripping | opng |
| 8.8 Glass and glazing | |
| 03 Acoustical | sf |
| 09 Faced | sf |
| 12 Full vision | sf |
| 18 Glazed variables | story/sf/lf/inch |
| 21 Insulating | sf |
| 24 Laminated | sf |
| 27 Mirror | sf |
| 30 Obscure glass | sf |
| 33 Patterned glass | sf |
| 36 Plate glass | sf |
| 39 Plexiglass | sf |
| 42 Polycarbonate | sf |
| 45 Reflective | sf |
| 48 Sandblasted | sf |
| 51 Sheet or float glass | sf |
| 54 Spandrel glass | sf |
| 57 Vinyl | sf/total |
| 60 Window glass | sf/lf |
| 66 Wire glass | sf |
| 8.9 Window/curtain walls | |
| 10 Curtain walls | sf |
| 80 Window walls | sf |

**FIGURE 10.4** (*continued*)

The storefront and curtain wall panels are normally taken off by the square footage by the general contractor. The subcontractor, however, will do a detailed takeoff of the materials for the storefront and curtain wall panels, price them, and submit a bid to the general contractor.

# FINISHES

Division 9 is probably the most diversified in that it covers most of the building's finishes, including lath and plaster, wallboard, tile, flooring, acoustical systems, carpet, painting, and wall coverings. Refer to Fig. 10.5 for a list of the items contained in this division along with the appropriate units of measure for takeoff.

Most of the items in this division are subcontracted. The general contractor should make a subcontractor analysis takeoff of the items; the subcontractor will make a detailed takeoff of the materials.

| | |
|---|---|
| 9.1  Lath and plaster | |
| 10  Accessories, plaster | clf/m/cwt |
| 15  Furring | sf |
| 16  Studding | sf |
| 17  Gauging plaster | bag |
| 20  Gypsum lath | sy |
| 21  Gypsum plaster | bag/sy |
| 22  High rise | sy |
| 24  Keenes cement | bag/sy |
| 25  Metal lath | sy/sf |
| 30  Partition walls | sf |
| 35  Perlite or vermiculite paper | bag/sy |
| 50  Sprayed | sf |
| 55  Stucco | sy |
| 56  Thin coat | sy |
| 57  Tile or terrazzo base | st |
| 60  Wood fiber plaster | sy |
| 9.2  Drywall | |
| 02  Accessories, drywall | clf/m |
| 05  Drywall | sf/bag/lf/ea |
| 20  Metal studs with runners | sf |
| 30  Partition walls | sf |
| 45  Shaft wall | sf |
| 9.3  Tile and terrazzo | |
| 05  Ceramic tile | lf/ea/sf |
| 10  Ceramic tile panels | sf |
| 15  Glazed mosaics | sf |
| 20  Marble | sf |
| 25  Metal tile | lf/sf |
| 30  Plastic tile | lf/sf |
| 35  Quarry tile | lf/sf/ea |
| 37  Slate tile | sf |
| 40  Terrazzo, cast in place | lf/sf |
| 45  Terrazzo, precast | lf/sf |
| 50  Terra cotta tile | sf |

**FIGURE 10.5**
Division 9: finishes.

| | | |
|---|---|---|
| 9.5 | Acoustical treatment | |
| | 05  Barriers | sf |
| | 10  Ceiling tile | sf |
| | 15  Suspended acoustical ceiling | sf/ea |
| | 20  Suspended systems | sf |
| | 25  Suspended ceiling, complete | sf |
| | 30  Sound absorbing panels | sf |
| | 40  Sound attenuation | sf |
| 9.6 | Flooring | |
| | 05  Carpet | sy/sf |
| | 09  Carpet maintenance | sf |
| | 10  Composition | sf |
| | 20  Resilient | sf/lf/ea/gal |
| | 25  Stair treads & risers | lf/sf |
| | 40  Wood — fir | sf |
| | 45  Wood block flooring | sf |
| 9.8 | Painting and wall covering | |
| | 05  Corner guards | lf |
| | 10  Galvanizing | gal |
| | 15  Paint | cwt |
| | 20  Painting | ea/sf/lf/riser |
| | 25  Sanding | sf/lf |
| | 30  Varnish | sf |
| | 35  Wall coatings | sf |
| | 40  Wall covering | sf/gal |
| | 45  Wallguard | lf/ea |

**FIGURE 10.5** (*continued*)

In most cases the initial takeoff calculation is in square units, such as square feet. The specialty subcontractor will need to convert this measurement to a unit that is used to order the material, such as number of $12'' \times 12''$ floor tiles, square yards of carpet, or gallons of paint. The balance of this section examines how to estimate some of the major items in division 9.

## Taking Off Drywall, Lath, and Plaster

Gypsum drywall is available in many different types, thicknesses, and sizes. In addition, there are many accessories used in drywall construction, such as corner bead, channel, and hangers for ceiling systems and others.

Drywall is taken off by square feet. A waste factor of 5 percent to 10 percent is added and the total converted to the number of specific type and size panels. One must also include amount of nails, screws, tape, joint compound, and texturing material. The exact quantities of each of these and other materials depend on the area of drywall to be installed, the type and size of drywall, and the method of installation. The subcontractor estimating this type of work determines the quantities of the various needed materials.

Lath is also available in different sizes and gauges for wire type. Lath can be purchased in various forms, such as panels and bundles. The detail estimator must determine how the product will be purchased and the coverage in square feet of each unit.

There are various types and thicknesses of plaster. The estimator should refer to the specifications for this information. The takeoff is based on the number of square feet of a certain type of plaster system. Since plaster is comprised of various components, the estimator will have to calculate the quantity of each component knowing such information as type of gypsum plaster required, amount of water per volume to be added, and the quantities of any admixtures such as coloring agents. An experienced contractor will have historical information that can be used to estimate the cost per square foot or yard for a specific plaster system. A waste factor of 5 percent to 10 percent is used for plaster. Stucco is taken off in the same manner as plaster.

The estimator for the general contractor needs to calculate the square footage of plaster or drywall. The estimator then multiplies the square footage by a factor to obtain an approximate cost for the drywall or plaster work.

## Taking Off Tile and Terrazzo

Tile is available in many different styles, sizes, and materials. Tile is taken off by the square foot or square yard. Accessories such as tile base, dividing strips, capping, and corners are taken off by linear feet or by piece. The estimator will also need to include the method of fastening the tile to the surface, such as the number of gallons of adhesive required.

Tile is available in different forms, such as $12'' \times 12''$ pieces or sheet stock in rolls or panels. Once the total square footage or yardage is calculated and waste added, this figure must be converted to the number of units to be purchased, knowing the area that one unit will cover. Waste for tile material ranges from 2 percent to 10 percent.

Terrazzo is a very specialized flooring material and requires contractors experienced in the procedure. There are many different types of terrazzo floors; refer to the specifications for specific information on the makeup of the system.

## Taking Off Carpeting

Carpeting is taken off by the square yard of the specified type, paying special attention to the layout of the space for the most economical use of material. The more care taken in this activity, the smaller the waste factor. Some carpet comes in tiles and others in rolls. In some cases, only a small amount of carpeting is needed but a roll of it has to be purchased. In this case there is a great amount of waste.

Besides carpeting itself, padding is usually also required. It is taken off in the same manner as carpeting. In addition, there may be need for accessories such as nailing strips for wall-to-wall installation, cap strips, and others. The waste factor for an average installation ranges from 5 percent to 10 percent.

## Taking Off Painting and Wall Coverings

Many variables affect the painting estimate. Both the painting contractor estimator and the general contractor estimator need to be aware of these variables. These include material to be painted, shape and location of surface to be painted, type of paint and other related products specified, number of coats required, extent of touch-up work (such as for structural steel), and amount of cleanup. The estimator will have to refer to the drawings and specifications for this information.

The painting contractor will need to determine the square footage of surface for each type of paint, number of coats required of the same paint, and application method. Knowing the coverage of one gallon of paint, the total gallons can be determined. A waste factor of 10 percent should be included in the calculations. For trim, the estimator should calculate the linear feet to be painted and convert it to square feet based on one linear foot equal to one square foot. Since the preparation of the surface is just as important as the painting itself, the detail estimate will need to include the materials needed for this activity in the stated units. The following is an example of a takeoff for paint:

Determine the gallons of paint required to paint the building shown in Fig. 10.6 assuming no deductions for windows and 5 percent waste. The specifications call for two coats of the same paint; assume the coverage is 450 sf per gallon. The results of the takeoff are documented on the worksheet in Fig. 10.7.

Wall coverings are available in many different materials and patterns. They are usually purchased in rolls. The estimator will have to determine the area covered by one roll. Once the total area to be covered in square feet or yards is taken off, the estimator can determine the number of rolls of covering needed. A waste factor between 5 percent and 15 percent should be used depending on the size of the pattern, if one occurs. The larger the pattern, the more the waste.

As in painting, there will be required preparation activities. The detail estimator will need to takeoff the materials required for this task. Finally, accessories such as corner trim may be needed. This will be taken off by linear feet per type.

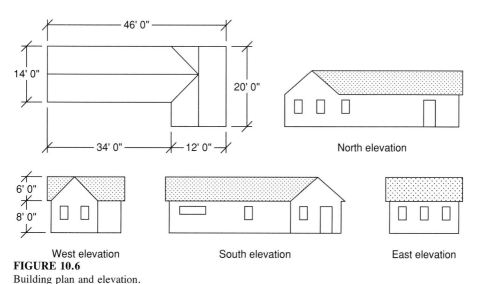

**FIGURE 10.6**
Building plan and elevation.

| COMPUTED BY: KB | | PROJECT: | Hatfield House | | | | | | DATE: 12-14 |
| CHECKED BY: RL | | ARCHITECT: | Clem + Son, AIA | | | | | | PAGE: 1 OF 1 |
| | | | | | | | | | INDEX NO: |

| REF | DESCRIPTION | DIMENSIONS | | | | SUBTOTAL | | TOTAL | | REMARKS |
|---|---|---|---|---|---|---|---|---|---|---|
| | | QUAN. | LENGTH | WIDTH | HEIGHT | QUAN. | UN. | QUAN. | UN. | |
| A-1 | North wall | 2 | | 46 | 8 | 736 | SF | | | |
| | " Gable | 2 | | 12 | 3 | 72 | SF | | | |
| | East wall | 2 | | 20 | 8 | 320 | SF | | | |
| | South walls | 2 | | 46 | 8 | 736 | SF | | | |
| | " Gable | 2 | | 12 | 3 | 72 | SF | | | |
| | West walls | 2 | | 20 | 8 | 320 | SF | | | |
| | " Gable | 2 | | 14 | 3 | 84 | SF | | | |
| | | | | | | | | | | |
| | Subtotal | | | | | 2340 | SF | | | |
| | Waste | | | | | 117 | SF | | | 5% |
| | Total | | | | | 2457 | SF | | 6 GAL | 450SF/GAL |

| TOTAL FROM PREVIOUS PAGE: | | 0 | | 0 | |
| TOTAL: | | 0 | | 6 | GAL |

**FIGURE 10.7**
Painting worksheet.

## SPECIALTIES, EQUIPMENT, FURNISHINGS, SPECIAL CONSTRUCTION, AND CONVEYING SYSTEMS

Divisions 10, 11, 12, 13, and 14 cover what is known as "special" types of equipment and construction. Most of these items are subcontracted to specialty contractors. In most cases, the items are taken off by units. However, there are exceptions. Figures 10.8 through 10.12 provide the estimator with the appropriate unit of takeoff for the items in the five divisions. The estimator should fully describe the items in question to ensure that the items are correctly quoted by the subcontractor. It is important that the estimator work closely with the subcontractor installing the items contained in these divisions to ensure that all products meet the specified requirements.

## MATERIAL PRICING

Most of the items in divisions 8 through 14 are subcontracted. Any material items that are to be installed by the general contractor will be bid to the general

---

10.1 Specialties

| | | |
|---|---|---|
| 02 | Bathroom accessories | ea/lf |
| 05 | Bulletin board | sf/lf/ea |
| 07 | Canopies | ea/sf |
| 10 | Chalkboard | sf/lf/total/ea |
| 12 | Chutes | floor/ea |
| 17 | Control boards | ea |
| 20 | Directory boards | ea |
| 22 | Disappearing stairway | ea |
| 25 | Display cases | ea/section |
| 30 | Fireplace, prefabricated | ea/vlf/set |
| 32 | Flagpole | ea |
| 37 | Lockers | opng/basket/lf |
| 40 | Mail boxes | ea |
| 42 | Medicine cabinets | ea |
| 45 | Partitions, folding accordian | sf |
| 47 | Partitions, folding leaf | sf |
| 50 | Partitions, hospital | lf |
| 52 | Partitions, movable office | sf/lf/ea |
| 55 | Partitions, operable | sf/lf |
| 56 | Partitions, portable | lf |
| 57 | Partitions, shower | ea |
| 60 | Partitions, toilet | lf/ea |
| 62 | Partitions, woven wire | ea |
| 65 | Parts bins | ea |
| 67 | Projection screens | sf/ea |
| 70 | Scales | ea |
| 72 | Security gates | opng |
| 75 | Shelving | sf/shlf |
| 77 | Signs | ea/sf/lf |
| 80 | Telephone enclosure | ea |
| 82 | Turnstiles | ea |

---

**FIGURE 10.8**
Division 10: specialties.

| 11.1 | Architectural equipment | |
|---|---|---|
| | 03 Appliances | ea |
| | 06 Automotive compressors | ea/set |
| | 07 Bank equipment | station/ea/lf/total |
| | 10 Barber equipment | ea |
| | 12 Church equipment | ea/lf/person |
| | 13 Checkout equipment | ea |
| | 15 Darkroom equipment | ea |
| | 16 Dental equipment | ea |
| | 19 Dentition equipment | ea |
| | 22 Dock equipment | ea/lf |
| | 25 Equipment installation | ton |
| | 28 Kitchen equipment | ea/sf |
| | 31 Laboratory equipment | lf/sf/ea/hood |
| | 32 Laundry equipment | ea |
| | 34 Library equipment | lf/ea |
| | 37 Medical equipment | ea |
| | 38 Movie equipment | ea/sf/system |
| | 40 Parking equipment | ea |
| | 42 Refrigerated food cases | ea |
| | 43 Safe | ea |
| | 46 Sauna | ea |
| | 49 School equipment | ea/set/seat/sf |
| | 52 Stage equipment | ea/lf/sf |
| | 58 Steam bath | ea |
| | 61 Vacuum cleaning | total |
| | 62 Vocational shop equipment | ea |
| | 64 Waste handling | ea/ton/day/ton |
| | 67 Wine vault | ea |

**FIGURE 10.9**
Division 11: equipment.

| 12.1 | Furnishings | |
|---|---|---|
| | 05 Blinds, exterior | pr |
| | 10 Blinds, interior | sf/pr |
| | 15 Cabinets | lf/ea |
| | 30 Dormitory furniture | ea/lf/student |
| | 34 Draperies | sf/lf |
| | 40 Floor mats | sf/lf/ea |
| | 45 Hospital furniture | ea/room |
| | 50 Hotel furnishings | room |
| | 52 Ironing centers | ea |
| | 53 Office furniture | person |
| | 55 Posts | ea/lf |
| | 60 Restaurant furniture | lf/set/ea |
| | 65 Seating | set/ea |
| | 70 Shades | sf/shades |
| | 73 Tables | ea |
| | 75 Wardrobes | lf |

**FIGURE 10.10**
Division 12: furnishings.

13.1 Special construction
- 01 Acoustical — sf/lf
- 02 Air curtains — lf/total
- 05 Air supported structures — sf/ea/total
- 07 Air supported storage tank covers — sf/total
- 10 Anechoic chambers — sf
- 12 Audiometric rooms — sf
- 15 Bowling alley — lane
- 17 Chimney foundations — vlf/ea
- 20 Comfort stations — sf/fixture
- 22 Control towers — ea
- 25 Darkrooms — sf
- 27 Domes — ea
- 30 Garage costs — car/total
- 32 Garden house — sf
- 33 Geodesic dome — ea
- 35 Grandstands — seat
- 37 Greenhouse — sf/total/mcf/ea
- 40 Hangers — sf
- 42 Ice skating — total
- 45 Integrated ceilings — sf/ea
- 46 Kiosks — ea
- 47 Music practice room — ea
- 50 Pedestal floors — sf/ea/lf
- 52 Portable booths — sf/ea
- 55 Radio towers — ea
- 57 Refrigerators — lf/sf/bf
- 59 Shelters — ea
- 60 Shielding, lead — sf/ea/total
- 62 Shielding, radio frequency — sf/surf
- 63 Shooting range — point
- 67 Squash court walls — sf/court
- 70 Swimming pool enclosure — sf
- 72 Swimming pool equipment — ea/total/lf/sf
- 75 Swimming pools — sf/pool/total
- 77 Tanks — ea/gal
- 78 Tension structures — sf/ea
- 80 Therapeutic pools — ea

**FIGURE 10.11**
Division 13: special construction.

14.1 Conveying systems
- 10 Correspondence lift — ea
- 15 Dumbwaiters — ea/stop
- 20 Elevators — ea/stop/system
- 25 Escalators — ea
- 30 Material handling — ea/lf
- 32 Motorized car — station/total
- 35 Moving ramps & walks — lf
- 40 Parcel lift — ea
- 45 Pneumatic tube systems — total/lf/system/ea
- 50 Vertical conveyors — total/floor

**FIGURE 10.12**
Division 14: conveying systems.

contractor from the material suppliers in the form of a lump sum price or a unit price. However, on occasion the specifications may contain a material allowance that should be included in the bid. Finish hardware often includes a material allowance. Refer to Chapter 4 for more information on allowances.

## LABOR AND EQUIPMENT PRICING

The labor and equipment required to install the items covered in this chapter will vary considerably depending on the material and/or system. Most of the items are subcontracted by the general contractor; however, a few items (such as doors, frames, and finish hardware) may be installed by the general contractor. The contractor may use the unit price method as a basis for the labor calculations, or the contractor may develop a labor hour per unit.

The pricing for the labor on doors and finish hardware is unique. As the general contractor develops labor standards for the company, it is important to decide how much of the finish hardware goes with the initial hanging of the door. This is often called the "swinging of the door." Usually only the hinges are used from the hardware group for this purpose and are included in the labor cost of hanging the door. The labor for the remainder of the hardware is priced separately.

The specialty contractor responsible for the construction will have both labor and equipment productivity rates based on similar past projects. In addition, the subcontractor will know what skill classifications of labor will be needed along with the types of required equipment and tools. Based on the material quantity, unit cost of material, productivity rate, wage rates, cost per hour for the equipment, the specialty contractor's overhead expenses, and profit, the specialty contractor will submit a bid to the general contractor for the work.

To ensure that the specialty contractor has included everything in accordance with the drawings and specifications, a system takeoff and a price applied to the system will need to be completed by the general contractor. In addition, the general contractor must make a comprehensive list of all items that are part of the system (including other cost-related factors such as those in the reminder lists contained in the previous chapters that apply to the respective type of construction being estimated). The estimator for the general contractor will then need to discuss each of the items on the list with the specialty contractor to ensure that all items are included in the bid. The general contractor will then need to perform a subcontractor bid analysis to determine who is the low bidder. See Chapter 4 for additional information on the subcontractor bid analysis.

## STUDENT EXERCISES

**10.1.** Determine the total cost of installing 6-ft.-wide vinyl sheet flooring in the room shown in Fig. 10.13. The costs for materials are 0.45/sf for the tile and 0.15/sf for underlayment. No special equipment is needed. Labor productivities and wage rates are as follows. Crew: 2 tile layers and helper. Wage rates: tile layer, $18.00/hr; helper, $10.50/hr. Productivity: 500 sf/8-hour day.

**10.2.** Referring to Fig. 10.14, takeoff the quantity of drywall for walls and ceiling. Drywall for walls is 4' × 8' and 4' × 10'; for the ceiling, it is 4' × 12'.

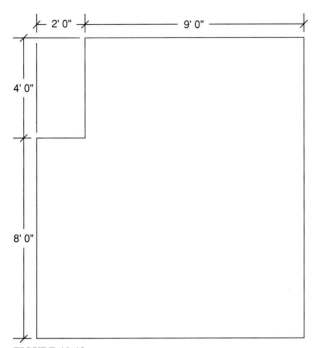

**FIGURE 10.13**
Floor plan.

**10.3.** For Exercise 10.2, determine the number of gallons of paint required based on the following: all surfaces to receive one coat of primer (450 sf/gallon); walls to receive two coats of latex-based paint (500 sf/gallon); and ceiling to receive texture coating (200 sf/gallon). Record the information on a standard worksheet.

**10.4.** Determine the quantity of wood shingles required to side the building shown in Fig. 10.15. Complete a worksheet.

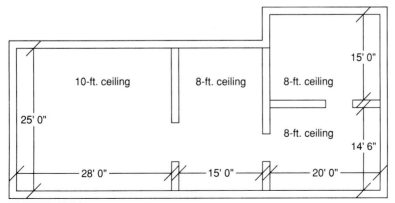

**FIGURE 10.14**
House plan for Exercise 10.2.

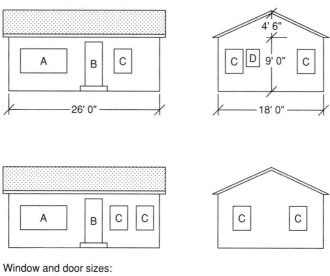

Window and door sizes:
   A = 8' 0" × 4' 0"    C = 3' 0" × 4' 0"
   B = 3' 0" × 7' 4"    D = 2' 0" × 2' 8"

**FIGURE 10.15**
House elevations for Exercise 10.4.

**10.5.** From Exercise 10.4 and the following information, determine the direct cost of installing the shingles. Crew: 1 carpenter and 1 laborer. Wages: carpenter, $15/hr; laborer, $9/hr. Crew productivity: 0.25 squares/hr. Complete a summary sheet.

**10.6.** Using the set of drawings provided by the instructor, perform a general takeoff, list the components of the subcontract, and price the system for roofing, sheet metal, and insulation. The instructor will provide the needed cost and labor productivity information.

**10.7.** Using the set of drawings provided by the instructor, do a detailed takeoff and pricing for caulking, metal doors, and frames. The instructor will provide the needed cost and labor productivity information.

# CHAPTER

# 11

# PLUMBING, MECHANICAL, AND ELECTRICAL

The development of a detailed estimate for plumbing, mechanical, or electrical work requires the estimator to have experience in these areas. As in the specialty work covered in Chapter 10, contractors specializing in the plumbing, mechanical, or electrical trades will, in most cases, develop the detailed estimate based on the design of the respective system utilizing experienced personnel.

Once the price is derived, the subcontractor submits it to the general contractor for inclusion in the total bid. If the subcontractor is acting as a prime contractor, which may occur on some projects, the bid is submitted to the owner or the owner's representative (such as a construction manager). The general contractor or other party then has to analyze all the bids for each specialty to be sure that items were not left out and that the bids from various subcontractors are comparable. (See Chapters 1 and 4 for additional information on subcontractor analysis.) At times, the general contractor may wish to evaluate the bids by performing a system estimate of the work, such as determining the cost per square foot or price per fixture, outlet, or piece of equipment installed (which includes the system serving it). The general contractor will rarely, if ever, develop a detailed estimate for plumbing, mechanical, or electrical work. However, this type of work often includes the most expensive components in the building and therefore deserves special attention by the general contractor.

The purpose of this chapter is to (1) provide enough background so that the estimator understands the areas covered; (2) give a basis for estimating plumbing, mechanical, and electrical work associated with the general contractor; and (3) provide an introduction to the specialized areas of plumbing, mechanical and electrical contracting. For more detailed discussions of the areas covered in this chapter, refer to the bibliography.

## MECHANICAL AND PLUMBING

Division 15 of the Uniform Construction Index (CSI format) includes fresh- and wastewater systems, fire protection, power and heat generation, refrigeration, air distribution, and controls and instrumentation. Refer to Fig. 11.1 for a list of items contained in this division along with the units used to take them off.

### Taking Off Plumbing Work

Plumbing is the installation of all piping required to supply fresh water and remove wastewater from the building. Special piping systems for natural gas, steam, and other substances may also be required, especially for institutional and industrial buildings. These and other piping systems are known as rough plumbing. The other type of plumbing is known as finish plumbing and includes all fixtures and equipment that the piping systems serve.

| | | |
|---|---|---|
| 15.1 | Pipe and fittings | |
| | 04 Backflow | ea |
| | 07 Cleanouts | ea |
| | 10 Cleanout tee | ea |
| | 13 Connectors | ea |
| | 16 Drains | ea |
| | 22 Faucets/fittings | ea |
| | 28 Hydrants | ea |
| | 34 Pipe, brass | lf/lb |
| | 40 Pipe, copper | lf |
| | 43 Pipe, corrosion resistant | lf |
| | 46 Pipe, glass | lf |
| | 49 Pipe, plastic | lf |
| | 52 Pipe, stainless steel | lf |
| | 55 Pipe, steel | lf |
| | 61 Pipe, grooved joint steel | lf/ea |
| | 67 Shock absorbers | ea |
| | 70 Supports/carriers | ea |
| | 73 Traps | ea |
| | 76 Vacuum breakers | ea |
| | 79 Valves, brass | ea |
| | 80 Valves, bronze | ea |
| | 82 Valves, iron body | ea |
| | 85 Valves, plastic | ea |
| | 88 Valves, steel | ea |
| | 93 Valves, semi-steel | ea |
| | 95 Vent flashing | ea |
| | 97 Water supply meters | ea |
| 15.2 | Plumbing fixtures | |
| | 01 Fixtures | ea |
| | 04 Baths | ea |
| | 12 Dental fountain | ea |
| | 16 Drinking fountain | ea |
| | 20 Hot water dispensers | ea |

**FIGURE 11.1**
Division 15: mechanical.

| | | |
|---|---|---|
| 24 | Industrial safety fixtures | ea |
| 28 | Interceptors | ea |
| 32 | Lavatories | ea |
| 36 | Laundry trays | ea |
| 41 | Pumps, circulating | ea |
| 43 | Pumps, condensate return system | ea |
| 47 | Pumps, grinder system | ea |
| 49 | Pumps, pressure booster system | ea |
| 51 | Pumps, pedestal sump | ea |
| 52 | Pumps, sewage ejector | ea |
| 53 | Pumps, sprinkler | ea |
| 54 | Pumps, submergible | ea |
| 55 | Pumps, well | ea |
| 56 | Showers | ea |
| 60 | Sinks | ea |
| 68 | Urinals | ea |
| 76 | Wash fountains | ea |
| 80 | Water closets | ea |

15.3 Plumbing appliances

| | | |
|---|---|---|
| 45 | Water cooler | ea |
| 50 | Water heaters | ea |

15.4 Fire extinguishing systems

| | | |
|---|---|---|
| 02 | Auto fire suppression systems | ea |
| 10 | Fire equipment cabinets | ea |
| 20 | Fire extinguisher | ea |
| 30 | Fire hose & equipment | lf/ea |
| 40 | Fire pumps | ea |
| 50 | Fire valves | ea |
| 60 | Sprinkler system components | ea |
| 70 | Sprinkler systems | head |

15.5 Heating

| | | |
|---|---|---|
| 06 | Boilers, electric, ASME | ea |
| 08 | Boilers, gas fired | ea |
| 10 | Boilers, oil fired | ea |
| 12 | Boilers, gas/oil | ea |
| 27 | Duct furnaces | ea |
| 29 | Duct heaters | ea |
| 40 | Heat exchangers | ea |
| 45 | Heating & ventilating units | ea |
| 48 | Heat recovery package | cfm |
| 51 | Hot water heating | lf/section/ea |
| 54 | Humidifiers | ea |
| 57 | Induced draft fans | ea |
| 59 | Industrial heating | sf/lf/cf |
| 62 | Infra-red | ea |
| 65 | Insulation | sf/lf |
| 68 | Make-up air unit | ea |
| 71 | Radiant heating | sf |
| 77 | Solar energy | ea |
| 80 | Space heaters | ea |
| 86 | Swimming pool heaters | ea |
| 89 | Tanks | ea |
| 90 | Vent chimney | vlf |

**FIGURE 11.1** (*continued*)

| | | |
|---|---|---|
| 15.6 | HVAC piping specialties | |
| | 04  Automatic air vent | ea |
| | 08  Air control | ea |
| | 20  Expansion joints | ea |
| | 28  Flexible metal hose | ea |
| | 32  Heating control valve | ea |
| | 44  Pressure regulator | ea |
| | 55  Steam condensate meter | ea |
| | 60  Steam trap | ea |
| | 70  Strainers, bronze | ea |
| | 75  Strainers, iron body | ea |
| | 85  Venturi flow | ea |
| 15.7 | Air conditioning and ventilating | |
| | 04  Absorption cold generators | ea |
| | 10  Air filters | mcfm/ea |
| | 16  Balancing, air | ea |
| | 19  Balancing, water | ea |
| | 25  Coils, flanged | ea |
| | 31  Computer room units | ea |
| | 43  Control systems, pneumatic | ea |
| | 46  Control systems, electronic | ea |
| | 49  Cooling towers | ton |
| | 52  Diffusers | ea |
| | 55  Grilles | ea |
| | 58  Registers | ea |
| | 61  Duct accessories | ea/lf/mcfm/sf |
| | 64  Duct work | lb/lf/sf |
| | 70  Fans | ea |
| | 73  Fan coil air conditioners | ea |
| | 76  Heat pumps | ea |
| | 79  Louvers | sf/ea |
| | 82  Packaged terminal air conditioners | ea |
| | 88  Self-contained single package | ea |
| | 96  Ventilators | ea |
| | 98  Water chillers | ea |

**FIGURE 11.1** (*continued*)

As noted, the general contractor would usually not develop a detailed estimate for plumbing work. However, he or she must be able to evaluate the reasonableness of plumbing estimates received from subcontractors. Three ways in which the general contractor can approximate the cost of the plumbing work are:

1. Cost per fixture
2. Percent of total project cost
3. Square feet of building

The first method relates to the number and type of plumbing fixtures. For a certain building design, there is usually a relationship between the quantity and installation of piping and the type of plumbing fixtures. Based on historical unit cost data, the general contractor would have information on the average cost for materials and installation to install a specific type of fixture. To obtain a total approximate cost for all the plumbing work, the general contractor would take off the quantity of each type of fixture, multiply by the respective unit cost, and sum all the costs for all the fixtures.

The second method is also based on historical data in that for a certain type of building, the cost to install the plumbing work is about the same percentage of the total project cost. For instance, for an elementary school building the plumbing work might be 9 percent of the total project cost. Therefore, to obtain an approximate cost to perform the plumbing work, the general contractor would multiply the percentage by the total estimated project cost.

The last method requires the general contractor to obtain the total square feet of floor area. This quantity is then multiplied by the average cost per square foot to perform the plumbing work to obtain the approximate cost of installing the plumbing. The unit cost is based on historical records for a specific type of building.

Preparing a detailed estimate requires a working knowledge of the craft. All work must be laid out on paper. That is, piping diagrams must be developed, preferably to scale. The estimator should not use the riser diagram to determine exact lengths of pipe. This diagram helps the estimator only in determining the size of pipe and obtaining a general location in the building (runs in the walls, slab, etc.) Piping diagrams are usually prepared by the plumbing contractor or engineer.

The estimate itself consists of the itemizing of all pipe lengths of the various diameters, fittings, valves, traps, and other items, including the quantity and type. In addition, the various numbers, types, and sizes of fixtures and equipment are also taken off and placed by item on the worksheet. Therefore, the takeoff consists of determining linear feet of pipe and counting fittings, fixtures, and other items.

The trenches required for plumbing constructions may be the responsibility of the plumbing contractor or some other contractor (possibly the general). The specifications should be checked to determine whose responsibility it is, and the specified contractor should perform the earthwork estimate in accordance with the information presented in Chapter 5.

Besides excavations, there may be other items that the plumbing contractor must coordinate with the other contractors. These include:

1. Sleeves and supports used at entrances into the building
2. Supports and anchors for mechanical room equipment
3. Outlets, drains, vents, and methods of support for fixtures
4. Sleeves, hangers, chases, vents, and access doors for piping systems
5. Factory or field finishes
6. Field provisions and storage of special equipment

Figure 11.2 illustrates how a plumbing takeoff for pipe and fixtures is documented on a standard worksheet.

| COMPUTED BY: | DB | PROJECT: | TRI-COUNTY REALTY | DATE: | 10-26 |
| CHECKED BY: | RL | ARCHITECT: | ACE MECHANICAL | PAGE: | 1 OF 1 |
| | | | | INDEX NO: | 342 |

| REF. | DESCRIPTION | QUAN. | DIMENSIONS | | | SUBTOTAL | | TOTAL | | REMARKS |
|---|---|---|---|---|---|---|---|---|---|---|
| | | | LENGTH | WIDTH | HEIGHT | QUAN. | UN. | QUAN. | UN. | |
| P2 | 1/2" Copper Tubing | | 96 | | | | | 96 | LF | Room 6 |
| P2 | " | | 102 | | | | | 102 | LF | Room 8 |
| P2 | " | | 38 | | | | | 38 | LF | Room 15 |
| | TOTAL | | | | | | | 236 | LF | |
| P2 | 3/4" Copper Tubing | | 57 | | | | | 57 | LF | Room 20 |
| P2 | " | | 92 | | | | | 92 | LF | Room 31 |
| | TOTAL | | | | | | | 149 | LF | |
| P3 | LAVATORIES | 4 | | | | | | 4 | EA | Room 6 |
| P3 | " | 4 | | | | | | 4 | EA | Room 8 |
| P3 | " | 2 | | | | | | 2 | EA | Room 20 |
| P3 | " | 4 | | | | | | 4 | EA | Room 31 |
| | TOTAL | | | | | | | 14 | EA | |
| P2 | WATER METER | 1 | | | | | | 1 | EA | |
| P3 | FLOOR DRAINS | 2 | | | | | | 2 | EA | |

| TOTAL FROM PREVIOUS PAGE: | |
| TOTAL: | |

**FIGURE 11.2**
Plumbing worksheet.

## Taking Off Mechanical Work

Mechanical work—known as heating, ventilating, and air conditioning (HVAC)—may be bid under single or separate contracts. The detailed estimate is prepared by a contractor specializing in this type of work. The estimator must have field experience, an understanding of design principles, and the HVAC drawings and specifications. In most cases the HVAC system is designed by a mechanical engineer.

The general contractor should evaluate all HVAC bids to see that all items have been included. The three methods described for plumbing can be used to calculate an approximate cost. Because there are so many different types of mechanical equipment that can exist in any one type of building, it is often difficult to maintain effective historical records of average cost per square foot or percent of total project cost. The unit cost for a specific type of equipment is thus a more reliable method of approximating the total cost of the mechanical work.

The takeoff for mechanical items includes piping, ductwork, equipment, and accessories. The estimator must have complete drawings from which to take off the linear feet of pipe, ductwork, and other linear components to the mechanical systems and the number of each type of equipment and accessories. This information is documented by type and size.

The mechanical contractor must review the specifications carefully to ensure that all items within their scope have been included in the estimate. Certain areas have to be closely coordinated with the other contractors. These include:

1. Location, size, and excavation responsibility for underground utilities
2. Wall sleeves, size limitations, chases, expansion compensators, and access doors for piping
3. Method of support and anchorage, roof curbs, size limitations, and access for receiving and installing equipment
4. Sizes, support, access doors, outlet sizes, chases, roof curbs, and exterior air louvers for ductwork

## ELECTRICAL

Division 16 of the Uniform Construction Index (CSI format) includes such items as conduit, wire, circuit breakers, switches, transformers, lighting fixtures, telephone, telecommunications, computer networking, fiber optics, and other special electrical systems. Figure 11.3 contains a list of the various items in this division along with their units of takeoff.

As always, the estimator must have a thorough knowledge of the area being estimated—in this case, electrical construction. The estimator must have a complete set of electrical drawings (wiring diagrams, lighting plan, etc.) and a complete set of electrical technical specifications. In addition, the estimator will need any electrical codes that pertain to the specific project. A typical set of construction drawings usually does not consist of a sufficient amount of information to develop a detailed estimate. Additional drawings, mainly wiring diagrams, are needed. These and other electrical-related drawings are usually prepared by an electrical engineer with input from electrical contractors.

| | | |
|---|---|---|
| 16.0 | Raceways | |
| | 10 Cable tray | lf |
| | 20 Conduit to 15′ high | lf |
| | 30 Conduit to concrete slab | lf |
| | 50 Conduit in trench | lf |
| | 80 Under floor duct | ea/lf |
| | 90 Wiremold raceway | lf/ea |
| | 95 Wireway | lf |
| 16.1 | Conductors and grounding | |
| | 10 Wire | clf |
| | 20 Armored cable | clf/lf |
| | 30 Control cable | clf |
| | 60 Shielded cable | clf |
| | 70 Non-metallic cable 600 volt | clf |
| 16.2 | Boxes and wiring devices | |
| | 10 Pull boxes &cabinets | ea |
| | 20 Outlet boxes | ea |
| | 30 Wiring devices | ea |
| | 35 Low voltage switching | ea |
| 16.3 | Starters, boards, and switches | |
| | 10 Circuit breakers | ea |
| | 15 Control stations | ea |
| | 20 Fuse cabinets | ea |
| | 27 Motor connections | ea |
| | 30 Motor starters &controls | ea |
| | 50 Panel boards | ea |
| | 53 Panel board circuit breakers | ea |
| | 55 Safety boards | ea |
| | 60 Switch boards | ea |
| | 65 Distribution section | ea |
| | 70 Feeder section | ea |
| | 80 Switchboard instruments | ea |
| 16.4 | Transformers and bus ducts | |
| | 01 Oil filled transformer | ea |
| | 10 Dry type transformer | ea |
| | 30 Copper bus duct | lf/ea |
| 16.5 | Power systems and capacitors | |
| | 05 Capacitors | ea |
| | 10 Generator set | ea |
| | 20 Total energy systems | ea |
| | 30 Uninterrupted power systems | ea |
| 16.6 | Lighting | |
| | 10 Interior lighting fixtures | ea |
| | 25 Exit light | ea |
| | 50 Exterior fixtures | ea |
| | 75 Lamps | ea |
| 16.7 | Electrical utilities | |
| | 01 Electric &telephone sitework | ea/lf |
| | 90 Transite duct | lf/ea |
| 16.8 | Special systems | |
| | 01 Clocks | ea |
| | 05 Clock systems | ea |
| | 15 Detection systems | ea |

**FIGURE 11.3**
Division 16: electrical.

| | | |
|---|---|---|
| 28 | Doctors' in-out register | ea |
| 30 | Doorbell systems | ea |
| 33 | Electric heating | sf/kw/ea |
| 35 | Nurses' call systems | ea/total |
| 38 | Public address systems | speaker |
| 50 | Sound system | ea/name |
| 80 | Wiring, residential | ea/total |

**FIGURE 11.3** (*continued*)

## Taking Off Electrical Work

Electrical construction can be divided into two phases. The first entails all the items used to bring power to an outlet, fixture, or piece of equipment (conduit, wire, boxes, etc). The other phase is the outlets, fixtures, and equipment. The estimator develops the estimate and prepares the worksheets based on these two phases.

The estimator uses the wiring diagrams to determine the number of linear feet of each type and size of linear component such as conduit and wire (electrical, telephone, etc.). There are various types of mechanical devices available, such as the rotometer, to help the estimator if scaled drawings are being used. The resulting information is placed in the appropriate manner on the worksheet. The estimator should be cautious about using riser diagrams in that they are provided only to help orient one to where the power lines are located in the building and the relationships of all the components of the electrical system. The diagram is not usually drawn to scale and thus should not be used directly in any takeoff work.

Once all phase 1 items are taken off, the next step is to obtain, through counting, each type and size of outlet, fixture, equipment, and other phase 2 items and record each on the worksheet separately. Figure 11.4 shows an example of a worksheet containing phase 1 and phase 2 electrical items.

The electrical contractor prepares a detailed estimate. The general contractor evaluates the subcontractor's bid using one of the three methods discussed in the plumbing section of this chapter to obtain a total approximate cost.

The electrical contractor must take time to closely review the specifications to determine their complete scope of work. The following areas may require close coordination with other contractors on the project:

1. Location, size, and responsibility for excavating for underground utilities
2. Supports, recessed depths, size of access openings, method of feed, and any size limitations for equipment
3. Field provisions and storage of special equipment
4. Location, method of support, finish, color, and material of terminal fixtures and devices
5. Locations of outlets, materials, method of feed, chases, and other special considerations for distribution systems
6. Allowable mounting surfaces

**WORKSHEET -A-**

| COMPUTED BY: | DB | | | | | | | | DATE: | 10-27 |
|---|---|---|---|---|---|---|---|---|---|---|
| CHECKED BY: | RL | PROJECT: HARTWELL BOAT SHOP | | | | | | | PAGE: 1 OF 1 | |
| | | ARCHITECT: VOLTAGE ENGINEERS | | | | | | | INDEX NO: 351 | |

| REF. | DESCRIPTION | QUAN. | DIMENSIONS LENGTH | WIDTH | HEIGHT | SUBTOTAL QUAN. | UN. | TOTAL QUAN. | UN. | REMARKS |
|---|---|---|---|---|---|---|---|---|---|---|
| E1 | 1/2" ELEC CONDUIT | | 975 | | | | | 975 | LF | Room E-7 |
| E1 | " | | 320 | | | | | 320 | LF | Room E-9 |
| E2 | " | | 915 | | | | | 915 | LF | Room E-12 |
| | TOTAL | | | | | | | 2210 | LF | |
| E2 | 3/4" ELEC CONDUIT | | 580 | | | | | 580 | LF | Room E-12 |
| E2 | " | | 250 | | | | | 250 | LF | Room E-14 |
| | TOTAL | | | | | | | 830 | LF | |
| E1 | DUPLEX RECEP | 15 | | | | | | 15 | EA | Room E-7 |
| E1 | " | 8 | | | | | | 8 | EA | Room E-9 |
| E3 | " | 27 | | | | | | 27 | EA | Room E-12 |
| E2 | " | 12 | | | | | | 12 | EA | Room E-14 |
| | TOTAL | | | | | | | 62 | EA | |
| E3 | 25 KVA TRANS | 1 | | | | | | 1 | EA | |

TOTAL FROM PREVIOUS PAGE:
TOTAL:

**FIGURE 11.4**
Electrical worksheet.

284

| COMPUTED BY: KB | | PROJECT: Tri-County Realty | | | | | | DATE: 10-27 | | | | | | | | |
| CHECKED BY: RL | | ARCHITECT: ACE Mechanical | | | | | | PAGE: 1 OF 1 | | | | | | | | |
| | | | | | | | | INDEX NO: 359 | | | | | | | | |

| | | QUANTITY | | MATERIAL COST | | DAILY PROD. OF CREW | CREW MAKE-UP | LABOR COST | | | | | EQUIPMENT COST | | SUB OR OTHER | TOTAL COST |
|---|---|---|---|---|---|---|---|---|---|---|---|---|---|---|---|---|
| REF. | DESCRIPTION | TOTAL | UN. | UNIT COST | MATERIAL SUBTOTAL | | | MAN-HOUR PER UNIT | TOTAL MAN HOURS | TOTAL CREW HOURS | AVG. WAGE RATE | LABOR SUBTOTAL | RATE PER HOUR | EQUIP. SUBTOTAL | | |
| 3/4 | 1/2" Copper Pipe | 960 | LF | 1.18 | 113 | 81 | 1 | .098 | 10 | 10 | 15 | 142 | | 0 | 0 | 255 |
| 3/4 | 3" Cast Iron Pipe | 164 | LF | 2.83 | 464 | 60 | 2 | 2.67 | 44 | 22 | 12.50 | 547 | | 0 | 0 | 1011 |
| 3/4 | 4" PVC | 396 | LF | 0.96 | 380 | 42 | 1 | .19 | 76 | 76 | 15 | 1131 | | 0 | 0 | 1511 |
| 3/4 | Urinals | 2 | EA | 325 | 670 | 5.33 | 2 | 3 | 6 | 3 | 12.50 | 75 | | 0 | 0 | 745 |
| 3/4 | Lavatories | 4 | EA | 134 | 586 | 64 | 2 | 2.5 | 10 | 5 | 12.50 | 125 | | 0 | 0 | 861 |
| 3/4 | Water Closets | 4 | EA | 418 | 1672 | 5.3 | 2 | 3.02 | 12 | 6 | 12.50 | 151 | | 0 | 0 | 1823 |
| 3/4 | Service Sink | 1 | EA | 315 | 315 | 4 | 2 | 4 | 4 | 2 | 12.50 | 50 | | 0 | 0 | 365 |
| 3/4 | Fountain | 1 | EA | 365 | 365 | 4 | 1 | 2 | 2 | 2 | 15.00 | 30 | | 0 | 0 | 395 |
| 3/4 | Floor Drains | 2 | EA | 33 | 66 | 12 | 2 | 1.333 | 2.67 | 1.33 | 12.50 | 33 | | 0 | 0 | 99 |
| | TOTAL FROM PREVIOUS PAGE: | | | | 0 | | | | | | | 0 | | 0 | 0 | 0 |
| | TOTAL: | | | | 4571 | | | | | | | 2287 | | 0 | 0 | 6865 |

**FIGURE 11.5**
Summary sheet.

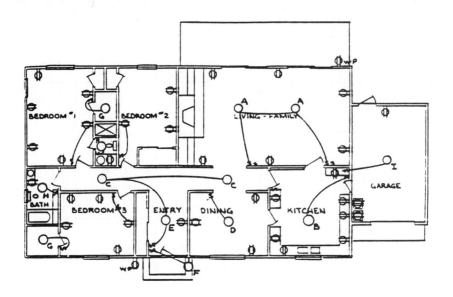

FIXTURE SCHEDULE

| NO. | TYPE | REMARKS |
|---|---|---|
| A | 12", 4-60 WATT LAMPS | SURFACE MOUNTED, OPAL GLASS |
| B | 2'X4' FLUORESCENT | SURFACE MOUNTED, 4-40 WATT |
| C | 2'X2' FLUORESCENT | RECESS MOUNTED, 2-U40 WATT |
| D | 10", 2-60 WATT LAMPS | SURFACE MOUNTED, OPAL GLASS |
| E | 8", 1-60 WATT LAMP | SURFACE MOUNTED, OPAL GLASS |
| F | INCANDESCENT, 100 WATT | WALL MOUNTED |
| G | FLUOR. STRIP FIXTURE | SURFACE MOUNTED, 1 (4'-40 WATT) |
| H | 2'X2' FLUORESCENT | SURFACE MOUNTED, 2-U40 WATT |
| I | FLOODLIGHT, 250 WATT | MERCURY VAPOR |

LEGEND

⌽    Duplex Receptacle

$    Switch

⌻    240 Volt Receptacle

$₃   Switch (3-Way)

⌽ᵂᴾ  Weatherproof Receptacle

**FIGURE 11.6**
Electrical floor plan.

# PRICING PLUMBING, MECHANICAL, AND ELECTRICAL WORK

As with any other item, to develop a complete cost, the estimator must know the labor requirements, productivity, wage rates, equipment requirements, and costs. In addition, the unit price of the material is needed. This information must be known when preparing the estimate. If it is not, the cost of the material can be obtained from the vendor, labor and equipment productivities from historical records, and wage rates and equipment costs from company records.

All of this information comes together on the summary sheet. An example, utilizing the information contained on the worksheets presented in this chapter, is shown in Fig. 11.5.

# STUDENT EXERCISES

**11.1.** List some of the temporary work items included in a plumbing takeoff.

**11.2.** What omissions should an estimator look for in a mechanical estimate?

**11.3.** What overlaps with other trades might occur in an electrical estimate?

**11.4.** In estimating piping, can the lengths be scaled from a riser diagram? Why or why not?

**11.5.** Develop a completed worksheet for all the outlets and fixtures shown in Fig. 11.6.

**11.6.** Using the drawings and other information provided by the instructor, perform a subcontractor system takeoff for plumbing, HVAC, and electrical.

# CHAPTER
# 12

# TRANSFER OF THE ESTIMATE TO THE CONSTRUCTION PROCESS

The estimate is the basis for all of the functions involved with the construction process. The estimator has the greatest knowledge of the project after it is awarded; it is the estimator's responsibility to assist in the transfer of the project to purchasing, accounting, and project management. During the project management process a project schedule and a schedule of values must be developed. In addition, projected cost estimates, progress estimates, and change order estimates will need to be completed during the progress of the project.

The estimator will have a varying degree of involvement in the different transfer functions. For example, in some construction companies the estimator might do all the change order estimates; in others, the project manager might do the change order estimates.

## TRANSFER TO PURCHASING

After the project is awarded, the construction company must purchase all the material, all the equipment in the building, all the equipment required to install the

PROJECT STATUS REPORT

Project name — Kroger store number 234
Superintendent — Jim Smith
Project manager — Hank Williams

| Cost Code | Work Description | Unit Measure | ESTIMATED LABOR | | | | |
|---|---|---|---|---|---|---|---|
| | | | Quantity | Total Man Hours | MH/U | Total Cost | Unit Cost |
| 3115 | Form footing | SFCA | 264 | 44 | 0.167 | $ 660 | $ 2.50 |
| 3117 | Reinforce foo | LB | 3500 | 53 | 0.015 | 788 | 0.23 |
| 3119 | Place footing | CY | 275 | 756 | 2.750 | 11,344 | 41.25 |
| 5115 | Set steel stai | RISE | 15 | 68 | 4.500 | 1,013 | 67.50 |
| 5487 | Set hand rail | LF | 200 | 50 | 0.250 | 750 | 3.75 |
| 6122 | Rafter framin | BF | 3600 | 234 | 0.065 | 3,510 | 0.98 |

**FIGURE 12.1**
Labor project status.

material, and all subcontracts. For a general building contractor this can be in excess of 80 percent of the contract price. Depending on the company organization, the purchasing could be the responsibility of the project manager, the purchasing agent, or the estimator.

The estimator will need to transfer all of the knowledge gained during the bidding process to the person doing the purchasing. The person responsible for the purchasing must check the quantity to be ordered, inclusions and exclusions of material on quotations, delivery times, and the scope of work on subcontract bids. Normally, the purchaser will purchase the material or write the subcontract with the same sources that were used during the bidding process. However, all purchases must be confirmed with the supplier or subcontractor before the final subcontract or material purchase order is sent. For some materials or subcontracted items, the estimator may not have had a quotation during the bidding process. The purchaser must then obtain quotations that meet the prescribed qualifications of the project.

In some cases the material quantities must be in a different unit of measure for the purposes of purchasing. For example, the lumber for a project may have been priced in board feet during the estimate. However, when the lumber is purchased it must be in terms of quantity, size, and length of boards.

The purchaser must also determine if all subcontractors and material suppliers are in compliance with the specifications. A variation from this could cost the general contractor a considerable amount of money. In addition, the purchaser must make sure that all purchases are in accordance with the method of construction and construction schedule.

The estimator must transfer the following information to the purchaser:

1. Quantity of materials
2. Name of subcontractors and material suppliers used during the bidding process
3. Delivery times

BOILER CONSTRUCTION COMPANY

| | TO DATE | | | | ESTIMATE REVISION | | | PROJECTED | | OVER OR UNDER | |
|---|---|---|---|---|---|---|---|---|---|---|---|
| | | | | | | | | | | − | + |
| Quantity | Total Man Hours | MH/U | Total Cost | Unit Cost | Quantity | MH/ | Total Cost | Total Man Hours | Total Cost | Total Man Hours | Total Cost |
| 45 | 9 | 0.2 | $132 | $ 2.94 | 300 | 0.175 | $788 | 60 | $  883 | −7.5 | $ (95) |
| 850 | 13 | 0.01529 | 191 | 0.22 | | | 0 | 53.529 | 785 | −1.029 | 2 |
| 6 | 18 | 3 | 226 | 37.67 | | | 0 | 825 | 10,358 | −68.75 | 985 |
| 0 | 0 | 0 | 0 | 0.00 | | | 0 | 0 | 0 | | |
| 0 | 0 | 0 | 0 | 0.00 | | | 0 | 0 | 0 | | |
| 0 | 0 | 0 | 0 | 0.00 | | | 0 | 0 | 0 | | |

**FIGURE 12.1** (*continued*)

4. Inclusions such as taxes, delivery cost, unloading cost, and shop-drawing cost
5. Does the material meet the specified quality?
6. Short supply items
7. Long-lead (long delivery time) items

## TRANSFER TO ACCOUNTING

Field costs are tracked in substantial detail because excessive costs in the field can be corrected only if the exact causes can be isolated. Also, the detailed actual costs of a project can, with adjustments for inflation and project variations, be used on future bids. The tracking of the actual cost and the projection of future cost are based on the original estimate. During construction the original estimate is compared to the actual costs. Figure 12.1 illustrates the comparison of the original estimated labor cost to the current actual labor cost and projects what the cost will be if the production stays at the same rate. To accomplish the comparisons and projections, the original estimate must be put into the company cost coding or code of accounts system (the first column in Fig. 12.1). Each estimated cost will need to be aligned with a cost code.

Figure 12.1 is the final file (PS.WQ1) of a series of files (CODE.WSF, QUAN.WQ1, TIME.WQ1, and PS.WQ1) that track the labor time and quantity of materials installed in the cost-projection process. The files are all linked together to calculate the final cost of the project. File CODE.WSF is used to activate the linkage to all of the other files. This file should be retrieved first. In file QUAN.WQ1 the quantities of material installed will be entered (see Fig. 12.2). File TIME.WQ1 is a time card. The amount of time that each worker spends on a cost code is entered in this file (see Fig. 12.3). The Lotus files PS.WK1, QUAN.WK1, and TIME.WK1 are also provided on the disk. However, they do not contain the linking characteristic of the WQ1 files used on Quattro Pro.

| QUANTITY REPORT | | BOILER CONSTRUCTION COMPANY | | | | | |
|---|---|---|---|---|---|---|---|
| PERIOD: May 1–5 | | | | | | | |
| | | | Enter the quantity for each date | | | | |
| Cost Code | Description | Unit of Measure | May 1 | May 2 | May 3 | May 4 | May 5 |
| 3115 | Form footings | SFCA | 45 | | | | |
| 3117 | Reinforce foo | LB | | 850 | | | |
| 3119 | Place footing | CY | | | 6 | | |
| 5115 | Set steel stair | RISER | | | | | |
| 5487 | Set hand rail | LF | | | | | |
| 6122 | Rafter framin | BF | | | | | |
| 6255 | Floor framing | BF | | | | | |
| 6455 | Install base bo | LF | | | | | |
| 6825 | Trim doors | LF | | | | | |

**FIGURE 12.2**
Quantities of materials installed.

A manually completed estimate can take a considerable amount of time to transfer to the company cost accounting system because the coding system and the method of estimating manually may not be compatible. The transfer of the estimate to the accounting department can be uncomplicated if the estimate is computerized and the estimating software is compatible with the accounting software.

## TRANSFER TO PROJECT MANAGEMENT

The transfer of the estimate to project management involves the use of the estimate for the development of the project schedule and the schedule of values. As the project progresses, estimates and change order estimates will have to be completed.

### Development of the Construction Schedule

The original estimate and preliminary schedule developed during the estimating process serves as the basis for the development of the final construction schedule. The estimator should make sure that all information pertaining to the schedule is available to the project manager.

In Fig. 12.4 (file PRICE.WQ1 or PRICE.WK1) the duration of each line item of the estimate that has a calculated labor cost is indicated in the second column from the right side. The project manager should study these durations and possibly adjust the crew size or combine several similar line items of the estimate to develop schedule activities. The planned construction method of the project could make it go over budget and/or duration if the project manager does not use the original estimate in the calculation of activity durations. By using the original estimate, the project manager may discover a more effective and efficient method of construction.

```
┌──────────────────────────────────────────────────────────────────────────────┐
│                                                                                │
│  TIME CARD                      BOILER CONSTRUCTION COMPANY                     │
│                                                                                │
│  PERIOD:  May 1–5                                                              │
│  ┌──────────────────────────────────────────────────────────────────────────┐│
│  │                    ENTER THE NUMBER OF HOURS WORKED THIS PERIOD            ││
│  │                                                                            ││
│  │                  Form  Reinf  Place  Set   Set  Rafter Floor  Base  Trim   ││
│  │          WAGE    Foot  Foot   Ft/Co  Stair Rail Frame  Frame Board Doors   ││
│  │  NAME    RATE    3115  3117   3119   5115  5487 6122   6255  6455  6825     ││
│  │                                                                            ││
│  │  Bill Smith       $15.00    3    3     2                                    ││
│  │  Bubby Jones      $10.15    3    5                                          ││
│  │  Mike Harrington  $15.75               8                                    ││
│  │  Doug Jones       $19.00    3    5                                          ││
│  │  Tom Anderson     $ 8.75               8                                    ││
│  │                                                                            ││
│  │             Total           9   13    18   0    0    0    0    0    0       ││
│  └──────────────────────────────────────────────────────────────────────────┘│
│                                                                                │
└──────────────────────────────────────────────────────────────────────────────┘
```

**FIGURE 12.3**
Labor time card.

The duration for the subcontracted items should be noted on the original subcontract quotation. The project manager may have to contact the subcontractors for a detailed breakdown of their activities.

## Development of a Schedule of Values

The schedule of values is a breakdown of the project costs before the project begins and is used to determine the value of the work completed for the subsequent monthly pay requests. For a lump-sum contract, the breakdown is submitted to the owner or architect by the contractor for approval before any payment request is presented. The line items of the schedule of values includes the bare cost, overhead, and profit from the estimate. It is derived by breaking down a project estimate's pricing sheet line items into measurable elements or work packages and then adding profit and overhead to each work package. The sum of all these work package prices should equal the total contract amount. The work packages and the actual construction schedule are then juxtaposed to provide the owner with a payment schedule for work completed. As the schedule of values inevitably determines a contractor's cash flow on a particular project, the derivation of them is not a task that should be taken lightly. Unfortunately, deriving a schedule of values is often a tedious, time-consuming, and inexact process. There are many methods when determining the amount of overhead and profit that should be added to each line item of the schedule of values. One method is to allocate the overhead and profit on the basis of risk. Items that have higher risk should be marked up a greater amount. Figure 12.5 (file VALUE.WQ1 or VALUE.WK1) illustrates the distribution of overhead and profit on a schedule of values by risk. The goal of this computer program is to enable the contractor to input several fundamental elements of the construction schedule and cost estimate into a spreadsheet and then integrate these elements into a schedule of values for the project. Derivation

| | | | | | MATERIAL | | --ENTER CREW MAKEUP-- | | |
|---|---|---|---|---|---|---|---|---|---|
| ENTER ESITMATE INDEX NO. | ENTER ITEM DESCRIPTION | ENTER TOTAL QUANTIT | UN | ENTER COST/UNI | TOTAL MATERIAL $8,952 | # OF MECHAN | # OF HELPER | # OF FOREME | |
| 4.00 | CONCRETE FTGS | 20.00 | CY | $50.00 | $1,000 | 1.00 | 1.00 | 1.00 |
| 3.00 | CONCRETE SLAB | 120.00 | CY | $53.00 | $6,360 | 4.00 | 5.00 | |
| 4.00 | BRICK PERIMETER | 5000.00 | EA | $0.04 | $200 | 2.00 | 3.00 | |
| 8.00 | METAL DOORS | 7.00 | EA | $198.90 | $1,392 | | 2.00 | |
| 11.00 | PUMP | | | | $0 | | | |
| 9.00 | CERAMIC TILE INSTA | | | | $0 | | | |
| | | | | | $0 | | | |

Project: ACE OFFICE BLDG. Estimato ANN, Location LAYAFETTE IND., Date MAY 7, Page No 1 OF 10. Enter Wages: MECHANI $8.55, HELPERS $7.70, FOREME $14.67.

**FIGURE 12.4**
Pricing sheet.

of the schedule of values using this program is virtually instantaneous, so the contractor can use this program in a trial and error modeling process to obtain a schedule of values that optimizes his resources and minimizes risk.

## Data Entry Explanation and Help Notes for VALUE.WQ.1 (VALUE.WK1)

All data entry items will appear in blue when entered.

1. **Project Name** Enter the project name.
2. **Owner** Enter the owner's name.
3. **Contract Amount** This is a critical entry because the dollar amount less material, labor, equipment, subcontract, other bare costs, and finance costs is the basis for the derivation of the calculated markup to be distributed.
4. **Item Number and Description** These entries vary from project to project. The estimator should combine line items from the summary sheets into quantifiable work packages that are then entered here as a schedule of values line item.
5. **Material Tax** Enter as a decimal.
6. **Labor Burden (Taxes and Insurance)** Enter as a decimal.
7. **Bare Costs** For each schedule of values line item, enter the bare costs (excluding taxes and insurance) for materials, labor, equipment, subcontractors, and other.
8. **Pay Materials Before We Are Paid** If the contractor intends to wait on payment from the owner prior to disbursing funds to material suppliers, enter **NO**, else enter **YES**.
9. **Expense Occurrence To Payment (Days)** Enter the number of days of payment lag from the time a request for payment is submitted to the owner

* If hours are not entered, the equipment hours will be calculated from labor durations.

| --ENTER ONE PRODUCTION METHOD-- | | | | TOTAL | -----EQUIPMENT----- | | TOTAL | ENTER | LINE ITEM | |
| DAILY PRODUCTI OF CREW | WORKER HOUR PER UNIT | TOTAL WORKER HOURS | UNIT PRICE | LABOR $15,080 | ENTER RATE PER HOUR | * HOURS REQUIRE HOURS | EQUIP. $822 | SUBCONTRA $8,000 | TOTAL DAYS | TOTAL $32,854 |
|---|---|---|---|---|---|---|---|---|---|---|
| | | 1.00 | | $10 | $12.00 | 0.000 | $4 | | 0.04 | $1,014 |
| | 1.0000 | | | $969 | $2.00 | | $27 | | 1.67 | $7,356 |
| 120.00 | | | | $13,400 | $2.00 | | $667 | | 41.67 | $14,267 |
| | | | 100.00 | $700 | $1.00 | 125.000 | $125 | | 5.68 | $2,217 |
| | | | | $0 | | | $0 | | 0.00 | $0 |
| | | | | $0 | | | $0 | $8,000 | 0.00 | $8,000 |
| | | | | $0 | | | $0 | | 0.00 | $0 |

**FIGURE 12.4** (*continued*)

until the time at which the owner remits payment to the contractor. (See **Explanation of How the Program Works** for assumptions made for this input.)

10. **Pay Subs Before We Are Paid**  If the contractor intends to wait on payment from the owner prior to disbursing funds to the subcontractors, enter **NO**, else enter **YES**.

11. **Interest Rate**  Enter as a decimal the discount rate the contractor's lending institution uses for short-term loans to the contractor.

12. **Retainage Requirements**  The percent of the payment the owner intends to withhold from each of the contractor's pay requests, as outlined in the contract documents.

13. **Hold Retainage On Subs**  Enter **YES** or **NO**.

14. **Number of Months After Completion That the Last Payment Is Expected**  The contractor must consider lag of billings from subcontractors and suppliers as well as payment lag from the owner. Typically, add two months to the expense occurrence to payment (#9 above) to calculate this number.

15. **Enter Month of Activity**  This number is derived from the contractor's schedule. For example, if the activity will occur in the sixth month from the project's commencement, enter **6**. If an activity spans more than one month, choose a month in which most of the activity will take place.

16. **Include Interest On Subs**  Enter **NO** if the contractor wants finance charges for subcontractor work to be distributed over the entire project. Enter **YES** if the contractor wants subcontractor finance charges to be applied to the applicable line item.

17. **Distribution of Risk:**
    A. First determine what percentage of the job will be considered the start-up phase of the project. For example, if the project duration is 12 months and the contractor feels the project will not be in full swing (due to mobilization, site layout, learning curve, etc.) until after month 3, the

SCHEDULE OF VALUES BY STEVE SCHUETTE 803-656-3081

AAA CONSTRUCTION COMPANY
SCHEDULE OF VALUES

BARE COST
ENTER THE ESTIMATED AMOUNTS (DO NOT INCLUDE TAXES AND I
SHOW TAX AND INSURANCE % RATES BELOW

PROJECT: Hardware

OWNER: Sam Smith

ENTER MATEIAL TA 5.00%
ENTER LABOR T&I 25.00%

PROJECT MANAGER: Jack Kennedy

ENTER CONTRACT AMO $1,370,000

| ITE | DESCRIPTION | MATERIAL | LABOR | SUBCONTR | TOTAL | % CONT | ENTER MAT. | ENTER LABOR | ENTER EQUIP. | ENTER SUB. | ENTER OTHER |
|---|---|---|---|---|---|---|---|---|---|---|---|
| 1 | BONDS AND PERMITS | $0 | $0 | $45,000 | $45,000 | 3.28% | | | | $45,000 | $0 |
| 2 | GRADING AND CLEARING | $11,950 | $0 | $0 | $11,950 | 0.87% | $8,523 | | | | |
| 3 | STORM DRAINAGE | $0 | $0 | $0 | $0 | 0.00% | | | | | |
| 4 | BUILDING CONCRETE | $64,569 | $166,837 | $0 | $231,406 | 16.89% | $45,826 | $98,000 | $2,500 | | |
| 5 | MASONRY | $18,930 | $17,827 | $0 | $36,757 | 2.68% | $15,000 | $8,560 | $4,203 | | |
| 6 | SITE CONCRETE | $9,879 | $10,530 | $0 | $20,408 | 1.49% | $7,856 | $5,065 | $2,500 | | |
| 7 | PAVING | $63,875 | $0 | $0 | $63,875 | 4.66% | $45,555 | | | | |
| 8 | STRUCTURAL AND MISC | $57,815 | $56,248 | $0 | $114,062 | 8.33% | $45,896 | $25,630 | $15,060 | | |
| 9 | FRAMING AND SHEATHIN | $107,731 | $8,743 | $0 | $116,475 | 8.50% | $85,630 | $5,866 | | | |
| 10 | BUILD-UP ROOFING AND | $0 | $0 | $15,563 | $15,563 | 1.14% | | | | $15,563 | |
| 11 | BUILDING INSULATION | $0 | $0 | $10,253 | $10,253 | 0.75% | | | | $10,253 | |
| 12 | CAULKING | $5,655 | $6,338 | $0 | $11,992 | 0.88% | $4,500 | $4,256 | | | |
| 13 | MILLWORK | $73,964 | $38,069 | $0 | $112,034 | 8.18% | $58,963 | $25,604 | | | |
| 14 | WINDOWS | $6,111 | $5,218 | $0 | $11,330 | 0.83% | $4,856 | $3,500 | | | |
| 15 | DOORS, FRAMES, GLASS | $19,397 | $5,206 | $0 | $24,604 | 1.80% | $15,455 | $3,500 | | | |
| 16 | HARDWARE | $61,047 | $0 | $0 | $61,047 | 4.46% | $48,696 | | | | |
| 17 | OVERHEAD DOORS | $0 | $0 | $25,000 | $25,000 | 1.82% | | | | $25,000 | |
| 18 | DRYWALL | $0 | $0 | $89,562 | $89,562 | 6.54% | | | | $89,562 | |
| 19 | ACOUSTICAL CEILING | $0 | $0 | $0 | $0 | 0.00% | | | | $0 | |
| 20 | RESILIENT FLOORING | $0 | $0 | $5,000 | $5,000 | 0.36% | | | | $5,000 | |
| 21 | CARPET | $0 | $0 | $15,362 | $15,362 | 1.12% | | | | $15,362 | |
| 22 | CERAMIC TILE | $0 | $0 | $4,523 | $4,523 | 0.33% | | | | $4,523 | |
| 23 | PAINT | $0 | $0 | $12,500 | $12,500 | 0.91% | | | | $12,500 | |
| 24 | SPECIALTIES | $0 | $0 | $45,696 | $45,696 | 3.34% | | | | $45,696 | |
| 25 | HVAC | $0 | $0 | $85,600 | $85,600 | 6.25% | | | | $85,600 | |
| 26 | PLUMBING | $0 | $0 | $75,000 | $75,000 | 5.47% | | | | $75,000 | |
| 27 | ELECTRICAL | $0 | $0 | $125,000 | $125,000 | 9.12% | | | | $125,000 | |

**FIGURE 12.5**
Calculations of a schedule of values.

percentage of the job considered start-up phase will be $\frac{3}{12} = 25\%$. Enter this number as a decimal in the **? % of Job =** cell.

B. The contractor must next determine what portion of the mark-up can be attributed to start-up costs. Affecting this decision are the following factors:

1. The skill level and expected productivity of craftsworkers at the beginning of the job
2. Mobilization, layout, permit and licensing fees, temporary utility installation, etc; costs not included in other schedule of values line items
3. Method of construction
4. Owner and contractual constraints
5. Adequacy of the design documents (specifications and drawings)
6. Owner-contractor and architect-contractor relationships
7. Start-up specific construction risks
8. Other job-dependent factors

When the contractor has established a percentage of the total markup that will be attributed to the cost of start-up, enter the figure as a decimal form in the **Start-Up** cell.

IF CONSIDERING FINANCING COST ENTER.
PAY MATERIAL BEFORE WE ARE PAI NO
EXPENSE INCURANCE TO PAYMENT 30
PAY SUBS BEFORE WE ARE PAID YES
INTEREST RATE = 8%
RETAINAGE REQUIRMENTS 10%
HOLD RETAINAGE ON SUBS. YES O YES
NUMBER OF MONTHS AFTER COMPLETION
THAT THE LAST PAYMENT IS EXPEC 2

INCLUDE INTEREST ON SUBS. YES or NO -> NO    SEE NOT
ENTER THE PER CENTAGE (%) OF MARK-UP THAT IS TO BE
DISTRIBUTED TO EACH RISK CATAGORY - 4 CATAGORY MUST =

| | | |
|---|---|---|
| START UP 20.00% | ? % OF JOB 25.00% | CALCULATED AMOU |
| LABOR 30.00% | SUBCONT. 0.00% | OF MARK-UP TO BE |
| MATERIAL 50.00% | | DISTRIBUT $156 039 |

\* If entry is "No" the interest will be added to the mark-up.

BARE COST WITH TAXES, INSUR, AND FINANCE COST COMPARED TO C

| ENTER MONTH OF ACTIVITY | TOTAL $8,210 | CASH FL FINANC | RETAINA FINANC | MATERIAL & OTHER BARE COST | CHARGE O | LABOR & EQUIPMENT BARE COST | CHARGE O | SUBCONTRACT BARE COS | CHARGE |
|---|---|---|---|---|---|---|---|---|---|
| 1 | $295 | $0 | $0 | $0 | $0 | $0 | $0 | $45,000 | $45,000 |
| 2 | | $0 | $68 | $9,017 | $11,950 | $0 | $0 | $0 | $0 |
| | | $0 | $0 | $0 | $0 | $0 | $0 | $0 | $0 |
| 1 | | $661 | $1,268 | $48,721 | $64,569 | $126,325 | $156,837 | $0 | $0 |
| 4 | | $84 | $185 | $15,895 | $18,930 | $15,027 | $17,827 | $0 | $0 |
| 10 | | $50 | $41 | $8,295 | $9,879 | $8,876 | $10,530 | $0 | $0 |
| 2 | | $0 | $364 | $48,197 | $63,875 | $0 | $0 | $0 | $0 |
| 7 | | $268 | $404 | $48,547 | $57,815 | $47,413 | $56,248 | $0 | $0 |
| 5 | | $39 | $549 | $90,461 | $107,731 | $7,370 | $8,743 | $0 | $0 |
| 7 | | $102 | $0 | $0 | $0 | $0 | $0 | $15,563 | $15,563 |
| 10 | | $67 | $0 | $0 | $0 | $0 | $0 | $10,253 | $10,253 |
| 11 | | $28 | $18 | $4,748 | $5,656 | $5,342 | $6,338 | $0 | $0 |
| 12 | | $168 | $113 | $62,107 | $73,964 | $32,090 | $38,069 | $0 | $0 |
| 8 | | $23 | $33 | $5,132 | $6,111 | $4,399 | $5,218 | $0 | $0 |
| 10 | | $23 | $51 | $16,288 | $19,397 | $4,389 | $5,206 | $0 | $0 |
| 10 | | $0 | $130 | $51,261 | $61,047 | $0 | $0 | $0 | $0 |
| 11 | | $164 | $0 | $0 | $0 | $0 | $0 | $25,000 | $25,000 |
| 10 | | $589 | $0 | $0 | $0 | $0 | $0 | $89,562 | $89,562 |
| 11 | | $0 | $0 | $0 | $0 | $0 | $0 | $0 | $0 |
| 12 | | $33 | $0 | $0 | $0 | $0 | $0 | $5,000 | $5,000 |
| 12 | | $101 | $0 | $0 | $0 | $0 | $0 | $15,362 | $15,362 |
| 12 | | $30 | $0 | $0 | $0 | $0 | $0 | $4,523 | $4,523 |
| 11 | | $82 | $0 | $0 | $0 | $0 | $0 | $12,500 | $12,500 |
| 11 | | $300 | $0 | $0 | $0 | $0 | $0 | $45,698 | $45,698 |
| 11 | | $563 | $0 | $0 | $0 | $0 | $0 | $85,600 | $85,600 |
| 11 | | $493 | $0 | $0 | $0 | $0 | $0 | $75,000 | $75,000 |
| 11 | | $822 | $0 | $0 | $0 | $0 | $0 | ******** | $125,000 |

**FIGURE 12.5** (*continued*)

**C.** The contractor should repeat the risk analysis for labor, material, and subcontractor costs. Each cost should be assigned a percentage based on the risk inherent to each of these construction costs. The risk percentage should be entered in decimal form in the appropriate spreadsheet cell. The sum of all the percentages (start-up + labor + material + subcontractor) must equal 100 percent. As each job is different, the job specific facts will dictate the percentage of risk distribution. For example, if skilled craftsworkers are scarce on one job, the contractor may input a high risk factor for labor. If the contractor did not have a signed contract for the electrical work or the subcontractors seem to be questionable on their financial ability, a high risk factor for subcontractor should be entered. If the construction is to be accomplished in a remote location where certain critical materials are scarce, the contractor may assign a high percentage of the markup to materials. The key is that the estimator or project manager should try several different scenarios to optimize the disbursement of markup on the particular project based on the risks inherent to it.

## Explanation of How VALUE.WQ1 (VALUE.WK1) Works

**THE END RESULT.** The end result of this program is found in column F of the spreadsheet or the **TOTAL** column of the program. A quantifiable work package is assigned a total dollar amount by this program. As such, the contractor and owner know the total amount due for the completed work package. This information, coupled with the estimated time period in which the work package will be accomplished (obtained from the project schedule), give the contractor and the owner anticipated cash inflow and outflow, respectively.

**STEPS IN DERIVING THE TOTAL PRICE FOR A WORK PACKAGE.** This derivation process begins with entering each schedule of values line item's bare cost for material, labor, equipment, subcontractor, and other.

The sales tax is calculated for material bare costs and labor T&I is calculated for labor bare costs. These costs and the finance costs are then added to the bare costs to calculate the **MATERIAL & OTHER, LABOR & EQUIPMENT,** and **SUBCONTRACT** total bare costs.

The financial costs are calculated for **CASH FLOW FINANCE** and **RE-TAINAGE FINANCE**. Retainage finance calculates the contractor's missed opportunity earnings for reinvesting the portion of each payment retained by the owner. Since the contractor has earned this money but cannot let these funds work to the company's advantage, this is an opportunity cost that must be documented. If the contractor pays the equipment suppliers, subcontractors, or materials suppliers before they pay the contractor, the cash flow finance cost must be documented in the schedule of values. This program assumes that the subcontractors and suppliers bill the contractor on the same date the contractor bills the owner. It also assumes that the contractor pays the subcontractors and suppliers on the same date that the bill is received or on the same date the owner pays the general, depending on which option is indicated in the general information above the spreadsheet. As such, if the contractor pays any of the bills before payment is received, the contractor must finance the expense for the number of days indicated in the **EX-PENSE OCCURRENCE TO PAYMENT** input cell. Note that whether or not the contractor actually has to borrow these funds from a lending institution, there is still a cash flow finance cost due to the opportunity cost of the contractor's funds that could have been otherwise invested. Once the program calculates the cash flow and retainage finance costs, these figures are added to the **MATERIAL & OTHER, LABOR & EQUIPMENT,** and **SUBCONTRACT** total bare costs on a pro rata basis, as mentioned previously.

Once the total bare costs have been calculated, the program next calculates the charge-out rate for each construction cost category. This is accomplished by adding the total bare cost to the distributed markup amount for each line item construction cost. The derivation of the distributed markup amount for each line item construction cost must therefore be examined. First, the total amount of markup to be distributed is calculated by taking the input contract amount and subtracting the input bare costs and the calculated taxes, labor burden, and finance costs from it. This total markup amount is then divided among four categories: start-up markup, labor markup, material markup, and subcontractor markup. The contractor will decide, based on the risk and cash flow analyses, what portion of the total markup to assign each of these four categories. The total markup multiplied by the percentage risk factor entered by the contractor will yield the total markup for each category. This number is then distributed over all of the schedule of values line item total bare costs for that particular category based on the weighted percentage of a particular line item's category cost with respect to the total category cost. Note that the start-up costs apply to all construction categories, but only in the months of the project that fall within the start-up percentage (input by the contractor in the **? % of Job =** cell of the spread sheet) with respect to the total project duration.

Once the charge-out cost for each category of work for a particular schedule of values line item is calculated, these charge-out costs are summed to provide the **TOTAL** line item schedule of values cost. If all schedule of values line item total costs are added together, the resulting figure will be the total contract amount.

## Projected Cost Estimates

To perform an internal project cost estimate, the project manager must study each line item of the project status report, sometimes called an *over-and-under* report (see Fig. 12.6). Figure 12.1 showed the project status of labor; Fig. 12.6 includes all costs on the project. The project manager must verify the correctness of any projected over-or-under items on the project status report. The projections are based on a pro rata basis and are equally distributed over the total duration of the project. If the activity has just begun, the report will often show an over budget condition. This could be false because the start-up phase is usually inefficient. The project manager will have to study and reestimate each line item that is excessively over or under budget.

## Progress Estimate

A progress estimate is performed during the pay request process. For each line item of the schedule of values, the project manager must estimate the progress of the project. This is done by measuring the quantities of materials that have been installed or stored on the job site. The number of cubic yards of concrete placed in the foundation wall or the number of tons of structural steel delivered to the job site are examples of measurable items on the schedule of values. Because the project manager must prepare the progress estimate for the pay request, the line items of the schedule of values should be in measurable terms.

## Change Order Estimate

It is common to make changes to a construction contract. Figure 12.7 illustrates the process of making a change to a stipulated-sum contract. Note that the change can originate from the owner/architect or contractor. Changes might involve additions to or deletions from the contract, changes of owner preference, changes in methods, changes in owner-provided materials, changes in time requirements, or errors and omissions in the contract documents. Regardless of the reason, a cost estimate of the work to be performed for the change often needs to be prepared. Changes on a unit price or cost-plus contract will not usually need to be estimated unless the changed work involves items that were not included in the original contract, the changes are so extensive that the contractor or owner is authorized

Timberline Construction, Inc.　　　　Job Cost Job Report　　　　8-07-89　　Page 1

1  Hall Street Warehouse　　　　Contract Amount　　152,000

| | Estimated | | | Period to date | | | Job to date | | | Pct | To date | Cost to |
|---|---|---|---|---|---|---|---|---|---|---|---|---|
| | Units | $/unit | Cost | Units | $/unit | Cost | Units | $/unit | Cost | Comp | Variance | Complete |
| **2　　SITEWORK** | | | | | | | | | | | | |
| **2.100 Site Preparation** | | | | | | | | | | | | |
| Subcontract | 3,000 | | 1,475 | 1,305 | | 2,900 | 2,002 | | 4,450 | 100 | 527- | |
| **2.150 Site Cleanup** | | | | | | | | | | | | |
| Labor | 100 | 6.00 | 600 | 44 | 6.00 | 264 | 68 | 6.00 | 408 | 25 | 258- | 450 |
| Material | 3 | 100.00 | 300 | 1 | 200.00 | 200 | 1 | 300.00 | 300 | 25 | 225- | 225 |
| TOTAL | 103 | | 900 | 45 | | 464 | 69 | | 708 | 79 | 483- | 675 |

**FIGURE 12.6**
Project status report.

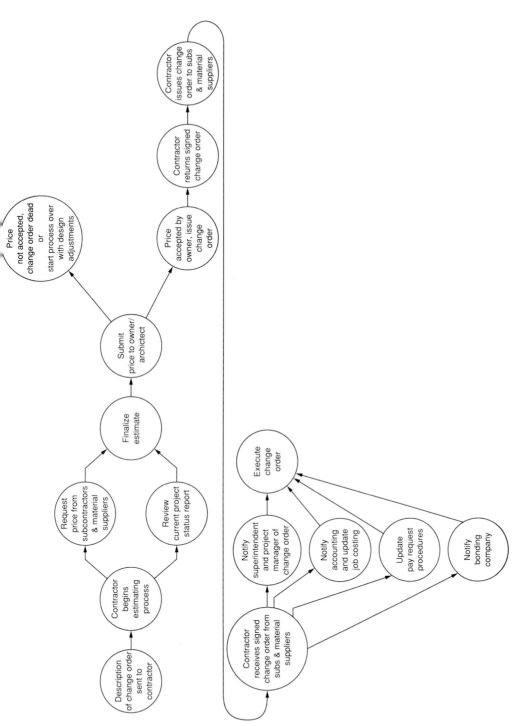

**FIGURE 12.7**
Change order process.

by the contract to request adjustments in the unit prices affected, or an extension of time will be required.

When a change is to be made, the owner or architect prepares a description of the change and presents it to the contractor for evaluation. Most contract documents require this to be done before the work is performed.

The change order estimate should be prepared in the same manner that the original estimate was prepared. The estimate should contain a material quantity takeoff, pricing of work performed with the general contractor work force, subcontract and material quotations, job overhead cost, taxes, insurance cost, bond cost, general overhead cost, and profit.

The estimator must determine if any of the proposed changes will affect any previously placed work. If previous work is affected, the cost impact should be included in the estimate. For example, if the size of the reinforcing needs to be increased and the footing has already been placed, the cost of removing the old footing will need to be included in the estimate. Material already ordered by the general contractor or subcontractors can be affected. For example, the shop drawings may have been completed, material may have been fabricated, or material may have been delivered that is to be changed. The cost of rework and shipping and handling will need to be included in the estimate.

The project status report should be reviewed to determine the actual cost of similar work being estimated. If there is similar work, the actual unit cost should be studied and used when pricing the change order.

For work that is to be deducted from the contract, the estimator should carefully evaluate the cost to make the change. It is obvious that the material, labor, and equipment cost of installation will not be a cost to the contractor, but there will be a cost of overhead to make sure that all parties are informed. There could be some cost for restocking material, renegotiating subcontracts, or material purchase orders for the project. The estimator must study all of the ramifications of a deductive change order before the amount of the deduction is forwarded to the owner or architect.

Contracts often limit the general contractor's markup for changes, such as a 15-percent markup for overhead and profit on all work performed by the general contractor and a 10-percent markup on subcontracts. For this reason, the estimator must list all possible costs in the estimate, probably with more precision than in the original estimate.

## STUDENT EXERCISES

**12.1.** Using file VALUE.WQ1, develop a schedule of values for the project that you have been estimating during the course.

**12.2.** Expand file PS.WQ1 to include material cost, equipment cost, and subcontract cost. For each of the categories include the estimated cost, cost to date, revisions to the estimate, and projected over- or underestimate.

# APPENDIX
# A

# THE AMERICAN
# INSTITUTE
# OF ARCHITECTS
# DOCUMENT A201

T H E      A M E R I C A N      I N S T I T U T E      O F      A R C H I T E C T S

Copies of the current edition of this AIA document may be purchased from The American Institute of Architects or its local distributors. The text of this document is not "model language" and is not intended for use in other documents without permission of the AIA.

*AIA Document A201*

# General Conditions of the Contract for Construction

*THIS DOCUMENT HAS IMPORTANT LEGAL CONSEQUENCES; CONSULTATION WITH AN ATTORNEY IS ENCOURAGED WITH RESPECT TO ITS MODIFICATION*

## 1987 EDITION

### TABLE OF ARTICLES

1. GENERAL PROVISIONS

2. OWNER

3. CONTRACTOR

4. ADMINISTRATION OF THE CONTRACT

5. SUBCONTRACTORS

6. CONSTRUCTION BY OWNER OR BY SEPARATE CONTRACTORS

7. CHANGES IN THE WORK

8. TIME

9. PAYMENTS AND COMPLETION

10. PROTECTION OF PERSONS AND PROPERTY

11. INSURANCE AND BONDS

12. UNCOVERING AND CORRECTION OF WORK

13. MISCELLANEOUS PROVISIONS

14. TERMINATION OR SUSPENSION OF THE CONTRACT

This document has been approved and endorsed by the Associated General Contractors of America.

 CAUTION: You should use an original AIA document which has this caution printed in red. An original assures that changes will not be obscured as may occur when documents are reproduced.

## INDEX

**Acceptance of Nonconforming Work** . . . . . . . 9.6.6, 9.9.3, **12.3**
Acceptance of Work . . . . . . . . . 9.6.6, 9.8.2, 9.9.3, 9.10.1, 9.10.3
**Access to Work** . . . . . . . . . . . . . . . . . . . . **3.16**, 6.2.1, 12.1
Accident Prevention . . . . . . . . . . . . . . . . . . . . . . . . 4.2.3, 10
Acts and Omissions . . . . 3.2.1, 3.2.2, 3.3.2, 3.12.8, 3.18, 4.2.3, 4.3.2,
4.3.9, 8.3.1, 10.1.4, 10.2.5, 13.4.2, 13.7, 14.1
Addenda . . . . . . . . . . . . . . . . . . . . . . . . . . . . 1.1.1, 3.11
Additional Cost, Claims for . . . . . . 4.3.6, 4.3.7, 4.3.9, 6.1.1, 10.3
Additional Inspections and Testing . . . . 4.2.6, 9.8.2, 12.2.1, 13.5
Additional Time, Claims for . . . . . . . . 4.3.6, 4.3.8, 4.3.9, 8.3.2
**ADMINISTRATION OF THE CONTRACT** . . . . 3.3.3, **4**, 9.4, 9.5
Advertisement or Invitation to Bid . . . . . . . . . . . . . . . . 1.1.1
Aesthetic Effect . . . . . . . . . . . . . . . . . . . . . . 4.2.13, 4.5.1
**Allowances** . . . . . . . . . . . . . . . . . . . . . . . . . . . . **3.8**
All-risk Insurance . . . . . . . . . . . . . . . . . . . . . . . . . 11.3.1.1
**Applications for Payment** . . . 4.2.5, 7.3.7, 9.2, **9.3**, 9.4, 9.5.1, 9.6.3,
9.8.3, 9.10.1, 9.10.3, 9.10.4, 11.1.3, 14.2.4
Approvals . . . . . 2.4, 3.3.3, 3.5, 3.10.2, 3.12.4 through 3.12.8, 3.18.3,
4.2.7, 9.3.2, 11.3.1.4, 13.4.2, 13.5
**Arbitration** . . . . . . . . . . . . 4.1.4, 4.3.2, 4.3.4, 4.4.4, **4.5**,
8.3.1, 10.1.2, 11.3.9, 11.3.10
**Architect** . . . . . . . . . . . . . . . . . . . . . . . . . . . . **4.1**
Architect, Definition of . . . . . . . . . . . . . . . . . . . . . . . 4.1.1
Architect, Extent of Authority . . . . 2.4, 3.12.6, 4.2, 4.3.2, 4.3.6,
4.4, 5.2, 6.3, 7.1.2, 7.2.1, 7.3.6, 7.4, 9.2, 9.3.1,
9.4, 9.5, 9.6.3, 9.8.2, 9.8.3, 9.10.3, 12.1, 12.2.1,
13.5.1, 13.5.2, 14.2.2, 14.2.4
Architect, Limitations of Authority and Responsibility 3.3.3, 3.12.8,
3.12.11, 4.1.2, 4.2.1, 4.2.2, 4.2.3, 4.2.6, 4.2.7, 4.2.10, 4.2.12,
4.2.13, 4.3.2, 5.2.1, 7.4, 9.4.2, 9.6.4, 9.6.6
Architect's Additional Services and Expenses . . . . . . 2.4, 9.8.2,
11.3.1.1, 12.2.1, 12.2.4, 13.5.2, 13.5.3, 14.2.4
**Architect's Administration of the Contract** . . . . . **4.2**, 4.3.6,
4.3.7, 4.4, 9.4, 9.5
Architect's Approvals 2.4, 3.5.1, 3.10.2, 3.12.6, 3.12.8, 3.18.3, 4.2.7
Architect's Authority to Reject Work . . . 3.5.1, 4.2.6, 12.1.2, 12.2.1
Architect's Copyright . . . . . . . . . . . . . . . . . . . . . . . 1.3
Architect's Decisions . . . . . . . . 4.2.6, 4.2.7, 4.2.11, 4.2.12, 4.2.13,
4.3.2, 4.3.6, 4.4.1, 4.4.4, 4.5, 6.3, 7.3.6, 7.3.8, 8.1.3,
9.2, 9.4, 9.5.1, 9.8.2, 9.9.1, 10.1.2, 13.5.2, 14.2.2, 14.2.4
9.9.2, 10.1.2, 13.5.2, 14.2.4
Architect's Inspections . . . . . . 4.2.2, 4.2.9, 4.3.6, 9.4.2, 9.8.2,
9.9.2, 13.5
Architect's Instructions . . . 4.2.6, 4.2.7, 4.2.8, 7.4.1, 12.1, 13.5.2
Architect's Interpretations . . . . . . . . . . . . 4.2.11, 4.2.12, 4.3.7
Architect's On-Site Observations . . . . . 4.2.2, 4.2.5, 4.3.6, 9.4.2,
9.5.1, 9.10.1, 13.5
Architect's Project Representative . . . . . . . . . . . . . . . 4.2.10
Architect's Relationship with Contractor . . . . 1.1.2, 3.2.1, 3.2.2,
3.3.3, 3.5.1, 3.7.3, 3.11, 3.12.8, 3.12.11, 3.16, 3.18, 4.2.3, 4.2.4,
4.2.6, 4.2.12, 5.2, 6.2.2, 7.3.4, 9.8.2, 11.3.7, 12.1, 13.5
Architect's Relationship with Subcontractors . . . . . 1.1.2, 4.2.3, 4.2.4,
4.2.6, 9.6.3, 9.6.4, 11.3.7
Architect's Representations . . . . . . . . 9.4.2, 9.5.1, 9.10.1
Architect's Site Visits . . . . . . 4.2.2, 4.2.5, 4.2.9, 4.3.6, 9.4.2, 9.5.1,
9.8.2, 9.9.2, 9.10.1, 13.5
Asbestos . . . . . . . . . . . . . . . . . . . . . . . . . . . . . . 10.1
Attorneys' Fees . . . . . . . . . . . . . . . 3.18.1, 9.10.2, 10.1.4
Award of Separate Contracts . . . . . . . . . . . . . . . . . . . 6.1.1
**Award of Subcontracts and Other Contracts for**
**Portions of the Work** . . . . . . . . . . . . . . . . . . . . . **5.2**
**Basic Definitions** . . . . . . . . . . . . . . . . . . . . . . . . **1.1**
Bidding Requirements . . . . . . . . . . . . 1.1.1, 1.1.7, 5.2.1, 11.4.1
**Boiler and Machinery Insurance** . . . . . . . . . . . . . . . **11.3.2**
Bonds, Lien . . . . . . . . . . . . . . . . . . . . . . . . . . . . 9.10.2
Bonds, Performance and Payment . . . . 7.3.6.4, 9.10.3, 11.3.9, 11.4

**Building Permit** . . . . . . . . . . . . . . . . . . . . . . . . . . 3.7.1
**Capitalization** . . . . . . . . . . . . . . . . . . . . . . . . . . **1.4**
Certificate of Substantial Completion . . . . . . . . . . . . . . 9.8.2
**Certificates for Payment** . . . 4.2.5, 4.2.9, 9.3.3, **9.4**, 9.5, 9.6.1,
9.6.6, 9.7.1, 9.8.3, 9.10.1, 9.10.3, 13.7, 14.1.1.3, 14.2.4
Certificates of Inspection, Testing or Approval . . . 3.12.11, 13.5.4
Certificates of Insurance . . . . . . . . . . . 9.3.2, 9.10.2, 11.1.3
**Change Orders** . . . . . 1.1.1, 2.4.1, 3.8.2.4, 3.11, 4.2.8, 4.3.3, 5.2.3,
7.1, **7.2**, 7.3.2, 8.3.1, 9.3.1.1, 9.10.3, 11.3.1.2,
11.3.4, 11.3.9, 12.1.2
Change Orders, Definition of . . . . . . . . . . . . . . . . . . . 7.2.1
**Changes** . . . . . . . . . . . . . . . . . . . . . . . . . . . . . **7.1**
**CHANGES IN THE WORK** . . . . . 3.11, 4.2.8, **7**, 8.3.1, 9.3.1.1, 10.1.3
Claim, Definition of . . . . . . . . . . . . . . . . . . . . . . . . 4.3.1
**Claims and Disputes** . . . . . . . . . . . . . . . . **4.3**, 4.4, 4.5, 6.2.5, 8.3.2,
9.3.1.2, 9.3.3, 9.10.4, 10.1.4
**Claims and Timely Assertion of Claims** . . . . . . . . . . . . . **4.5.6**
**Claims for Additional Cost** . . . . . . . . . 4.3.6, **4.3.7**, 4.3.9, 6.1.1, 10.3
**Claims for Additional Time** . . . . . . . . . 4.3.6, **4.3.8**, 4.3.9, 8.3.2
**Claims for Concealed or Unknown Conditions** . . . . . . . . . **4.3.6**
Claims for Damages . . . . 3.18, 4.3.9, 6.1.1, 6.2.5, 8.3.2, 9.5.1.2, 10.1.4
Claims Subject to Arbitration . . . . . . . . . 4.3.2, 4.4.4, 4.5.1
**Cleaning Up** . . . . . . . . . . . . . . . . . . . . . . . . **3.15**, 6.3
**Commencement of Statutory Limitation Period** . . . . . . . . . **13.7**
Commencement of the Work, Conditions Relating to . . . . . 2.1.2,
2.2.1, 3.2.1, 3.2.2, 3.7.1, 3.10.1, 3.12.6, 4.3.7, 5.2.1,
6.2.2, 8.1.2, 8.2.2, 9.2, 11.1.3, 11.3.6, 11.4.1
Commencement of the Work, Definition of . . . . . . . . . . . . 8.1.2
Communications Facilitating Contract
Administration . . . . . . . . . . . . . . . 3.9.1, 4.2.4, 5.2.1
Completion, Conditions Relating to . . . 3.11, 3.15, 4.2.2, 4.2.9,
4.3.2, 9.4.2, 9.8, 9.9.1, 9.10, 11.3.5, 12.2.2, 13.7.1
**COMPLETION, PAYMENTS AND** . . . . . . . . . . . . . . . . . . . **9**
Completion, Substantial . . . . 4.2.9, 4.3.5.2, 8.1.1, 8.1.3, 8.2.3,
9.8, 9.9.1, 12.2.2, 13.7
Compliance with Laws . . . . . 1.3, 3.6, 3.7, 3.13, 4.1.1, 10.2.2, 11.1,
11.3, 13.1, 13.5.1, 13.5.2, 13.6, 14.1.1, 14.2.1.3
Concealed or Unknown Conditions . . . . . . . . . . . . . . . . 4.3.6
Conditions of the Contract . . . . . . . . . . . . . 1.1.1, 1.1.7, 6.1.1
Consent, Written . . . . . . . . . . . . . 1.3.1, 3.12.8, 3.14.2, 4.1.2,
4.3.4, 4.5.5, 9.3.2, 9.8.2, 9.9.1, 9.10.2, 9.10.3, 10.1.2, 10.1.3,
11.3.1, 11.3.1.4, 11.3.11, 13.2, 13.4.2
**CONSTRUCTION BY OWNER OR BY SEPARATE**
**CONTRACTORS** . . . . . . . . . . . . . . . . . . . . . . 1.1.4, **6**
Construction Change Directive, Definition of . . . . . . . . . . 7.3.1
**Construction Change Directives** . . . . . 1.1.1, 4.2.8, 7.1, **7.3**, 9.3.1.1
Construction Schedules, Contractor's . . . . . . . . . . 3.10, 6.1.3
**Contingent Assignment of Subcontracts** . . . . . . . . . . . . **5.4**
**Continuing Contract Performance** . . . . . . . . . . . . . . . . **4.3.4**
Contract, Definition of . . . . . . . . . . . . . . . . . . . . . . . 1.1.2
**CONTRACT, TERMINATION OR**
**SUSPENSION OF THE** . . . . . . . . . . . . 4.3.7, 5.4.1.1, **14**
Contract Administration . . . . . . . . . . . 3.3.3, 4, 9.4, 9.5
Contract Award and Execution, Conditions Relating to . . . . 3.7.1,
3.10, 5.2, 9.2, 11.1.3, 11.3.6, 11.4.1
**Contract Documents, The** . . . . . . . . . . . . . . . . . . **1.1**, 1.2.7
Contract Documents, Copies Furnished and Use of . . . . 1.3, 2.2.5, 5.3
Contract Documents, Definition of . . . . . . . . . . . . . . . . 1.1.1
Contract Performance During Arbitration . . . . . . . . 4.3.4, 4.5.3
**Contract Sum** . . . . . . . . . . . . . 3.8, 4.3.6, 4.3.7, 4.4.4, 5.2.3,
6.1.3, 7.2, 7.3, **9.1**, 9.7, 11.3.1, 12.2.4, 12.3, 14.2.4
**Contract Sum**, Definition of . . . . . . . . . . . . . . . . . . . **9.1**
Contract Time . . . . . . . . . . . . . 4.3.6, 4.3.8, 4.4.4, 7.2.1.3, 7.3,
8.2.1, 8.3.1, 9.7, 12.1.1
Contract Time, **Definition** of . . . . . . . . . . . . . . . . . . **8.1.1**

**CONTRACTOR** . . . . . . . . . . . . . . . . . . . . . . . . . . . . . . . **3**
Contractor, **Definition** of . . . . . . . . . . . . . . . . . . **3.1**, 6.1.2
Contractor's Bid . . . . . . . . . . . . . . . . . . . . . . . . . . . . . . 1.1.1
**Contractor's Construction Schedules** . . . . . . . . . . **3.10**, 6.1.3
Contractor's Employees . . . . . . . . . 3.3.2, 3.4.2, 3.8.1, 3.9, 3.18, 4.2.3,
    4.2.6, 8.1.2, 10.2, 10.3, 11.1.1, 14.2.1.1
**Contractor's Liability Insurance** . . . . . . . . . . . . . . . . . **11.1**
Contractor's Relationship with Separate Contractors
   and Owner's Forces . . . . . . 2.2.6, 3.12.5, 3.14.2, 4.2.4.6, 12.2.5
Contractor's Relationship with Subcontractors . . . . 1.2.4, 3.3.2,
   3.18.1, 3.18.2, 5.2, 5.3, 5.4, 9.6.2, 11.3.7, 11.3.8, 14.2.1.2
Contractor's Relationship with the Architect . . . . 1.1.2, 3.2.1, 3.2.2,
   3.3.3, 3.5.1, 3.7.3, 3.11, 3.12.8, 3.16, 3.18, 4.2.3, 4.2.4, 4.2.6
   4.2.12, 5.2, 6.2.2, 7.3.4, 9.8.2, 11.3.7, 12.1, 13.5
Contractor's Representations . . . 1.2.2, 3.5.1, 3.12.7, 6.2.2, 8.2.1, 9.3.3
Contractor's Responsibility for Those
   Performing the Work . . . . . . . . . . 3.3.2, 3.18, 4.2.3, 10
Contractor's Review of Contract Documents . . . . . . 1.2.2, 3.2, 3.7.3
Contractor's Right to Stop the Work . . . . . . . . . . . . . . . . . 9.7
Contractor's Right to Terminate the Contract . . . . . . . . . . . 14.1
Contractor's Submittals . . . . . . 3.10, 3.11, 3.12, 4.2.7, 5.2.1, 5.2.3,
   7.3.6, 9.2, 9.3.1, 9.8.2, 9.9.1, 9.10.2,
   9.10.3, 10.1.2, 11.4.2, 11.4.3
Contractor's Superintendent . . . . . . . . . . . . . . . . 3.9, 10.2.6
Contractor's Supervision and Construction Procedures . . . 1.2.4,
   3.3, 3.4, 4.2.3, 8.2.2, 8.2.3, 10
Contractual Liability Insurance . . . . . . . . . . . . 11.1.1.7, 11.2.1
Coordination and Correlation . . . . . . . . . 1.2.2, 1.2.4, 3.3.1,
   3.10, 3.12.7, 6.1.3, 6.2.1
Copies Furnished of Drawings and Specifications . . . 1.3, 2.2.5, 3.11
Correction of Work . . . . . . . . . . . . . . . 2.3, 2.4, 4.2.1, 9.8.2,
   9.9.1, 12.1.2, 12.2, 13.7.1.3
Cost, Definition of . . . . . . . . . . . . . . . . . . . . . 7.3.6, 14.3.5
Costs . . . . . 2.4, 3.2.1, 3.7.4, 3.8.2, 3.15.2, 4.3.6, 4.3.7, 4.3.8.1, 5.2.3,
   6.1.1, 6.2.3, 6.3, 7.3.3.3, 7.3.6, 7.3.7, 9.7, 9.8.2, 9.10.2, 11.3.1.2,
   11.3.1.3, 11.3.4, 11.3.9, 12.1, 12.2.1, 12.2.4, 12.2.5, 13.5, 14
Cutting and Patching . . . . . . . . . . . . . . . . . . **3.14**, 6.2.6
Damage to Construction of Owner or Separate Contractors . . 3.14.2,
   6.2.4, 9.5.1.5, 10.2.1.2, 10.2.5, 10.3, 11.1, 11.3, 12.2.5
Damage to the Work . . . . . . . . 3.14.2, 9.9.1, 10.2.1.2, 10.2.5, 10.3, 11.3
Damages, Claims for . . . . 3.18, 4.3.9, 6.1.1, 6.2.5, 8.3.2, 9.5.1, 9.6.1.1
Damages for Delay . . . . . . . . . . . . . 6.1.1, 8.3.3, 9.5.1.6, 9.7
Date of Commencement of the Work, Definition of . . . . . . . 8.1.2
Date of Substantial Completion, Definition of . . . . . . . . . . 8.1.3
Day, Definition of . . . . . . . . . . . . . . . . . . . . . . . . . . 8.1.4
Decisions of the Architect . . . . . . 4.2.6, 4.2.7, 4.2.11, 4.2.12, 4.2.13,
   4.3.2, 4.3.6, 4.4.1, 4.4.4, 4.5, 6.3, 7.3.6, 7.3.8, 8.1.3, 8.3.1, 9.2,
   9.4, 9.5.1, 9.8.2, 9.9.1, 10.1.2, 13.5.2, 14.2.2, 14.2.4
**Decisions to Withhold Certification** . . . . . **9.5**, 9.7, 14.1.1.3
Defective or Nonconforming Work, Acceptance,
   Rejection and Correction of . . . . . 2.3, 2.4, 3.5.1, 4.2.1,
   4.2.6, 4.3.5, 9.5.2, 9.8.2, 9.9.1, 10.2.5, 12, 13.7.1.3
Defective Work, Definition of . . . . . . . . . . . . . . . . . . . 3.5.1
Definitions . . . . . . . . . . . 1.1, 2.1.1, 3.1, 3.5.1, 3.12.1, 3.12.2, 3.12.3, 4.1.1,
   4.3.1, 5.1, 6.1.2, 7.2.1, 7.3.1, 7.3.6, 8.1, 9.1, 9.8.1
**Delays and Extensions of Time** . . . . . . . 4.3.1, 4.3.8.1, 4.3.8.2,
   6.1.1, 6.2.3, 7.2.1, 7.3.1, 7.3.4, 7.3.5, 7.3.8,
   7.3.9, 8.1.1, **8.3**, 10.3.1, 14.1.1.4
Disputes . . . . . . . . 4.1.4, 4.3, 4.4, 4.5, 6.2.5, 6.3, 7.3.8, 9.3.1.2
Documents and Samples at the Site . . . . . . . . . . . . . . . . 3.11
Drawings, Definition of . . . . . . . . . . . . . . . . . . . . . . . 1.1.5
Drawings and Specifications, Use and Ownership of . . . 1.1.1, 1.3,
   2.2.5, 3.11, 5.3
Duty to Review Contract Documents and Field Conditions . . . 3.2
Effective Date of Insurance . . . . . . . . . . . . . . . 8.2.2, 11.1.2

Emergencies . . . . . . . . . . . . . . . . . . . . . . . 4.3.7, **10.3**
Employees, Contractor's . . . . . . 3.3.2, 3.4.2, 3.8.1, 3.9, 3.18.1,
   3.18.2, 4.2.3, 4.2.6, 8.1.2, 10.2, 10.3, 11.1.1, 14.2.1.1
Equipment, Labor, Materials and . . . . . . 1.1.3, 1.1.6, 3.4, 3.5.1,
   3.8.2, 3.12.3, 3.12.7, 3.12.11, 3.13, 3.15.1, 4.2.7,
   6.2.1, 7.3.6, 9.3.2, 9.3.3, 11.3, 12.2.4, 14
Execution and Progress of the Work . . . . . . 1.1.3, 1.2.3, 3.2, 3.4.1,
   3.5.1, 4.2.2, 4.2.3, 4.3.4, 4.3.8, 6.2.2, 7.1.3,
   7.3.9, 8.2, 8.3, 9.5, 9.9.1, 10.2, 14.2, 14.3
**Execution, Correlation and Intent** of the
   Contract Documents . . . . . . . . . . . . . . . . . **1.2**, 3.7.1
Extensions of Time . . . . . . . . . . . 4.3.1, 4.3.8, 7.2.1.3, 8.3, 10.3.1
Failure of Payment by Contractor . . . . . . . . . . . . 9.5.1.3, 14.2.1.2
Failure of Payment by Owner . . . . . . . . . . 4.3.7, 9.7, 14.1.3
Faulty Work (See Defective or Nonconforming Work)
**Final Completion and Final Payment** . . . . . 4.2.1, 4.2.9, 4.3.2,
   4.3.5, **9.10**, 11.1.2, 11.1.3, 11.3.5, 12.3.1, 13.7
Financial Arrangements, Owner's . . . . . . . . . . . . . . . . . 2.2.1
Fire and Extended Coverage Insurance . . . . . . . . . . . . . . 11.3
**GENERAL PROVISIONS** . . . . . . . . . . . . . . . . . . . . . **1**
**Governing Law** . . . . . . . . . . . . . . . . . . . . . . . . . . **13.1**
Guarantees (See Warranty and Warranties)
Hazardous Materials . . . . . . . . . . . . . . . . . . . 10.1, 10.2.4
Identification of Contract Documents . . . . . . . . . . . . . . . 1.2.1
Identification of Subcontractors and Suppliers . . . . . . . . . . 5.2.1
**Indemnification** . . . . . . . . . 3.17, **3.18**, 9.10.2, 10.1.4, 11.3.1.2, 11.3.7
**Information and Services Required of the Owner** . . . 2.1.2, **2.2**,
   4.3.4, 6.1.3, 6.1.4, 6.2.6, 9.3.2, 9.6.1, 9.6.4, 9.8.3, 9.9.2,
   9.10.3, 10.1.4, 11.2, 11.3, 13.5.1, 13.5.2
**Injury or Damage to Person or Property** . . . . . . . . . . **4.3.9**
Inspections . . . . . . . . . . . . . 3.3.3, 3.3.4, 3.7.1, 4.2.2,
   4.2.6, 4.2.9, 4.3.6, 9.4.2, 9.8.2, 9.9.2, 9.10.1, 13.5
Instructions to Bidders . . . . . . . . . . . . . . . . . . . . . . . 1.1.1
Instructions to the Contractor . . . . . 3.8.1, 4.2.8, 5.2.1, 7, 12.1, 13.5.2
**Insurance** . . . . . . . . . 3.18.1, 6.1.1, 7.3.6.4, 9.3.2, 9.8.2, 9.9.1, 9.10.2, 11
**Insurance, Boiler and Machinery** . . . . . . . . . . . . . . . **11.3.2**
**Insurance, Contractor's Liability** . . . . . . . . . . . . . . . . **11.1**
Insurance, Effective Date of . . . . . . . . . . . . . . . . 8.2.2, 11.1.2
**Insurance, Loss of Use** . . . . . . . . . . . . . . . . . . . . . . 11.3.3
**Insurance, Owner's Liability** . . . . . . . . . . . . . . . . . . **11.2**
**Insurance, Property** . . . . . . . . . . . . . . . . . . . 10.2.5, **11.3**
Insurance, Stored Materials . . . . . . . . . . . . . . 9.3.2, 11.3.1.4
**INSURANCE AND BONDS** . . . . . . . . . . . . . . . . . . . . **11**
Insurance Companies, Consent to Partial Occupancy . 9.9.1, 11.3.11
Insurance Companies, Settlement with . . . . . . . . . . . . . . 11.3.10
Intent of the Contract Documents . . . . . . . . . . 1.2.3, 3.12.4,
   4.2.6, 4.2.7, 4.2.12, 4.2.13, 7.4
**Interest** . . . . . . . . . . . . . . . . . . . . . . . . . . . . . . . **13.6**
**Interpretation** . . . . . . . . . 1.2.5, 1.4, **1.5**, 4.1.1, 4.3.1, 5.1, 6.1.2, 8.1.4
Interpretations, Written . . . . . . . . . . . 4.2.11, 4.2.12, 4.3.7
Joinder and Consolidation of Claims Required . . . . . . . . . . **4.5.6**
**Judgment on Final Award** . . . . . . . . . . . 4.5.1, 4.5.4.1, **4.5.7**
**Labor and Materials**, Equipment . . . . . 1.1.3, 1.1.6, **3.4**, 3.5.1, 3.8.2,
   3.12.2, 3.12.3, 3.12.7, 3.12.11, 3.13, 3.15.1,
   4.2.7, 6.2.1, 7.3.6, 9.3.2, 9.3.3, 12.2.4, 14
Labor Disputes . . . . . . . . . . . . . . . . . . . . . . . . . . . 8.3.1
Laws and Regulations . . . . . . . 1.3, 3.6, 3.7, 3.13, 4.1.1, 4.5.5, 4.5.7,
   9.9.1, 10.2.2, 11.1, 11.3, 13.1, 13.4, 13.5.1, 13.5.2, 13.6
Liens . . . . . . . . . 2.1.2, 4.3.2, 4.3.5.1, 8.2.2, 9.3.3, 9.10.2
**Limitation on Consolidation or Joinder** . . . . . . . . . . **4.5.5**
Limitations, Statutes of . . . . . . . . . . 4.5.4.2, 12.2.6, 13.7
Limitations of Authority . . . . . . . . . . 3.3.1, 4.1.2, 4.2.1,
   4.2.3, 4.2.7, 4.2.10, 5.2.2, 5.2.4, 7.4, 11.3.10

Limitations of Liability . . . . . . 2.3, 3.2.1, 3.5.1, 3.7.3, 3.12.8, 3.12.11,
3.17, 3.18, 4.2.6, 4.2.7, 4.2.12, 6.2.2, 9.4.2, 9.6.4, 9.10.4,
10.1.4, 10.2.5, 11.1.2, 11.2.1, 11.3.7, 13.4.2, 13.5.2

Limitations of Time, General . . . . . . 2.2.1, 2.2.4, 3.2.1, 3.7.3,
3.8.2, 3.10, 3.12.5, 3.15.1, 4.2.1, 4.2.7, 4.2.11, 4.3.2,
4.3.3, 4.3.4, 4.3.6, 4.3.9, 4.5.4.2, 5.2.1, 5.2.3, 6.2.4, 7.3.4, 7.4,
8.2, 9.5, 9.6.2, 9.8, 9.9, 9.10, 11.1.3, 11.3.1, 11.3.2, 11.3.5,
11.3.6, 12.2.1, 12.2.2, 13.5, 13.7

Limitations of Time, Specific . . . . . . 2.1.2, 2.2.1, 2.4, 3.10, 3.11,
3.15.1, 4.2.1, 4.2.11, 4.3, 4.4, 4.5, 5.3, 5.4, 7.3.5, 7.3.9, 8.2,
9.2, 9.3.1, 9.3.3, 9.4.1, 9.6.1, 9.7, 9.8.2, 9.10.2, 11.1.3, 11.3.6,
11.3.10, 11.3.11, 12.2.2, 12.2.4, 12.2.6, 13.7, 14

**Loss of Use Insurance** . . . . . . . . . . . . . . . . . . . . . . . . . . . . . . **11.3.3**
Material Suppliers . . . . . . 1.3.1, 3.12.1, 4.2.4, 4.2.6, 5.2.1,
9.3.1, 9.3.1.2, 9.3.3, 9.4.2, 9.6.5, 9.10.4
Materials, Hazardous . . . . . . . . . . . . . . . . . . . . . . . 10.1, 10.2.4
Materials, Labor, Equipment and . . . . . . 1.1.3, 1.1.6, 3.4, 3.5.1, 3.8.2,
3.12.2, 3.12.3, 3.12.7, 3.12.11, 3.13, 3.15.1, 4.2.7, 6.2.1,
7.3.6, 9.3.2, 9.3.3, 12.2.4, 14
Means, Methods, Techniques, Sequences and
Procedures of Construction . . . . . . 3.3.1, 4.2.3, 4.2.7, 9.4.2
**Minor Changes in the Work** . . . . . . 1.1.1, 4.2.8, 4.3.7, 7.1, **7.4**
**MISCELLANEOUS PROVISIONS** . . . . . . . . . . . . . . . . . . . . . . **13**
Modifications, Definition of . . . . . . . . . . . . . . . . . . . . . . . . . 1.1.1
Modifications to the Contract . . . . . . 1.1.1, 1.1.2, 3.7.3, 3.11,
4.1.2, 4.2.1, 5.2.3, 7, 8.3.1, 9.7
**Mutual Responsibility** . . . . . . . . . . . . . . . . . . . . . . . . . . . . **8.2**
**Nonconforming Work, Acceptance of** . . . . . . . . . . . . . . . . . . **12.3**
Nonconforming Work, Rejection and Correction of . . . . . . 2.3.1,
4.3.5, 9.5.2, 9.8.2, 12, 13.7.1.3
Notice . . . . . . 2.3, 2.4, 3.2.1, 3.2.2, 3.7.3, 3.7.4, 3.9, 3.12.8,
3.12.9, 3.17, 4.3, 4.4.4, 4.5, 5.2.1, 5.3, 5.4.1.1, 8.2.2, 9.4.1,
9.5.1, 9.6.1, 9.7, 9.10, 10.1.2, 10.2.6, 11.1.3, 11.3, 12.2.2,
12.2.4, 13.3, 13.5.1, 13.5.2, 14
**Notice, Written** . . . . . . 2.3, 2.4, 3.9, 3.12.8, 3.12.9, 4.3,
4.4.4, 4.5, 5.2.1, 5.3, 5.4.1.1, 8.2.2, 9.4.1, 9.5.1, 9.7, 9.10,
10.1.2, 10.2.6, 11.1.3, 11.3, 12.2.2, 12.2.4, **13.3**, 13.5.2, 14
Notice of Testing and Inspections . . . . . . . . . . . . 13.5.1, 13.5.2
Notice to Proceed . . . . . . . . . . . . . . . . . . . . . . . . . . . . . . . 8.2.2
**Notices, Permits, Fees and** . . . . . . 2.2.3, **3.7**, 3.13, 7.3.6.4, 10.2.2
Observations, Architect's On-Site . . . . . . . . . . . 4.2.2, 4.2.5,
4.3.6, 9.4.2, 9.5.1, 9.10.1
Observations, Contractor's . . . . . . . . . . . . . . . . . . . . . . 1.2.2, 3.2.2
Occupancy . . . . . . . . . . . . . . . . 9.6.6, 9.8, 9.9, 11.3.11
On-Site Inspections by the Architect . . . . . . 4.2.2, 4.2.9, 4.3.6,
4.2.7, 9.8.2, 9.9.2, 9.10.1
On-Site Observations by the Architect . . . . . . 4.2.2, 4.2.5, 4.3.6,
9.4.2, 9.5.1, 9.10.1, 13.5
Orders, Written . . . . . . 2.3, 3.9, 4.3.7, 7, 8.2.2, 11.3.9, 12.1,
12.2, 13.5.2, 14.3.1

**OWNER** . . . . . . . . . . . . . . . . . . . . . . . . . . . . . . . . . . . . . . . . . . **2**
Owner, **Definition** of . . . . . . . . . . . . . . . . . . . . . . . . . . . . . . . **2.1**
**Owner, Information and Services Required of the** . . . . . . 2.1.2,
**2.2**, 4.3.4, 6, 9, 10.1.4, 11.2, 11.3, 13.5.1, 14.1.1.5, 14.1.3
Owner's Authority . . . . . . 3.8.1, 4.1.3, 4.2.9, 5.2.1, 5.2.4, 5.4.1,
7.3.1, 8.2.2, 9.3.1, 9.3.2, 11.4.1, 12.2.4, 13.5.2, 14.2, 14.3.1
Owner's Financial Capability . . . . . . . . . . 2.2.1, 14.1.1.5
**Owner's Liability Insurance** . . . . . . . . . . . . . . . . . . . . . . . . **11.2**
Owner's Loss of Use Insurance . . . . . . . . . . . . . . . . . . . . . . 11.3.3
Owner's Relationship with Subcontractors . . . . . . . . . . . . . 1.1.2,
5.2.1, 5.4.1, 9.6.4
Owner's Right to Carry Out the Work . . . . . . 2.4, 12.2.4, 14.2.2.2
**Owner's Right to Clean Up** . . . . . . . . . . . . . . . . . . . . . . . . . **6.3**

**Owner's Right to Perform Construction and to
Award Separate Contracts** . . . . . . . . . . . . . . . . . . . . . . . **6.1**
**Owner's Right to Stop the Work** . . . . . . . . . . . . . . . . . . **2.3**, 4.3.7
Owner's Right to Suspend the Work . . . . . . . . . . . . . . . . . . . 14.3
Owner's Right to Terminate the Contract . . . . . . . . . . . . . . . 14.2
**Ownership and Use of Architect's Drawings, Specifications
and Other Documents** . . . . . . 1.1.1, **1.3**, 2.2.5, 5.3
**Partial Occupancy or Use** . . . . . . . . . . . . . 9.6.6, **9.9**, 11.3.11
**Patching, Cutting and** . . . . . . . . . . . . . . . . . . . . . . . **3.14**, 6.2.6
**Patents, Royalties and** . . . . . . . . . . . . . . . . . . . . . . . . . . . . **3.17**
**Payment, Applications for** . . . . . . 4.2.5, 9.2, **9.3**, 9.4,
9.5.1, 9.8.3, 9.10.1, 9.10.3, 14.2.4
**Payment, Certificates for** . . . . . . 4.2.5, 4.2.9, 9.3.3, **9.4**, 9.5,
9.6.1, 9.6.6, 9.7.1, 9.8.3, 9.10.1, 9.10.3, 13.7, 14.1.1.3, 14.2.4
**Payment, Failure of** . . . . . . . . . . . . . . . . . . . . . . . . . . . . 9.5.1.3,
**9.7**, 9.10.2, 14.1.1.3, 14.2.1.2
Payment, Final . . . . . . 4.2.1, 4.2.9, 4.3.2, 4.3.5, 9.10, 11.1.2,
11.1.3, 11.3.5, 12.3.1
**Payment Bond, Performance Bond and** . . . . . . . . . . 7.3.6.4,
9.10.3, 11.3.9, **11.4**
Payments, Progress . . . . . . . . . . . . . . . . . . 4.3.4, 9.3, 9.6,
9.8.3, 9.10.3, 13.6, 14.2.3
**PAYMENTS AND COMPLETION** . . . . . . . . . . . . . . . . . . . . **9**, 14
Payments to Subcontractors . . . . . . . . . . . . 5.4.2, 9.5.1.3,
9.6.2, 9.6.3, 9.6.4, 11.3.8, 14.2.1.2
PCB . . . . . . . . . . . . . . . . . . . . . . . . . . . . . . . . . . . . . . . . . . . 10.1
Performance Bond and Payment Bond . . . . . . . . . . . . . 7.3.6.4,
9.10.3, 11.3.9, 11.4
**Permits, Fees and Notices** . . . . . . 2.2.3, **3.7**, 3.13, 7.3.6.4, 10.2.2
**PERSONS AND PROPERTY, PROTECTION OF** . . . . . . . . . **10**
Polychlorinated Biphenyl . . . . . . . . . . . . . . . . . . . . . . . . . . . 10.1
Product Data, Definition of . . . . . . . . . . . . . . . . . . . . . . . . 3.12.2
**Product Data and Samples, Shop Drawings** . . . . . 3.11, **3.12**, 4.2.7
**Progress and Completion** . . . . . . . . . . . . . . . 4.2.2, 4.3.4, **8.2**
**Progress Payments** . . . . . . . . . . . . . . . . . . . . . . . . . 4.3.4, 9.3,
**9.6**, 9.8.3, 9.10.3, 13.6, 14.2.3
**Project, Definition of the** . . . . . . . . . . . . . . . . . . . . . . . . . . **1.1.4**
**Project Manual, Definition of the** . . . . . . . . . . . . . . . . . . . **1.1.7**
Project Manuals . . . . . . . . . . . . . . . . . . . . . . . . . . . . . . . . . 2.2.5
Project Representatives . . . . . . . . . . . . . . . . . . . . . . . . . . . 4.2.10
**Property Insurance** . . . . . . . . . . . . . . . . . . . . . . . . 10.2.5, **11.3**
**PROTECTION OF PERSONS AND PROPERTY** . . . . . . . . . **10**
Regulations and Laws . . . . . . 1.3, 3.6, 3.7, 3.13, 4.1.1, 4.5.5,
4.5.7, 10.2.2, 11.1, 11.3, 13.1, 13.4, 13.5.1, 13.5.2, 13.6, 14
Rejection of Work . . . . . . . . . . . . . . . . . 3.5.1, 4.2.6, 12.2
Releases of Waivers and Liens . . . . . . . . . . . . . . . . . . . . . . 9.10.2
Representations . . . . . . . . . . . . . . . . . 1.2.2, 3.5.1, 3.12.7,
6.2.2, 8.2.1, 9.3.3, 9.4.2, 9.5.1, 9.8.2, 9.10.1
Representatives . . . . . . . . . . . . . . . . . . . . 2.1.1, 3.1.1, 3.9,
4.1.1, 4.2.1, 4.2.10, 5.1.1, 5.1.2, 13.2.1
**Resolution of Claims and Disputes** . . . . . . . . . . . . . . **4.4**, 4.5
Responsibility for Those Performing the Work . . . . . . . . . . 3.3.2,
4.2.3, 6.1.3, 6.2, 10
Retainage . . . . . . 9.3.1, 9.6.2, 9.8.3, 9.9.1, 9.10.2, 9.10.3
**Review of Contract Documents and Field
Conditions by Contractor** . . . . . . . . . . . . 1.2.2, **3.2**, 3.7.3, 3.12.7
Review of Contractor's Submittals by
Owner and Architect . . . . . . . . . . . . 3.10.1, 3.10.2, 3.11, 3.12,
4.2.7, 4.2.9, 5.2.1, 5.2.3, 9.2, 9.8.2
Review of Shop Drawings, Product Data
and Samples by Contractor . . . . . . . . . . . . . . . . . . . . . . 3.12.5
**Rights and Remedies** . . . . . . 1.1.2, 2.3, 2.4, 3.5.1, 3.15.2,
4.2.6, 4.3.6, 4.5, 5.3, 6.1, 6.3, 7.3.1, 8.3.1, 9.5.1, 9.7, 10.2.5,
10.3, 12.2.2, 12.2.4, **13.4**, 14
**Royalties and Patents** . . . . . . . . . . . . . . . . . . . . . . . . . . . . **3.17**

**4   A201-1987**      AIA DOCUMENT A201 • GENERAL CONDITIONS OF THE CONTRACT FOR CONSTRUCTION • FOURTEENTH EDITION
AIA® • ©1987 THE AMERICAN INSTITUTE OF ARCHITECTS, 1735 NEW YORK AVENUE, N.W., WASHINGTON, D.C. 20006

Rules and Notices for Arbitration ........................ **4.5.2**
Safety of Persons and Property ........................... **10.2**
Safety Precautions and Programs ..... 4.2.3, 4.2.7, **10.1**
Samples, Definition of ..................................... 3.12.3
Samples, Shop Drawings, Product Data and ... 3.11, **3.12**, 4.2.7
Samples at the Site, Documents and ..................... **3.11**
Schedule of Values ................................... **9.2**, 9.3.1
Schedules, Construction ................................... 3.10
Separate Contracts and Contractors ... 1.1.4, 3.14.2, 4.2.4
 .................... 4.5.5, 6, 11.3.7, 12.1.2, 12.2.5
Shop Drawings, Definition of ............................. 3.12.1
Shop Drawings, Product Data and Samples ... 3.11, **3.12**, 4.2.7
Site, Use of ........................................ **3.13**, 6.1.1, 6.2.1
Site Inspections ... 1.2.2, 3.3.4, 4.2.2, 4.2.9, 4.3.6, 9.8.2, 9.10.1, 13.5
Site Visits, Architect's ... 4.2.2, 4.2.5, 4.2.9, 4.3.6,
 ........... 9.4.2, 9.5.1, 9.8.2, 9.9.2, 9.10.1, 13.5
Special Inspections and Testing ... 4.2.6, 12.2.1, 13.5
Specifications, Definition of the ....................... **1.1.6**
Specifications, The ... 1.1.1, **1.1.6**, 1.1.7, 1.2.4, 1.3, 3.11
Statutes of Limitations ........... 4.5.4.2, 12.2.6, 13.7
Stopping the Work .......... 2.3, 4.3.7, 9.7, 10.1.2, 10.3, 14.1
Stored Materials ... 6.2.1, 9.3.2, 10.2.1.2, 11.3.1.4, 12.2.4
Subcontractor, Definition of ............................ 5.1.1
**SUBCONTRACTORS** ........................................... **5**
Subcontractors, Work by ... 1.2.4, 3.3.2, 3.12.1,
 ........................ 4.2.3, 5.3, 5.4
Subcontractual Relations ... **5.3**, 5.4, 9.3.1.2, 9.6.2,
 ... 9.6.3, 9.6.4, 10.2.1, 11.3.7, 11.3.8, 14.1.1, 14.2.1.2, 14.3.2
Submittals ... 1.3, 3.2.3, 3.10, 3.11, 3.12, 4.2.7, 5.2.1, 5.2.3,
 ... 7.3.6, 9.2, 9.3.1, 9.8.2, 9.9.1, 9.10.2, 9.10.3, 10.1.2, 11.1.3
Subrogation, Waivers of ... 6.1.1, 11.3.5, **11.3.7**
Substantial Completion ... 4.2.9, 4.3.5.2, 8.1.1, 8.1.3,
 ... 8.2.3, **9.8**, 9.9.1, 12.2.1, 12.2.2, 13.7
Substantial Completion, Definition of ................... 9.8.1
Substitution of Subcontractors ................. 5.2.3, 5.2.4
Substitution of the Architect ........................... 4.1.3
Substitutions of Materials .............................. 3.5.1
Sub-subcontractor, Definition of ........................ 5.1.2
Subsurface Conditions ................................... 4.3.6
Successors and Assigns ................................. 13.2
Superintendent ................................. 3.9, 10.2.6
Supervision and Construction Procedures ... 1.2.4, 3.3, 3.4,
 ... 4.2.3, 4.3.4, 6.1.3, 6.2.4, 7.1.3, 7.3.4, 8.2, 8.3.1, 10, 12, 14
Surety ................. 4.4.1, 4.4.4, 5.4.1.2, 9.10.2, 9.10.3, 14.2.2
Surety, Consent of ................... 9.9.1, 9.10.2, 9.10.3
Surveys .................................. 2.2.2, 3.18.3

Suspension by the Owner for Convenience ............... **14.3**
Suspension of the Work ... 4.3.7, 5.4.2, 14.1.1.4, 14.3
Suspension or Termination of the Contract ... 4.3.7, 5.4.1.1, 14
Taxes .......................................... **3.6**, 7.3.6.4
Termination by the Contractor ......................... **14.1**
Termination by the Owner for Cause ......... 5.4.1.1, **14.2**
Termination of the Architect ........................... 4.1.3
Termination of the Contractor .......................... 14.2.2
**TERMINATION OR SUSPENSION OF THE CONTRACT** ........... **14**
Tests and Inspections ... 3.3.3, 4.2.6, 4.2.9, 9.4.2, 12.2.1, **13.5**
**TIME** ..................................................... **8**
Time, Delays and Extensions of ........ 4.3.8, 7.2.1, **8.3**
Time Limits, Specific ... 2.1.2, 2.2.1, 2.4, 3.10, 3.11, 3.15.1,
 ... 4.2.1, 4.2.11, 4.3, 4.4, 4.5, 5.3, 5.4, 7.3.5, 7.3.9, 8.2, 9.2, 9.3.1,
 ... 9.3.3, 9.4.1, 9.6.1, 9.7, 9.8.2, 9.10.2, 11.1.3, 11.3.6, 11.3.10,
 ... 11.3.11, 12.2.2, 12.2.4, 12.2.6, 13.7, 14
Time Limits on Claims ... 4.3.2, **4.3.3**, 4.3.6, 4.3.9, 4.4, 4.5
Title to Work ...................................... 9.3.2, 9.3.3
**UNCOVERING AND CORRECTION OF WORK** ................... **12**
Uncovering of Work ..................................... **12.1**
Unforeseen Conditions ................. 4.3.6, 8.3.1, 10.1
Unit Prices ...................................... 7.1.4, 7.3.3.2
Use of Documents ... 1.1.1, 1.3, 2.2.5, 3.12.7, 5.3
Use of Site ............................ **3.13**, 6.1.1, 6.2.1
Values, Schedule of ............................. **9.2**, 9.3.1
Waiver of Claims: Final Payment ... **4.3.5**, 4.5.1, 9.10.3
Waiver of Claims by the Architect ...................... 13.4.2
Waiver of Claims by the Contractor ... 9.10.4, 11.3.7, 13.4.2
Waiver of Claims by the Owner ... 4.3.5, 4.5.1, 9.9.3,
 ... 9.10.3, 11.3.3, 11.3.5, 11.3.7, 13.4.2
Waiver of Liens ........................................ 9.10.2
Waivers of Subrogation ... 6.1.1, 11.3.5, 11.3.7
Warranty and Warranties ...................... **3.5**, 4.2.9,
 ... 4.3.5.3, 9.3.3, 9.8.2, 9.9.1, 12.2.2, 13.7.1.3
Weather Delays ........................................ 4.3.8.2
When Arbitration May Be Demanded ..................... **4.5.4**
Work, Definition of ...................................... 1.1.3
Written Consent ... 1.3.1, 3.12.8, 3.14.2, 4.1.2, 4.3.4,
 ... 4.5.5, 9.3.2, 9.8.2, 9.9.1, 9.10.2, 9.10.3, 10.1.2, 10.1.3,
 ... 11.3.1, 11.3.1.4, 11.3.11, 13.2, 13.4.2
Written Interpretations ........... 4.2.11, 4.2.12, 4.3.7
Written Notice ... 2.3, 2.4, 3.9, 3.12.8, 3.12.9, 4.3, 4.4.4,
 ... 4.5, 5.2.1, 5.3, 5.4.1.1, 8.2.2, 9.4.1, 9.5.1, 9.7, 9.10, 10.1.2,
 ... 10.2.6, 11.1.3, 11.3, 12.2.2, 12.2.4, **13.3**, 13.5.2, 14
Written Orders ... 2.3, 3.9, 4.3.7,
 ... 7, 8.2.2, 11.3.9, 12.1, 12.2, 13.5.2, 14.3.1

## GENERAL CONDITIONS OF THE CONTRACT FOR CONSTRUCTION

### ARTICLE 1

### GENERAL PROVISIONS

**1.1 BASIC DEFINITIONS**

**1.1.1 THE CONTRACT DOCUMENTS**

The Contract Documents consist of the Agreement between Owner and Contractor (hereinafter the Agreement), Conditions of the Contract (General, Supplementary and other Conditions), Drawings, Specifications, addenda issued prior to execution of the Contract, other documents listed in the Agreement and Modifications issued after execution of the Contract. A Modification is (1) a written amendment to the Contract signed by both parties, (2) a Change Order, (3) a Construction Change Directive or (4) a written order for a minor change in the Work issued by the Architect. Unless specifically enumerated in the Agreement, the Contract Documents do not include other documents such as bidding requirements (advertisement or invitation to bid, Instructions to Bidders, sample forms, the Contractor's bid or portions of addenda relating to bidding requirements).

**1.1.2 THE CONTRACT**

The Contract Documents form the Contract for Construction. The Contract represents the entire and integrated agreement between the parties hereto and supersedes prior negotiations, representations or agreements, either written or oral. The Contract may be amended or modified only by a Modification. The Contract Documents shall not be construed to create a contractual relationship of any kind (1) between the Architect and Contractor, (2) between the Owner and a Subcontractor or Subsubcontractor or (3) between any persons or entities other than the Owner and Contractor. The Architect shall, however, be entitled to performance and enforcement of obligations under the Contract intended to facilitate performance of the Architect's duties.

**1.1.3 THE WORK**

The term "Work" means the construction and services required by the Contract Documents, whether completed or partially completed, and includes all other labor, materials, equipment and services provided or to be provided by the Contractor to fulfill the Contractor's obligations. The Work may constitute the whole or a part of the Project.

**1.1.4 THE PROJECT**

The Project is the total construction of which the Work performed under the Contract Documents may be the whole or a part and which may include construction by the Owner or by separate contractors.

**1.1.5 THE DRAWINGS**

The Drawings are the graphic and pictorial portions of the Contract Documents, wherever located and whenever issued, showing the design, location and dimensions of the Work, generally including plans, elevations, sections, details, schedules and diagrams.

**1.1.6 THE SPECIFICATIONS**

The Specifications are that portion of the Contract Documents consisting of the written requirements for materials, equip-

ment, construction systems, standards and workmanship for the Work, and performance of related services.

**1.1.7 THE PROJECT MANUAL**

The Project Manual is the volume usually assembled for the Work which may include the bidding requirements, sample forms, Conditions of the Contract and Specifications.

**1.2 EXECUTION, CORRELATION AND INTENT**

**1.2.1** The Contract Documents shall be signed by the Owner and Contractor as provided in the Agreement. If either the Owner or Contractor or both do not sign all the Contract Documents, the Architect shall identify such unsigned Documents upon request.

**1.2.2** Execution of the Contract by the Contractor is a representation that the Contractor has visited the site, become familiar with local conditions under which the Work is to be performed and correlated personal observations with requirements of the Contract Documents.

**1.2.3** The intent of the Contract Documents is to include all items necessary for the proper execution and completion of the Work by the Contractor. The Contract Documents are complementary, and what is required by one shall be as binding as if required by all; performance by the Contractor shall be required only to the extent consistent with the Contract Documents and reasonably inferable from them as being necessary to produce the intended results.

**1.2.4** Organization of the Specifications into divisions, sections and articles, and arrangement of Drawings shall not control the Contractor in dividing the Work among Subcontractors or in establishing the extent of Work to be performed by any trade.

**1.2.5** Unless otherwise stated in the Contract Documents, words which have well-known technical or construction industry meanings are used in the Contract Documents in accordance with such recognized meanings.

**1.3 OWNERSHIP AND USE OF ARCHITECT'S DRAWINGS, SPECIFICATIONS AND OTHER DOCUMENTS**

**1.3.1** The Drawings, Specifications and other documents prepared by the Architect are instruments of the Architect's service through which the Work to be executed by the Contractor is described. The Contractor may retain one contract record set. Neither the Contractor nor any Subcontractor, Subsubcontractor or material or equipment supplier shall own or claim a copyright in the Drawings, Specifications and other documents prepared by the Architect, and unless otherwise indicated the Architect shall be deemed the author of them and will retain all common law, statutory and other reserved rights, in addition to the copyright. All copies of them, except the Contractor's record set, shall be returned or suitably accounted for to the Architect, on request, upon completion of the Work. The Drawings, Specifications and other documents prepared by the Architect, and copies thereof furnished to the Contractor, are for use solely with respect to this Project. They are not to be used by the Contractor or any Subcontractor, Subsubcontractor or material or equipment supplier on other projects or for additions to this Project outside the scope of the

Work without the specific written consent of the Owner and Architect. The Contractor, Subcontractors, Sub-subcontractors and material or equipment suppliers are granted a limited license to use and reproduce applicable portions of the Drawings, Specifications and other documents prepared by the Architect appropriate to and for use in the execution of their Work under the Contract Documents. All copies made under this license shall bear the statutory copyright notice, if any, shown on the Drawings, Specifications and other documents prepared by the Architect. Submittal or distribution to meet official regulatory requirements or for other purposes in connection with this Project is not to be construed as publication in derogation of the Architect's copyright or other reserved rights.

### 1.4 CAPITALIZATION

**1.4.1** Terms capitalized in these General Conditions include those which are (1) specifically defined, (2) the titles of numbered articles and identified references to Paragraphs, Subparagraphs and Clauses in the document or (3) the titles of other documents published by the American Institute of Architects.

### 1.5 INTERPRETATION

**1.5.1** In the interest of brevity the Contract Documents frequently omit modifying words such as "all" and "any" and articles such as "the" and "an," but the fact that a modifier or an article is absent from one statement and appears in another is not intended to affect the interpretation of either statement.

## ARTICLE 2

## OWNER

### 2.1 DEFINITION

**2.1.1** The Owner is the person or entity identified as such in the Agreement and is referred to throughout the Contract Documents as if singular in number. The term "Owner" means the Owner or the Owner's authorized representative.

**2.1.2** The Owner upon reasonable written request shall furnish to the Contractor in writing information which is necessary and relevant for the Contractor to evaluate, give notice of or enforce mechanic's lien rights. Such information shall include a correct statement of the record legal title to the property on which the Project is located, usually referred to as the site, and the Owner's interest therein at the time of execution of the Agreement and, within five days after any change, information of such change in title, recorded or unrecorded.

### 2.2 INFORMATION AND SERVICES REQUIRED OF THE OWNER

**2.2.1** The Owner shall, at the request of the Contractor, prior to execution of the Agreement and promptly from time to time thereafter, furnish to the Contractor reasonable evidence that financial arrangements have been made to fulfill the Owner's obligations under the Contract. *[Note: Unless such reasonable evidence were furnished on request prior to the execution of the Agreement, the prospective contractor would not be required to execute the Agreement or to commence the Work.]*

**2.2.2** The Owner shall furnish surveys describing physical characteristics, legal limitations and utility locations for the site of the Project, and a legal description of the site.

**2.2.3** Except for permits and fees which are the responsibility of the Contractor under the Contract Documents, the Owner shall secure and pay for necessary approvals, easements, assess-ments and charges required for construction, use or occupancy of permanent structures or for permanent changes in existing facilities.

**2.2.4** Information or services under the Owner's control shall be furnished by the Owner with reasonable promptness to avoid delay in orderly progress of the Work.

**2.2.5** Unless otherwise provided in the Contract Documents, the Contractor will be furnished, free of charge, such copies of Drawings and Project Manuals as are reasonably necessary for execution of the Work.

**2.2.6** The foregoing are in addition to other duties and responsibilities of the Owner enumerated herein and especially those in respect to Article 6 (Construction by Owner or by Separate Contractors), Article 9 (Payments and Completion) and Article 11 (Insurance and Bonds).

### 2.3 OWNER'S RIGHT TO STOP THE WORK

**2.3.1** If the Contractor fails to correct Work which is not in accordance with the requirements of the Contract Documents as required by Paragraph 12.2 or persistently fails to carry out Work in accordance with the Contract Documents, the Owner, by written order signed personally or by an agent specifically so empowered by the Owner in writing, may order the Contractor to stop the Work, or any portion thereof, until the cause for such order has been eliminated; however, the right of the Owner to stop the Work shall not give rise to a duty on the part of the Owner to exercise this right for the benefit of the Contractor or any other person or entity, except to the extent required by Subparagraph 6.1.3.

### 2.4 OWNER'S RIGHT TO CARRY OUT THE WORK

**2.4.1** If the Contractor defaults or neglects to carry out the Work in accordance with the Contract Documents and fails within a seven-day period after receipt of written notice from the Owner to commence and continue correction of such default or neglect with diligence and promptness, the Owner may after such seven-day period give the Contractor a second written notice to correct such deficiencies within a second seven-day period. If the Contractor within such second seven-day period after receipt of such second notice fails to commence and continue to correct any deficiencies, the Owner may, without prejudice to other remedies the Owner may have, correct such deficiencies. In such case an appropriate Change Order shall be issued deducting from payments then or thereafter due the Contractor the cost of correcting such deficiencies, including compensation for the Architect's additional services and expenses made necessary by such default, neglect or failure. Such action by the Owner and amounts charged to the Contractor are both subject to prior approval of the Architect. If payments then or thereafter due the Contractor are not sufficient to cover such amounts, the Contractor shall pay the difference to the Owner.

## ARTICLE 3

## CONTRACTOR

### 3.1 DEFINITION

**3.1.1** The Contractor is the person or entity identified as such in the Agreement and is referred to throughout the Contract Documents as if singular in number. The term "Contractor" means the Contractor or the Contractor's authorized representative.

## 3.2   REVIEW OF CONTRACT DOCUMENTS AND FIELD CONDITIONS BY CONTRACTOR

**3.2.1** The Contractor shall carefully study and compare the Contract Documents with each other and with information furnished by the Owner pursuant to Subparagraph 2.2.2 and shall at once report to the Architect errors, inconsistencies or omissions discovered. The Contractor shall not be liable to the Owner or Architect for damage resulting from errors, inconsistencies or omissions in the Contract Documents unless the Contractor recognized such error, inconsistency or omission and knowingly failed to report it to the Architect. If the Contractor performs any construction activity knowing it involves a recognized error, inconsistency or omission in the Contract Documents without such notice to the Architect, the Contractor shall assume appropriate responsibility for such performance and shall bear an appropriate amount of the attributable costs for correction.

**3.2.2** The Contractor shall take field measurements and verify field conditions and shall carefully compare such field measurements and conditions and other information known to the Contractor with the Contract Documents before commencing activities. Errors, inconsistencies or omissions discovered shall be reported to the Architect at once.

**3.2.3** The Contractor shall perform the Work in accordance with the Contract Documents and submittals approved pursuant to Paragraph 3.12.

## 3.3   SUPERVISION AND CONSTRUCTION PROCEDURES

**3.3.1** The Contractor shall supervise and direct the Work, using the Contractor's best skill and attention. The Contractor shall be solely responsible for and have control over construction means, methods, techniques, sequences and procedures and for coordinating all portions of the Work under the Contract, unless Contract Documents give other specific instructions concerning these matters.

**3.3.2** The Contractor shall be responsible to the Owner for acts and omissions of the Contractor's employees, Subcontractors and their agents and employees, and other persons performing portions of the Work under a contract with the Contractor.

**3.3.3** The Contractor shall not be relieved of obligations to perform the Work in accordance with the Contract Documents either by activities or duties of the Architect in the Architect's administration of the Contract, or by tests, inspections or approvals required or performed by persons other than the Contractor.

**3.3.4** The Contractor shall be responsible for inspection of portions of Work already performed under this Contract to determine that such portions are in proper condition to receive subsequent Work.

## 3.4   LABOR AND MATERIALS

**3.4.1** Unless otherwise provided in the Contract Documents, the Contractor shall provide and pay for labor, materials, equipment, tools, construction equipment and machinery, water, heat, utilities, transportation, and other facilities and services necessary for proper execution and completion of the Work, whether temporary or permanent and whether or not incorporated or to be incorporated in the Work.

**3.4.2** The Contractor shall enforce strict discipline and good order among the Contractor's employees and other persons carrying out the Contract. The Contractor shall not permit employment of unfit persons or persons not skilled in tasks assigned to them.

## 3.5   WARRANTY

**3.5.1** The Contractor warrants to the Owner and Architect that materials and equipment furnished under the Contract will be of good quality and new unless otherwise required or permitted by the Contract Documents, that the Work will be free from defects not inherent in the quality required or permitted, and that the Work will conform with the requirements of the Contract Documents. Work not conforming to these requirements, including substitutions not properly approved and authorized, may be considered defective. The Contractor's warranty excludes remedy for damage or defect caused by abuse, modifications not executed by the Contractor, improper or insufficient maintenance, improper operation, or normal wear and tear under normal usage. If required by the Architect, the Contractor shall furnish satisfactory evidence as to the kind and quality of materials and equipment.

## 3.6   TAXES

**3.6.1** The Contractor shall pay sales, consumer, use and similar taxes for the Work or portions thereof provided by the Contractor which are legally enacted when bids are received or negotiations concluded, whether or not yet effective or merely scheduled to go into effect.

## 3.7   PERMITS, FEES AND NOTICES

**3.7.1** Unless otherwise provided in the Contract Documents, the Contractor shall secure and pay for the building permit and other permits and governmental fees, licenses and inspections necessary for proper execution and completion of the Work which are customarily secured after execution of the Contract and which are legally required when bids are received or negotiations concluded.

**3.7.2** The Contractor shall comply with and give notices required by laws, ordinances, rules, regulations and lawful orders of public authorities bearing on performance of the Work.

**3.7.3** It is not the Contractor's responsibility to ascertain that the Contract Documents are in accordance with applicable laws, statutes, ordinances, building codes, and rules and regulations. However, if the Contractor observes that portions of the Contract Documents are at variance therewith, the Contractor shall promptly notify the Architect and Owner in writing, and necessary changes shall be accomplished by appropriate Modification.

**3.7.4** If the Contractor performs Work knowing it to be contrary to laws, statutes, ordinances, building codes, and rules and regulations without such notice to the Architect and Owner, the Contractor shall assume full responsibility for such Work and shall bear the attributable costs.

## 3.8   ALLOWANCES

**3.8.1** The Contractor shall include in the Contract Sum all allowances stated in the Contract Documents. Items covered by allowances shall be supplied for such amounts and by such persons or entities as the Owner may direct, but the Contractor shall not be required to employ persons or entities against which the Contractor makes reasonable objection.

**3.8.2** Unless otherwise provided in the Contract Documents:

    .1 materials and equipment under an allowance shall be selected promptly by the Owner to avoid delay in the Work;

    .2 allowances shall cover the cost to the Contractor of materials and equipment delivered at the site and all required taxes, less applicable trade discounts;

**AIA DOCUMENT A201** • GENERAL CONDITIONS OF THE CONTRACT FOR CONSTRUCTION • FOURTEENTH EDITION
AIA® • ©1987 THE AMERICAN INSTITUTE OF ARCHITECTS, 1735 NEW YORK AVENUE, N.W., WASHINGTON, D.C. 20006

.3 Contractor's costs for unloading and handling at the site, labor, installation costs, overhead, profit and other expenses contemplated for stated allowance amounts shall be included in the Contract Sum and not in the allowances;

.4 whenever costs are more than or less than allowances, the Contract Sum shall be adjusted accordingly by Change Order. The amount of the Change Order shall reflect (1) the difference between actual costs and the allowances under Clause 3.8.2.2 and (2) changes in Contractor's costs under Clause 3.8.2.3.

## 3.9 SUPERINTENDENT

**3.9.1** The Contractor shall employ a competent superintendent and necessary assistants who shall be in attendance at the Project site during performance of the Work. The superintendent shall represent the Contractor, and communications given to the superintendent shall be as binding as if given to the Contractor. Important communications shall be confirmed in writing. Other communications shall be similarly confirmed on written request in each case.

## 3.10 CONTRACTOR'S CONSTRUCTION SCHEDULES

**3.10.1** The Contractor, promptly after being awarded the Contract, shall prepare and submit for the Owner's and Architect's information a Contractor's construction schedule for the Work. The schedule shall not exceed time limits current under the Contract Documents, shall be revised at appropriate intervals as required by the conditions of the Work and Project, shall be related to the entire Project to the extent required by the Contract Documents, and shall provide for expeditious and practicable execution of the Work.

**3.10.2** The Contractor shall prepare and keep current, for the Architect's approval, a schedule of submittals which is coordinated with the Contractor's construction schedule and allows the Architect reasonable time to review submittals.

**3.10.3** The Contractor shall conform to the most recent schedules.

## 3.11 DOCUMENTS AND SAMPLES AT THE SITE

**3.11.1** The Contractor shall maintain at the site for the Owner one record copy of the Drawings, Specifications, addenda, Change Orders and other Modifications, in good order and marked currently to record changes and selections made during construction, and in addition approved Shop Drawings, Product Data, Samples and similar required submittals. These shall be available to the Architect and shall be delivered to the Architect for submittal to the Owner upon completion of the Work.

## 3.12 SHOP DRAWINGS, PRODUCT DATA AND SAMPLES

**3.12.1** Shop Drawings are drawings, diagrams, schedules and other data specially prepared for the Work by the Contractor or a Subcontractor, Sub-subcontractor, manufacturer, supplier or distributor to illustrate some portion of the Work.

**3.12.2** Product Data are illustrations, standard schedules, performance charts, instructions, brochures, diagrams and other information furnished by the Contractor to illustrate materials or equipment for some portion of the Work.

**3.12.3** Samples are physical examples which illustrate materials, equipment or workmanship and establish standards by which the Work will be judged.

**3.12.4** Shop Drawings, Product Data, Samples and similar submittals are not Contract Documents. The purpose of their submittal is to demonstrate for those portions of the Work for which submittals are required the way the Contractor proposes to conform to the information given and the design concept expressed in the Contract Documents. Review by the Architect is subject to the limitations of Subparagraph 4.2.7.

**3.12.5** The Contractor shall review, approve and submit to the Architect Shop Drawings, Product Data, Samples and similar submittals required by the Contract Documents with reasonable promptness and in such sequence as to cause no delay in the Work or in the activities of the Owner or of separate contractors. Submittals made by the Contractor which are not required by the Contract Documents may be returned without action.

**3.12.6** The Contractor shall perform no portion of the Work requiring submittal and review of Shop Drawings, Product Data, Samples or similar submittals until the respective submittal has been approved by the Architect. Such Work shall be in accordance with approved submittals.

**3.12.7** By approving and submitting Shop Drawings, Product Data, Samples and similar submittals, the Contractor represents that the Contractor has determined and verified materials, field measurements and field construction criteria related thereto, or will do so, and has checked and coordinated the information contained within such submittals with the requirements of the Work and of the Contract Documents.

**3.12.8** The Contractor shall not be relieved of responsibility for deviations from requirements of the Contract Documents by the Architect's approval of Shop Drawings, Product Data, Samples or similar submittals unless the Contractor has specifically informed the Architect in writing of such deviation at the time of submittal and the Architect has given written approval to the specific deviation. The Contractor shall not be relieved of responsibility for errors or omissions in Shop Drawings, Product Data, Samples or similar submittals by the Architect's approval thereof.

**3.12.9** The Contractor shall direct specific attention, in writing or on resubmitted Shop Drawings, Product Data, Samples or similar submittals, to revisions other than those requested by the Architect on previous submittals.

**3.12.10** Informational submittals upon which the Architect is not expected to take responsive action may be so identified in the Contract Documents.

**3.12.11** When professional certification of performance criteria of materials, systems or equipment is required by the Contract Documents, the Architect shall be entitled to rely upon the accuracy and completeness of such calculations and certifications.

## 3.13 USE OF SITE

**3.13.1** The Contractor shall confine operations at the site to areas permitted by law, ordinances, permits and the Contract Documents and shall not unreasonably encumber the site with materials or equipment.

## 3.14 CUTTING AND PATCHING

**3.14.1** The Contractor shall be responsible for cutting, fitting or patching required to complete the Work or to make its parts fit together properly.

**3.14.2** The Contractor shall not damage or endanger a portion of the Work or fully or partially completed construction of the Owner or separate contractors by cutting, patching or otherwise altering such construction, or by excavation. The Contractor shall not cut or otherwise alter such construction by the

Owner or a separate contractor except with written consent of the Owner and of such separate contractor; such consent shall not be unreasonably withheld. The Contractor shall not unreasonably withhold from the Owner or a separate contractor the Contractor's consent to cutting or otherwise altering the Work.

**3.15  CLEANING UP**

**3.15.1** The Contractor shall keep the premises and surrounding area free from accumulation of waste materials or rubbish caused by operations under the Contract. At completion of the Work the Contractor shall remove from and about the Project waste materials, rubbish, the Contractor's tools, construction equipment, machinery and surplus materials.

**3.15.2** If the Contractor fails to clean up as provided in the Contract Documents, the Owner may do so and the cost thereof shall be charged to the Contractor.

**3.16  ACCESS TO WORK**

**3.16.1** The Contractor shall provide the Owner and Architect access to the Work in preparation and progress wherever located.

**3.17  ROYALTIES AND PATENTS**

**3.17.1** The Contractor shall pay all royalties and license fees. The Contractor shall defend suits or claims for infringement of patent rights and shall hold the Owner and Architect harmless from loss on account thereof, but shall not be responsible for such defense or loss when a particular design, process or product of a particular manufacturer or manufacturers is required by the Contract Documents. However, if the Contractor has reason to believe that the required design, process or product is an infringement of a patent, the Contractor shall be responsible for such loss unless such information is promptly furnished to the Architect.

**3.18  INDEMNIFICATION**

**3.18.1** To the fullest extent permitted by law, the Contractor shall indemnify and hold harmless the Owner, Architect, Architect's consultants, and agents and employees of any of them from and against claims, damages, losses and expenses, including but not limited to attorneys' fees, arising out of or resulting from performance of the Work, provided that such claim, damage, loss or expense is attributable to bodily injury, sickness, disease or death, or to injury to or destruction of tangible property (other than the Work itself) including loss of use resulting therefrom, but only to the extent caused in whole or in part by negligent acts or omissions of the Contractor, a Subcontractor, anyone directly or indirectly employed by them or anyone for whose acts they may be liable, regardless of whether or not such claim, damage, loss or expense is caused in part by a party indemnified hereunder. Such obligation shall not be construed to negate, abridge, or reduce other rights or obligations of indemnity which would otherwise exist as to a party or person described in this Paragraph 3.18.

**3.18.2** In claims against any person or entity indemnified under this Paragraph 3.18 by an employee of the Contractor, a Subcontractor, anyone directly or indirectly employed by them or anyone for whose acts they may be liable, the indemnification obligation under this Paragraph 3.18 shall not be limited by a limitation on amount or type of damages, compensation or benefits payable by or for the Contractor or a Subcontractor under workers' or workmen's compensation acts, disability benefit acts or other employee benefit acts.

**3.18.3** The obligations of the Contractor under this Paragraph 3.18 shall not extend to the liability of the Architect, the Archi-

tect's consultants, and agents and employees of any of them arising out of (1) the preparation or approval of maps, drawings, opinions, reports, surveys, Change Orders, designs or specifications, or (2) the giving of or the failure to give directions or instructions by the Architect, the Architect's consultants, and agents and employees of any of them provided such giving or failure to give is the primary cause of the injury or damage.

## ARTICLE 4

### ADMINISTRATION OF THE CONTRACT

**4.1  ARCHITECT**

**4.1.1** The Architect is the person lawfully licensed to practice architecture or an entity lawfully practicing architecture identified as such in the Agreement and is referred to throughout the Contract Documents as if singular in number. The term "Architect" means the Architect or the Architect's authorized representative.

**4.1.2** Duties, responsibilities and limitations of authority of the Architect as set forth in the Contract Documents shall not be restricted, modified or extended without written consent of the Owner, Contractor and Architect. Consent shall not be unreasonably withheld.

**4.1.3** In case of termination of employment of the Architect, the Owner shall appoint an architect against whom the Contractor makes no reasonable objection and whose status under the Contract Documents shall be that of the former architect.

**4.1.4** Disputes arising under Subparagraphs 4.1.2 and 4.1.3 shall be subject to arbitration.

**4.2  ARCHITECT'S ADMINISTRATION OF THE CONTRACT**

**4.2.1** The Architect will provide administration of the Contract as described in the Contract Documents, and will be the Owner's representative (1) during construction, (2) until final payment is due and (3) with the Owner's concurrence, from time to time during the correction period described in Paragraph 12.2. The Architect will advise and consult with the Owner. The Architect will have authority to act on behalf of the Owner only to the extent provided in the Contract Documents, unless otherwise modified by written instrument in accordance with other provisions of the Contract.

**4.2.2** The Architect will visit the site at intervals appropriate to the stage of construction to become generally familiar with the progress and quality of the completed Work and to determine in general if the Work is being performed in a manner indicating that the Work, when completed, will be in accordance with the Contract Documents. However, the Architect will not be required to make exhaustive or continuous on-site inspections to check quality or quantity of the Work. On the basis of on-site observations as an architect, the Architect will keep the Owner informed of progress of the Work, and will endeavor to guard the Owner against defects and deficiencies in the Work.

**4.2.3** The Architect will not have control over or charge of and will not be responsible for construction means, methods, techniques, sequences or procedures, or for safety precautions and programs in connection with the Work, since these are solely the Contractor's responsibility as provided in Paragraph 3.3. The Architect will not be responsible for the Contractor's failure to carry out the Work in accordance with the Contract Documents. The Architect will not have control over or charge of and will not be responsible for acts or omissions of the Con-

**AIA DOCUMENT A201** • GENERAL CONDITIONS OF THE CONTRACT FOR CONSTRUCTION • FOURTEENTH EDITION
AIA® • ©1987 THE AMERICAN INSTITUTE OF ARCHITECTS, 1735 NEW YORK AVENUE, N.W., WASHINGTON, D.C. 20006

tractor, Subcontractors, or their agents or employees, or of any other persons performing portions of the Work.

**4.2.4 Communications Facilitating Contract Administration.** Except as otherwise provided in the Contract Documents or when direct communications have been specially authorized, the Owner and Contractor shall endeavor to communicate through the Architect. Communications by and with the Architect's consultants shall be through the Architect. Communications by and with Subcontractors and material suppliers shall be through the Contractor. Communications by and with separate contractors shall be through the Owner.

**4.2.5** Based on the Architect's observations and evaluations of the Contractor's Applications for Payment, the Architect will review and certify the amounts due the Contractor and will issue Certificates for Payment in such amounts.

**4.2.6** The Architect will have authority to reject Work which does not conform to the Contract Documents. Whenever the Architect considers it necessary or advisable for implementation of the intent of the Contract Documents, the Architect will have authority to require additional inspection or testing of the Work in accordance with Subparagraphs 13.5.2 and 13.5.3, whether or not such Work is fabricated, installed or completed. However, neither this authority of the Architect nor a decision made in good faith either to exercise or not to exercise such authority shall give rise to a duty or responsibility of the Architect to the Contractor, Subcontractors, material and equipment suppliers, their agents or employees, or other persons performing portions of the Work.

**4.2.7** The Architect will review and approve or take other appropriate action upon the Contractor's submittals such as Shop Drawings, Product Data and Samples, but only for the limited purpose of checking for conformance with information given and the design concept expressed in the Contract Documents. The Architect's action will be taken with such reasonable promptness as to cause no delay in the Work or in the activities of the Owner, Contractor or separate contractors, while allowing sufficient time in the Architect's professional judgment to permit adequate review. Review of such submittals is not conducted for the purpose of determining the accuracy and completeness of other details such as dimensions and quantities, or for substantiating instructions for installation or performance of equipment or systems, all of which remain the responsibility of the Contractor as required by the Contract Documents. The Architect's review of the Contractor's submittals shall not relieve the Contractor of the obligations under Paragraphs 3.3, 3.5 and 3.12. The Architect's review shall not constitute approval of safety precautions or, unless otherwise specifically stated by the Architect, of any construction means, methods, techniques, sequences or procedures. The Architect's approval of a specific item shall not indicate approval of an assembly of which the item is a component.

**4.2.8** The Architect will prepare Change Orders and Construction Change Directives, and may authorize minor changes in the Work as provided in Paragraph 7.4.

**4.2.9** The Architect will conduct inspections to determine the date or dates of Substantial Completion and the date of final completion, will receive and forward to the Owner for the Owner's review and records written warranties and related documents required by the Contract and assembled by the Contractor, and will issue a final Certificate for Payment upon compliance with the requirements of the Contract Documents.

**4.2.10** If the Owner and Architect agree, the Architect will provide one or more project representatives to assist in carrying

out the Architect's responsibilities at the site. The duties, responsibilities and limitations of authority of such project representatives shall be as set forth in an exhibit to be incorporated in the Contract Documents.

**4.2.11** The Architect will interpret and decide matters concerning performance under and requirements of the Contract Documents on written request of either the Owner or Contractor. The Architect's response to such requests will be made with reasonable promptness and within any time limits agreed upon. If no agreement is made concerning the time within which interpretations required of the Architect shall be furnished in compliance with this Paragraph 4.2, then delay shall not be recognized on account of failure by the Architect to furnish such interpretations until 15 days after written request is made for them.

**4.2.12** Interpretations and decisions of the Architect will be consistent with the intent of and reasonably inferable from the Contract Documents and will be in writing or in the form of drawings. When making such interpretations and decisions, the Architect will endeavor to secure faithful performance by both Owner and Contractor, will not show partiality to either and will not be liable for results of interpretations or decisions so rendered in good faith.

**4.2.13** The Architect's decisions on matters relating to aesthetic effect will be final if consistent with the intent expressed in the Contract Documents.

**4.3    CLAIMS AND DISPUTES**

**4.3.1 Definition.** A Claim is a demand or assertion by one of the parties seeking, as a matter of right, adjustment or interpretation of Contract terms, payment of money, extension of time or other relief with respect to the terms of the Contract. The term "Claim" also includes other disputes and matters in question between the Owner and Contractor arising out of or relating to the Contract. Claims must be made by written notice. The responsibility to substantiate Claims shall rest with the party making the Claim.

**4.3.2 Decision of Architect.** Claims, including those alleging an error or omission by the Architect, shall be referred initially to the Architect for action as provided in Paragraph 4.4. A decision by the Architect, as provided in Subparagraph 4.4.4, shall be required as a condition precedent to arbitration or litigation of a Claim between the Contractor and Owner as to all such matters arising prior to the date final payment is due, regardless of (1) whether such matters relate to execution and progress of the Work or (2) the extent to which the Work has been completed. The decision by the Architect in response to a Claim shall not be a condition precedent to arbitration or litigation in the event (1) the position of Architect is vacant, (2) the Architect has not received evidence or has failed to render a decision within agreed time limits, (3) the Architect has failed to take action required under Subparagraph 4.4.4 within 30 days after the Claim is made, (4) 45 days have passed after the Claim has been referred to the Architect or (5) the Claim relates to a mechanic's lien.

**4.3.3 Time Limits on Claims.** Claims by either party must be made within 21 days after occurrence of the event giving rise to such Claim or within 21 days after the claimant first recognizes the condition giving rise to the Claim, whichever is later. Claims must be made by written notice. An additional Claim made after the initial Claim has been implemented by Change Order will not be considered unless submitted in a timely manner.

**4.3.4 Continuing Contract Performance.** Pending final resolution of a Claim including arbitration, unless otherwise agreed in writing the Contractor shall proceed diligently with performance of the Contract and the Owner shall continue to make payments in accordance with the Contract Documents.

**4.3.5 Waiver of Claims: Final Payment.** The making of final payment shall constitute a waiver of Claims by the Owner except those arising from:

.1 liens, Claims, security interests or encumbrances arising out of the Contract and unsettled;

.2 failure of the Work to comply with the requirements of the Contract Documents; or

.3 terms of special warranties required by the Contract Documents.

**4.3.6 Claims for Concealed or Unknown Conditions.** If conditions are encountered at the site which are (1) subsurface or otherwise concealed physical conditions which differ materially from those indicated in the Contract Documents or (2) unknown physical conditions of an unusual nature, which differ materially from those ordinarily found to exist and generally recognized as inherent in construction activities of the character provided for in the Contract Documents, then notice by the observing party shall be given to the other party promptly before conditions are disturbed and in no event later than 21 days after first observance of the conditions. The Architect will promptly investigate such conditions and, if they differ materially and cause an increase or decrease in the Contractor's cost of, or time required for, performance of any part of the Work, will recommend an equitable adjustment in the Contract Sum or Contract Time, or both. If the Architect determines that the conditions at the site are not materially different from those indicated in the Contract Documents and that no change in the terms of the Contract is justified, the Architect shall so notify the Owner and Contractor in writing, stating the reasons. Claims by either party in opposition to such determination must be made within 21 days after the Architect has given notice of the decision. If the Owner and Contractor cannot agree on an adjustment in the Contract Sum or Contract Time, the adjustment shall be referred to the Architect for initial determination, subject to further proceedings pursuant to Paragraph 4.4.

**4.3.7 Claims for Additional Cost.** If the Contractor wishes to make Claim for an increase in the Contract Sum, written notice as provided herein shall be given before proceeding to execute the Work. Prior notice is not required for Claims relating to an emergency endangering life or property arising under Paragraph 10.3. If the Contractor believes additional cost is involved for reasons including but not limited to (1) a written interpretation from the Architect, (2) an order by the Owner to stop the Work where the Contractor was not at fault, (3) a written order for a minor change in the Work issued by the Architect, (4) failure of payment by the Owner, (5) termination of the Contract by the Owner, (6) Owner's suspension or (7) other reasonable grounds, Claim shall be filed in accordance with the procedure established herein.

**4.3.8 Claims for Additional Time**

**4.3.8.1** If the Contractor wishes to make Claim for an increase in the Contract Time, written notice as provided herein shall be given. The Contractor's Claim shall include an estimate of cost and of probable effect of delay on progress of the Work. In the case of a continuing delay only one Claim is necessary.

**4.3.8.2** If adverse weather conditions are the basis for a Claim for additional time, such Claim shall be documented by data substantiating that weather conditions were abnormal for the period of time and could not have been reasonably anticipated, and that weather conditions had an adverse effect on the scheduled construction.

**4.3.9 Injury or Damage to Person or Property.** If either party to the Contract suffers injury or damage to person or property because of an act or omission of the other party, of any of the other party's employees or agents, or of others for whose acts such party is legally liable, written notice of such injury or damage, whether or not insured, shall be given to the other party within a reasonable time not exceeding 21 days after first observance. The notice shall provide sufficient detail to enable the other party to investigate the matter. If a Claim for additional cost or time related to this Claim is to be asserted, it shall be filed as provided in Subparagraphs 4.3.7 or 4.3.8.

**4.4   RESOLUTION OF CLAIMS AND DISPUTES**

**4.4.1** The Architect will review Claims and take one or more of the following preliminary actions within ten days of receipt of a Claim: (1) request additional supporting data from the claimant, (2) submit a schedule to the parties indicating when the Architect expects to take action, (3) reject the Claim in whole or in part, stating reasons for rejection, (4) recommend approval of the Claim by the other party or (5) suggest a compromise. The Architect may also, but is not obligated to, notify the surety, if any, of the nature and amount of the Claim.

**4.4.2** If a Claim has been resolved, the Architect will prepare or obtain appropriate documentation.

**4.4.3** If a Claim has not been resolved, the party making the Claim shall, within ten days after the Architect's preliminary response, take one or more of the following actions: (1) submit additional supporting data requested by the Architect, (2) modify the initial Claim or (3) notify the Architect that the initial Claim stands.

**4.4.4** If a Claim has not been resolved after consideration of the foregoing and of further evidence presented by the parties or requested by the Architect, the Architect will notify the parties in writing that the Architect's decision will be made within seven days, which decision shall be final and binding on the parties but subject to arbitration. Upon expiration of such time period, the Architect will render to the parties the Architect's written decision relative to the Claim, including any change in the Contract Sum or Contract Time or both. If there is a surety and there appears to be a possibility of a Contractor's default, the Architect may, but is not obligated to, notify the surety and request the surety's assistance in resolving the controversy.

**4.5   ARBITRATION**

**4.5.1 Controversies and Claims Subject to Arbitration.** Any controversy or Claim arising out of or related to the Contract, or the breach thereof, shall be settled by arbitration in accordance with the Construction Industry Arbitration Rules of the American Arbitration Association, and judgment upon the award rendered by the arbitrator or arbitrators may be entered in any court having jurisdiction thereof, except controversies or Claims relating to aesthetic effect and except those waived as provided for in Subparagraph 4.3.5. Such controversies or Claims upon which the Architect has given notice and rendered a decision as provided in Subparagraph 4.4.4 shall be subject to arbitration upon written demand of either party. Arbitration may be commenced when 45 days have passed after a Claim has been referred to the Architect as provided in Paragraph 4.3 and no decision has been rendered.

**4.5.2 Rules and Notices for Arbitration.** Claims between the Owner and Contractor not resolved under Paragraph 4.4 shall, if subject to arbitration under Subparagraph 4.5.1, be decided by arbitration in accordance with the Construction Industry Arbitration Rules of the American Arbitration Association currently in effect, unless the parties mutually agree otherwise. Notice of demand for arbitration shall be filed in writing with the other party to the Agreement between the Owner and Contractor and with the American Arbitration Association, and a copy shall be filed with the Architect.

**4.5.3 Contract Performance During Arbitration.** During arbitration proceedings, the Owner and Contractor shall comply with Subparagraph 4.3.4.

**4.5.4 When Arbitration May Be Demanded.** Demand for arbitration of any Claim may not be made until the earlier of (1) the date on which the Architect has rendered a final written decision on the Claim, (2) the tenth day after the parties have presented evidence to the Architect or have been given reasonable opportunity to do so, if the Architect has not rendered a final written decision by that date, or (3) any of the five events described in Subparagraph 4.3.2.

**4.5.4.1** When a written decision of the Architect states that (1) the decision is final but subject to arbitration and (2) a demand for arbitration of a Claim covered by such decision must be made within 30 days after the date on which the party making the demand receives the final written decision, then failure to demand arbitration within said 30 days' period shall result in the Architect's decision becoming final and binding upon the Owner and Contractor. If the Architect renders a decision after arbitration proceedings have been initiated, such decision may be entered as evidence, but shall not supersede arbitration proceedings unless the decision is acceptable to all parties concerned.

**4.5.4.2** A demand for arbitration shall be made within the time limits specified in Subparagraphs 4.5.1 and 4.5.4 and Clause 4.5.4.1 as applicable, and in other cases within a reasonable time after the Claim has arisen, and in no event shall it be made after the date when institution of legal or equitable proceedings based on such Claim would be barred by the applicable statute of limitations as determined pursuant to Paragraph 13.7.

**4.5.5 Limitation on Consolidation or Joinder.** No arbitration arising out of or relating to the Contract Documents shall include, by consolidation or joinder or in any other manner, the Architect, the Architect's employees or consultants, except by written consent containing specific reference to the Agreement and signed by the Architect, Owner, Contractor and any other person or entity sought to be joined. No arbitration shall include, by consolidation or joinder or in any other manner, parties other than the Owner, Contractor, a separate contractor as described in Article 6 and other persons substantially involved in a common question of fact or law whose presence is required if complete relief is to be accorded in arbitration. No person or entity other than the Owner, Contractor or a separate contractor as described in Article 6 shall be included as an original third party or additional third party to an arbitration whose interest or responsibility is insubstantial. Consent to arbitration involving an additional person or entity shall not constitute consent to arbitration of a dispute not described therein or with a person or entity not named or described therein. The foregoing agreement to arbitrate and other agreements to arbitrate with an additional person or entity duly consented to by parties to the Agreement shall be specifically enforceable under applicable law in any court having jurisdiction thereof.

**4.5.6 Claims and Timely Assertion of Claims.** A party who files a notice of demand for arbitration must assert in the demand all Claims then known to that party on which arbitration is permitted to be demanded. When a party fails to include a Claim through oversight, inadvertence or excusable neglect, or when a Claim has matured or been acquired subsequently, the arbitrator or arbitrators may permit amendment.

**4.5.7 Judgment on Final Award.** The award rendered by the arbitrator or arbitrators shall be final, and judgment may be entered upon it in accordance with applicable law in any court having jurisdiction thereof.

## ARTICLE 5

## SUBCONTRACTORS

**5.1  DEFINITIONS**

**5.1.1** A Subcontractor is a person or entity who has a direct contract with the Contractor to perform a portion of the Work at the site. The term "Subcontractor" is referred to throughout the Contract Documents as if singular in number and means a Subcontractor or an authorized representative of the Subcontractor. The term "Subcontractor" does not include a separate contractor or subcontractors of a separate contractor.

**5.1.2** A Sub-subcontractor is a person or entity who has a direct or indirect contract with a Subcontractor to perform a portion of the Work at the site. The term "Sub-subcontractor" is referred to throughout the Contract Documents as if singular in number and means a Sub-subcontractor or an authorized representative of the Sub-subcontractor.

**5.2  AWARD OF SUBCONTRACTS AND OTHER CONTRACTS FOR PORTIONS OF THE WORK**

**5.2.1** Unless otherwise stated in the Contract Documents or the bidding requirements, the Contractor, as soon as practicable after award of the Contract, shall furnish in writing to the Owner through the Architect the names of persons or entities (including those who are to furnish materials or equipment fabricated to a special design) proposed for each principal portion of the Work. The Architect will promptly reply to the Contractor in writing stating whether or not the Owner or the Architect, after due investigation, has reasonable objection to any such proposed person or entity. Failure of the Owner or Architect to reply promptly shall constitute notice of no reasonable objection.

**5.2.2** The Contractor shall not contract with a proposed person or entity to whom the Owner or Architect has made reasonable and timely objection. The Contractor shall not be required to contract with anyone to whom the Contractor has made reasonable objection.

**5.2.3** If the Owner or Architect has reasonable objection to a person or entity proposed by the Contractor, the Contractor shall propose another to whom the Owner or Architect has no reasonable objection. The Contract Sum shall be increased or decreased by the difference in cost occasioned by such change and an appropriate Change Order shall be issued. However, no increase in the Contract Sum shall be allowed for such change unless the Contractor has acted promptly and responsively in submitting names as required.

**5.2.4** The Contractor shall not change a Subcontractor, person or entity previously selected if the Owner or Architect makes reasonable objection to such change

### 5.3 SUBCONTRACTUAL RELATIONS

**5.3.1** By appropriate agreement, written where legally required for validity, the Contractor shall require each Subcontractor, to the extent of the Work to be performed by the Subcontractor, to be bound to the Contractor by terms of the Contract Documents, and to assume toward the Contractor all the obligations and responsibilities which the Contractor, by these Documents, assumes toward the Owner and Architect. Each subcontract agreement shall preserve and protect the rights of the Owner and Architect under the Contract Documents with respect to the Work to be performed by the Subcontractor so that subcontracting thereof will not prejudice such rights, and shall allow to the Subcontractor, unless specifically provided otherwise in the subcontract agreement, the benefit of all rights, remedies and redress against the Contractor that the Contractor, by the Contract Documents, has against the Owner Where appropriate, the Contractor shall require each Subcontractor to enter into similar agreements with Sub-subcontractors. The Contractor shall make available to each proposed Subcontractor, prior to the execution of the subcontract agreement, copies of the Contract Documents to which the Subcontractor will be bound, and, upon written request of the Subcontractor, identify to the Subcontractor terms and conditions of the proposed subcontract agreement which may be at variance with the Contract Documents. Subcontractors shall similarly make copies of applicable portions of such documents available to their respective proposed Sub-subcontractors.

### 5.4 CONTINGENT ASSIGNMENT OF SUBCONTRACTS

**5.4.1** Each subcontract agreement for a portion of the Work is assigned by the Contractor to the Owner provided that:

    .1 assignment is effective only after termination of the Contract by the Owner for cause pursuant to Paragraph 14.2 and only for those subcontract agreements which the Owner accepts by notifying the Subcontractor in writing; and

    .2 assignment is subject to the prior rights of the surety, if any, obligated under bond relating to the Contract.

**5.4.2** If the Work has been suspended for more than 30 days, the Subcontractor's compensation shall be equitably adjusted.

## ARTICLE 6

### CONSTRUCTION BY OWNER OR BY SEPARATE CONTRACTORS

### 6.1 OWNER'S RIGHT TO PERFORM CONSTRUCTION AND TO AWARD SEPARATE CONTRACTS

**6.1.1** The Owner reserves the right to perform construction or operations related to the Project with the Owner's own forces, and to award separate contracts in connection with other portions of the Project or other construction or operations on the site under Conditions of the Contract identical or substantially similar to these including those portions related to insurance and waiver of subrogation. If the Contractor claims that delay or additional cost is involved because of such action by the Owner, the Contractor shall make such Claim as provided elsewhere in the Contract Documents.

**6.1.2** When separate contracts are awarded for different portions of the Project or other construction or operations on the site, the term "Contractor" in the Contract Documents in each case shall mean the Contractor who executes each separate Owner-Contractor Agreement

**6.1.3** The Owner shall provide for coordination of the activities of the Owner's own forces and of each separate contractor with the Work of the Contractor, who shall cooperate with them. The Contractor shall participate with other separate contractors and the Owner in reviewing their construction schedules when directed to do so. The Contractor shall make any revisions to the construction schedule and Contract Sum deemed necessary after a joint review and mutual agreement The construction schedules shall then constitute the schedules to be used by the Contractor, separate contractors and the Owner until subsequently revised.

**6.1.4** Unless otherwise provided in the Contract Documents, when the Owner performs construction or operations related to the Project with the Owner's own forces, the Owner shall be deemed to be subject to the same obligations and to have the same rights which apply to the Contractor under the Conditions of the Contract, including, without excluding others, those stated in Article 3, this Article 6 and Articles 10, 11 and 12.

### 6.2 MUTUAL RESPONSIBILITY

**6.2.1** The Contractor shall afford the Owner and separate contractors reasonable opportunity for introduction and storage of their materials and equipment and performance of their activities and shall connect and coordinate the Contractor's construction and operations with theirs as required by the Contract Documents.

**6.2.2** If part of the Contractor's Work depends for proper execution or results upon construction or operations by the Owner or a separate contractor, the Contractor shall, prior to proceeding with that portion of the Work, promptly report to the Architect apparent discrepancies or defects in such other construction that would render it unsuitable for such proper execution and results. Failure of the Contractor so to report shall constitute an acknowledgment that the Owner's or separate contractors' completed or partially completed construction is fit and proper to receive the Contractor's Work, except as to defects not then reasonably discoverable.

**6.2.3** Costs caused by delays or by improperly timed activities or defective construction shall be borne by the party responsible therefor.

**6.2.4** The Contractor shall promptly remedy damage wrongfully caused by the Contractor to completed or partially completed construction or to property of the Owner or separate contractors as provided in Subparagraph 10.2.5.

**6.2.5** Claims and other disputes and matters in question between the Contractor and a separate contractor shall be subject to the provisions of Paragraph 4.3 provided the separate contractor has reciprocal obligations.

**6.2.6** The Owner and each separate contractor shall have the same responsibilities for cutting and patching as are described for the Contractor in Paragraph 3.14.

### 6.3 OWNER'S RIGHT TO CLEAN UP

**6.3.1** If a dispute arises among the Contractor, separate contractors and the Owner as to the responsibility under their respective contracts for maintaining the premises and surrounding area free from waste materials and rubbish as described in Paragraph 3.15, the Owner may clean up and allocate the cost among those responsible as the Architect determines to be just

**AIA DOCUMENT A201** • GENERAL CONDITIONS OF THE CONTRACT FOR CONSTRUCTION • FOURTEENTH EDITION
AIA® • © 1987 THE AMERICAN INSTITUTE OF ARCHITECTS, 1735 NEW YORK AVENUE, N W, WASHINGTON, D C 20006

# ARTICLE 7

# CHANGES IN THE WORK

## 7.1 CHANGES

**7.1.1** Changes in the Work may be accomplished after execution of the Contract, and without invalidating the Contract, by Change Order, Construction Change Directive or order for a minor change in the Work, subject to the limitations stated in this Article 7 and elsewhere in the Contract Documents.

**7.1.2** A Change Order shall be based upon agreement among the Owner, Contractor and Architect; a Construction Change Directive requires agreement by the Owner and Architect and may or may not be agreed to by the Contractor; an order for a minor change in the Work may be issued by the Architect alone.

**7.1.3** Changes in the Work shall be performed under applicable provisions of the Contract Documents, and the Contractor shall proceed promptly, unless otherwise provided in the Change Order, Construction Change Directive or order for a minor change in the Work.

**7.1.4** If unit prices are stated in the Contract Documents or subsequently agreed upon, and if quantities originally contemplated are so changed in a proposed Change Order or Construction Change Directive that application of such unit prices to quantities of Work proposed will cause substantial inequity to the Owner or Contractor, the applicable unit prices shall be equitably adjusted.

## 7.2 CHANGE ORDERS

**7.2.1** A Change Order is a written instrument prepared by the Architect and signed by the Owner, Contractor and Architect, stating their agreement upon all of the following:

.1 a change in the Work;

.2 the amount of the adjustment in the Contract Sum, if any; and

.3 the extent of the adjustment in the Contract Time, if any.

**7.2.2** Methods used in determining adjustments to the Contract Sum may include those listed in Subparagraph 7.3.3.

## 7.3 CONSTRUCTION CHANGE DIRECTIVES

**7.3.1** A Construction Change Directive is a written order prepared by the Architect and signed by the Owner and Architect, directing a change in the Work and stating a proposed basis for adjustment, if any, in the Contract Sum or Contract Time, or both. The Owner may by Construction Change Directive, without invalidating the Contract, order changes in the Work within the general scope of the Contract consisting of additions, deletions or other revisions, the Contract Sum and Contract Time being adjusted accordingly.

**7.3.2** A Construction Change Directive shall be used in the absence of total agreement on the terms of a Change Order.

**7.3.3** If the Construction Change Directive provides for an adjustment to the Contract Sum, the adjustment shall be based on one of the following methods:

.1 mutual acceptance of a lump sum properly itemized and supported by sufficient substantiating data to permit evaluation;

.2 unit prices stated in the Contract Documents or subsequently agreed upon;

.3 cost to be determined in a manner agreed upon by the parties and a mutually acceptable fixed or percentage fee; or

.4 as provided in Subparagraph 7.3.6.

**7.3.4** Upon receipt of a Construction Change Directive, the Contractor shall promptly proceed with the change in the Work involved and advise the Architect of the Contractor's agreement or disagreement with the method, if any, provided in the Construction Change Directive for determining the proposed adjustment in the Contract Sum or Contract Time.

**7.3.5** A Construction Change Directive signed by the Contractor indicates the agreement of the Contractor therewith, including adjustment in Contract Sum and Contract Time or the method for determining them. Such agreement shall be effective immediately and shall be recorded as a Change Order.

**7.3.6** If the Contractor does not respond promptly or disagrees with the method for adjustment in the Contract Sum, the method and the adjustment shall be determined by the Architect on the basis of reasonable expenditures and savings of those performing the Work attributable to the change, including, in case of an increase in the Contract Sum, a reasonable allowance for overhead and profit. In such case, and also under Clause 7.3.3.3, the Contractor shall keep and present, in such form as the Architect may prescribe, an itemized accounting together with appropriate supporting data. Unless otherwise provided in the Contract Documents, costs for the purposes of this Subparagraph 7.3.6 shall be limited to the following:

.1 costs of labor, including social security, old age and unemployment insurance, fringe benefits required by agreement or custom, and workers' or workmen's compensation insurance;

.2 costs of materials, supplies and equipment, including cost of transportation, whether incorporated or consumed;

.3 rental costs of machinery and equipment, exclusive of hand tools, whether rented from the Contractor or others;

.4 costs of premiums for all bonds and insurance, permit fees, and sales, use or similar taxes related to the Work; and

.5 additional costs of supervision and field office personnel directly attributable to the change.

**7.3.7** Pending final determination of cost to the Owner, amounts not in dispute may be included in Applications for Payment. The amount of credit to be allowed by the Contractor to the Owner for a deletion or change which results in a net decrease in the Contract Sum shall be actual net cost as confirmed by the Architect. When both additions and credits covering related Work or substitutions are involved in a change, the allowance for overhead and profit shall be figured on the basis of net increase, if any, with respect to that change.

**7.3.8** If the Owner and Contractor do not agree with the adjustment in Contract Time or the method for determining it, the adjustment or the method shall be referred to the Architect for determination.

**7.3.9** When the Owner and Contractor agree with the determination made by the Architect concerning the adjustments in the Contract Sum and Contract Time, or otherwise reach agreement upon the adjustments, such agreement shall be effective immediately and shall be recorded by preparation and execution of an appropriate Change Order.

### 7.4 MINOR CHANGES IN THE WORK

**7.4.1** The Architect will have authority to order minor changes in the Work not involving adjustment in the Contract Sum or extension of the Contract Time and not inconsistent with the intent of the Contract Documents. Such changes shall be effected by written order and shall be binding on the Owner and Contractor. The Contractor shall carry out such written orders promptly.

# ARTICLE 8

## TIME

### 8.1 DEFINITIONS

**8.1.1** Unless otherwise provided, Contract Time is the period of time, including authorized adjustments, allotted in the Contract Documents for Substantial Completion of the Work.

**8.1.2** The date of commencement of the Work is the date established in the Agreement. The date shall not be postponed by the failure to act of the Contractor or of persons or entities for whom the Contractor is responsible.

**8.1.3** The date of Substantial Completion is the date certified by the Architect in accordance with Paragraph 9.8.

**8.1.4** The term "day" as used in the Contract Documents shall mean calendar day unless otherwise specifically defined.

### 8.2 PROGRESS AND COMPLETION

**8.2.1** Time limits stated in the Contract Documents are of the essence of the Contract. By executing the Agreement the Contractor confirms that the Contract Time is a reasonable period for performing the Work.

**8.2.2** The Contractor shall not knowingly, except by agreement or instruction of the Owner in writing, prematurely commence operations on the site or elsewhere prior to the effective date of insurance required by Article 11 to be furnished by the Contractor. The date of commencement of the Work shall not be changed by the effective date of such insurance. Unless the date of commencement is established by a notice to proceed given by the Owner, the Contractor shall notify the Owner in writing not less than five days or other agreed period before commencing the Work to permit the timely filing of mortgages, mechanic's liens and other security interests.

**8.2.3** The Contractor shall proceed expeditiously with adequate forces and shall achieve Substantial Completion within the Contract Time.

### 8.3 DELAYS AND EXTENSIONS OF TIME

**8.3.1** If the Contractor is delayed at any time in progress of the Work by an act or neglect of the Owner or Architect, or of an employee of either, or of a separate contractor employed by the Owner, or by changes ordered in the Work, or by labor disputes, fire, unusual delay in deliveries, unavoidable casualties or other causes beyond the Contractor's control, or by delay authorized by the Owner pending arbitration, or by other causes which the Architect determines may justify delay, then the Contract Time shall be extended by Change Order for such reasonable time as the Architect may determine.

**8.3.2** Claims relating to time shall be made in accordance with applicable provisions of Paragraph 4.3.

**8.3.3** This Paragraph 8.3 does not preclude recovery of damages for delay by either party under other provisions of the Contract Documents.

# ARTICLE 9

## PAYMENTS AND COMPLETION

### 9.1 CONTRACT SUM

**9.1.1** The Contract Sum is stated in the Agreement and, including authorized adjustments, is the total amount payable by the Owner to the Contractor for performance of the Work under the Contract Documents.

### 9.2 SCHEDULE OF VALUES

**9.2.1** Before the first Application for Payment, the Contractor shall submit to the Architect a schedule of values allocated to various portions of the Work, prepared in such form and supported by such data to substantiate its accuracy as the Architect may require. This schedule, unless objected to by the Architect, shall be used as a basis for reviewing the Contractor's Applications for Payment.

### 9.3 APPLICATIONS FOR PAYMENT

**9.3.1** At least ten days before the date established for each progress payment, the Contractor shall submit to the Architect an itemized Application for Payment for operations completed in accordance with the schedule of values. Such application shall be notarized, if required, and supported by such data substantiating the Contractor's right to payment as the Owner or Architect may require, such as copies of requisitions from Subcontractors and material suppliers, and reflecting retainage if provided for elsewhere in the Contract Documents.

**9.3.1.1** Such applications may include requests for payment on account of changes in the Work which have been properly authorized by Construction Change Directives but not yet included in Change Orders.

**9.3.1.2** Such applications may not include requests for payment of amounts the Contractor does not intend to pay to a Subcontractor or material supplier because of a dispute or other reason.

**9.3.2** Unless otherwise provided in the Contract Documents, payments shall be made on account of materials and equipment delivered and suitably stored at the site for subsequent incorporation in the Work. If approved in advance by the Owner, payment may similarly be made for materials and equipment suitably stored off the site at a location agreed upon in writing. Payment for materials and equipment stored on or off the site shall be conditioned upon compliance by the Contractor with procedures satisfactory to the Owner to establish the Owner's title to such materials and equipment or otherwise protect the Owner's interest, and shall include applicable insurance, storage and transportation to the site for such materials and equipment stored off the site.

**9.3.3** The Contractor warrants that title to all Work covered by an Application for Payment will pass to the Owner no later than the time of payment. The Contractor further warrants that upon submittal of an Application for Payment all Work for which Certificates for Payment have been previously issued and payments received from the Owner shall, to the best of the Contractor's knowledge, information and belief, be free and clear of liens, claims, security interests or encumbrances in favor of the Contractor, Subcontractors, material suppliers, or other persons or entities making a claim by reason of having provided labor, materials and equipment relating to the Work.

### 9.4 CERTIFICATES FOR PAYMENT

**9.4.1** The Architect will, within seven days after receipt of the Contractor's Application for Payment, either issue to the

**AIA DOCUMENT A201** • GENERAL CONDITIONS OF THE CONTRACT FOR CONSTRUCTION • FOURTEENTH EDITION
AIA® • ©1987 THE AMERICAN INSTITUTE OF ARCHITECTS, 1735 NEW YORK AVENUE, N.W., WASHINGTON, D.C. 20006

Owner a Certificate for Payment, with a copy to the Contractor, for such amount as the Architect determines is properly due, or notify the Contractor and Owner in writing of the Architect's reasons for withholding certification in whole or in part as provided in Subparagraph 9.5.1.

**9.4.2** The issuance of a Certificate for Payment will constitute a representation by the Architect to the Owner, based on the Architect's observations at the site and the data comprising the Application for Payment, that the Work has progressed to the point indicated and that, to the best of the Architect's knowledge, information and belief, quality of the Work is in accordance with the Contract Documents. The foregoing representations are subject to an evaluation of the Work for conformance with the Contract Documents upon Substantial Completion, to results of subsequent tests and inspections, to minor deviations from the Contract Documents correctable prior to completion and to specific qualifications expressed by the Architect. The issuance of a Certificate for Payment will further constitute a representation that the Contractor is entitled to payment in the amount certified. However, the issuance of a Certificate for Payment will not be a representation that the Architect has (1) made exhaustive or continuous on-site inspections to check the quality or quantity of the Work, (2) reviewed construction means, methods, techniques, sequences or procedures, (3) reviewed copies of requisitions received from Subcontractors and material suppliers and other data requested by the Owner to substantiate the Contractor's right to payment or (4) made examination to ascertain how or for what purpose the Contractor has used money previously paid on account of the Contract Sum.

## 9.5 DECISIONS TO WITHHOLD CERTIFICATION

**9.5.1** The Architect may decide not to certify payment and may withhold a Certificate for Payment in whole or in part, to the extent reasonably necessary to protect the Owner, if in the Architect's opinion the representations to the Owner required by Subparagraph 9.4.2 cannot be made. If the Architect is unable to certify payment in the amount of the Application, the Architect will notify the Contractor and Owner as provided in Subparagraph 9.4.1. If the Contractor and Architect cannot agree on a revised amount, the Architect will promptly issue a Certificate for Payment for the amount for which the Architect is able to make such representations to the Owner. The Architect may also decide not to certify payment or, because of subsequently discovered evidence or subsequent observations, may nullify the whole or a part of a Certificate for Payment previously issued, to such extent as may be necessary in the Architect's opinion to protect the Owner from loss because of:

.1 defective Work not remedied;

.2 third party claims filed or reasonable evidence indicating probable filing of such claims;

.3 failure of the Contractor to make payments properly to Subcontractors or for labor, materials or equipment;

.4 reasonable evidence that the Work cannot be completed for the unpaid balance of the Contract Sum;

.5 damage to the Owner or another contractor;

.6 reasonable evidence that the Work will not be completed within the Contract Time, and that the unpaid balance would not be adequate to cover actual or liquidated damages for the anticipated delay; or

.7 persistent failure to carry out the Work in accordance with the Contract Documents.

**9.5.2** When the above reasons for withholding certification are removed, certification will be made for amounts previously withheld.

## 9.6 PROGRESS PAYMENTS

**9.6.1** After the Architect has issued a Certificate for Payment, the Owner shall make payment in the manner and within the time provided in the Contract Documents, and shall so notify the Architect.

**9.6.2** The Contractor shall promptly pay each Subcontractor, upon receipt of payment from the Owner, out of the amount paid to the Contractor on account of such Subcontractor's portion of the Work, the amount to which said Subcontractor is entitled, reflecting percentages actually retained from payments to the Contractor on account of such Subcontractor's portion of the Work. The Contractor shall, by appropriate agreement with each Subcontractor, require each Subcontractor to make payments to Sub-subcontractors in similar manner.

**9.6.3** The Architect will, on request, furnish to a Subcontractor, if practicable, information regarding percentages of completion or amounts applied for by the Contractor and action taken thereon by the Architect and Owner on account of portions of the Work done by such Subcontractor.

**9.6.4** Neither the Owner nor Architect shall have an obligation to pay or to see to the payment of money to a Subcontractor except as may otherwise be required by law.

**9.6.5** Payment to material suppliers shall be treated in a manner similar to that provided in Subparagraphs 9.6.2, 9.6.3 and 9.6.4.

**9.6.6** A Certificate for Payment, a progress payment, or partial or entire use or occupancy of the Project by the Owner shall not constitute acceptance of Work not in accordance with the Contract Documents.

## 9.7 FAILURE OF PAYMENT

**9.7.1** If the Architect does not issue a Certificate for Payment, through no fault of the Contractor, within seven days after receipt of the Contractor's Application for Payment, or if the Owner does not pay the Contractor within seven days after the date established in the Contract Documents the amount certified by the Architect or awarded by arbitration, then the Contractor may, upon seven additional days' written notice to the Owner and Architect, stop the Work until payment of the amount owing has been received. The Contract Time shall be extended appropriately and the Contract Sum shall be increased by the amount of the Contractor's reasonable costs of shut-down, delay and start-up, which shall be accomplished as provided in Article 7.

## 9.8 SUBSTANTIAL COMPLETION

**9.8.1** Substantial Completion is the stage in the progress of the Work when the Work or designated portion thereof is sufficiently complete in accordance with the Contract Documents so the Owner can occupy or utilize the Work for its intended use.

**9.8.2** When the Contractor considers that the Work, or a portion thereof which the Owner agrees to accept separately, is substantially complete, the Contractor shall prepare and submit to the Architect a comprehensive list of items to be completed or corrected. The Contractor shall proceed promptly to complete and correct items on the list. Failure to include an item on such list does not alter the responsibility of the Contractor to complete all Work in accordance with the Contract Documents. Upon receipt of the Contractor's list, the Architect will make an inspection to determine whether the Work or designated portion thereof is substantially complete. If the Architect's inspection discloses any item, whether or not included on the Contractor's list, which is not in accordance with the requirements of the Contract Documents, the Contractor shall, before issuance of the Certificate of Substantial Completion, complete or correct such item upon notification by the Architect. The Contractor shall then submit a request for another inspection by the Architect to determine Substantial Completion. When the Work or designated portion thereof is substantially complete, the Architect will prepare a Certificate of Substantial Completion which shall establish the date of Substantial Completion, shall establish responsibilities of the Owner and Contractor for security, maintenance, heat, utilities, damage to the Work and insurance, and shall fix the time within which the Contractor shall finish all items on the list accompanying the Certificate. Warranties required by the Contract Documents shall commence on the date of Substantial Completion of the Work or designated portion thereof unless otherwise provided in the Certificate of Substantial Completion. The Certificate of Substantial Completion shall be submitted to the Owner and Contractor for their written acceptance of responsibilities assigned to them in such Certificate.

**9.8.3** Upon Substantial Completion of the Work or designated portion thereof and upon application by the Contractor and certification by the Architect, the Owner shall make payment, reflecting adjustment in retainage, if any, for such Work or portion thereof as provided in the Contract Documents.

## 9.9 PARTIAL OCCUPANCY OR USE

**9.9.1** The Owner may occupy or use any completed or partially completed portion of the Work at any stage when such portion is designated by separate agreement with the Contractor, provided such occupancy or use is consented to by the insurer as required under Subparagraph 11.3.11 and authorized by public authorities having jurisdiction over the Work. Such partial occupancy or use may commence whether or not the portion is substantially complete, provided the Owner and Contractor have accepted in writing the responsibilities assigned to each of them for payments, retainage if any, security, maintenance, heat, utilities, damage to the Work and insurance, and have agreed in writing concerning the period for correction of the Work and commencement of warranties required by the Contract Documents. When the Contractor considers a portion substantially complete, the Contractor shall prepare and submit a list to the Architect as provided under Subparagraph 9.8.2. Consent of the Contractor to partial occupancy or use shall not be unreasonably withheld. The stage of the progress of the Work shall be determined by written agreement between the Owner and Contractor or, if no agreement is reached, by decision of the Architect.

**9.9.2** Immediately prior to such partial occupancy or use, the Owner, Contractor and Architect shall jointly inspect the area to be occupied or portion of the Work to be used in order to determine and record the condition of the Work.

**9.9.3** Unless otherwise agreed upon, partial occupancy or use of a portion or portions of the Work shall not constitute acceptance of Work not complying with the requirements of the Contract Documents.

## 9.10 FINAL COMPLETION AND FINAL PAYMENT

**9.10.1** Upon receipt of written notice that the Work is ready for final inspection and acceptance and upon receipt of a final Application for Payment, the Architect will promptly make such inspection and, when the Architect finds the Work acceptable under the Contract Documents and the Contract fully performed, the Architect will promptly issue a final Certificate for Payment stating that to the best of the Architect's knowledge, information and belief, and on the basis of the Architect's observations and inspections, the Work has been completed in accordance with terms and conditions of the Contract Documents and that the entire balance found to be due the Contractor and noted in said final Certificate is due and payable. The Architect's final Certificate for Payment will constitute a further representation that conditions listed in Subparagraph 9.10.2 as precedent to the Contractor's being entitled to final payment have been fulfilled.

**9.10.2** Neither final payment nor any remaining retained percentage shall become due until the Contractor submits to the Architect (1) an affidavit that payrolls, bills for materials and equipment, and other indebtedness connected with the Work for which the Owner or the Owner's property might be responsible or encumbered (less amounts withheld by Owner) have been paid or otherwise satisfied, (2) a certificate evidencing that insurance required by the Contract Documents to remain in force after final payment is currently in effect and will not be cancelled or allowed to expire until at least 30 days' prior written notice has been given to the Owner, (3) a written statement that the Contractor knows of no substantial reason that the insurance will not be renewable to cover the period required by the Contract Documents, (4) consent of surety, if any, to final payment and (5), if required by the Owner, other data establishing payment or satisfaction of obligations, such as receipts, releases and waivers of liens, claims, security interests or encumbrances arising out of the Contract, to the extent and in such form as may be designated by the Owner. If a Subcontractor refuses to furnish a release or waiver required by the Owner, the Contractor may furnish a bond satisfactory to the Owner to indemnify the Owner against such lien. If such lien remains unsatisfied after payments are made, the Contractor shall refund to the Owner all money that the Owner may be compelled to pay in discharging such lien, including all costs and reasonable attorneys' fees.

**9.10.3** If, after Substantial Completion of the Work, final completion thereof is materially delayed through no fault of the Contractor or by issuance of Change Orders affecting final completion, and the Architect so confirms, the Owner shall, upon application by the Contractor and certification by the Architect, and without terminating the Contract, make payment of the balance due for that portion of the Work fully completed and accepted. If the remaining balance for Work not fully completed or corrected is less than retainage stipulated in the Contract Documents, and if bonds have been furnished, the written consent of surety to payment of the balance due for that portion of the Work fully completed and accepted shall be submitted by the Contractor to the Architect prior to certification of such payment. Such payment shall be made under terms and conditions governing final payment, except that it shall not constitute a waiver of claims. The making of final payment shall constitute a waiver of claims by the Owner as provided in Subparagraph 4.3.5.

**9.10.4** Acceptance of final payment by the Contractor, a Subcontractor or material supplier shall constitute a waiver of claims by that payee except those previously made in writing and identified by that payee as unsettled at the time of final Application for Payment. Such waivers shall be in addition to the waiver described in Subparagraph 4.3.5.

**AIA DOCUMENT A201** • GENERAL CONDITIONS OF THE CONTRACT FOR CONSTRUCTION • FOURTEENTH EDITION
AIA® • ©1987 THE AMERICAN INSTITUTE OF ARCHITECTS, 1735 NEW YORK AVENUE, N.W., WASHINGTON, D.C. 20006

## ARTICLE 10

## PROTECTION OF PERSONS AND PROPERTY

### 10.1 SAFETY PRECAUTIONS AND PROGRAMS

**10.1.1** The Contractor shall be responsible for initiating, maintaining and supervising all safety precautions and programs in connection with the performance of the Contract.

**10.1.2** In the event the Contractor encounters on the site material reasonably believed to be asbestos or polychlorinated biphenyl (PCB) which has not been rendered harmless, the Contractor shall immediately stop Work in the area affected and report the condition to the Owner and Architect in writing. The Work in the affected area shall not thereafter be resumed except by written agreement of the Owner and Contractor if in fact the material is asbestos or polychlorinated biphenyl (PCB) and has not been rendered harmless. The Work in the affected area shall be resumed in the absence of asbestos or polychlorinated biphenyl (PCB), or when it has been rendered harmless, by written agreement of the Owner and Contractor, or in accordance with final determination by the Architect on which arbitration has not been demanded, or by arbitration under Article 4.

**10.1.3** The Contractor shall not be required pursuant to Article 7 to perform without consent any Work relating to asbestos or polychlorinated biphenyl (PCB).

**10.1.4** To the fullest extent permitted by law, the Owner shall indemnify and hold harmless the Contractor, Architect, Architect's consultants and agents and employees of any of them from and against claims, damages, losses and expenses, including but not limited to attorneys' fees, arising out of or resulting from performance of the Work in the affected area if in fact the material is asbestos or polychlorinated biphenyl (PCB) and has not been rendered harmless, provided that such claim, damage, loss or expense is attributable to bodily injury, sickness, disease or death, or to injury to or destruction of tangible property (other than the Work itself) including loss of use resulting therefrom, but only to the extent caused in whole or in part by negligent acts or omissions of the Owner, anyone directly or indirectly employed by the Owner or anyone for whose acts the Owner may be liable, regardless of whether or not such claim, damage, loss or expense is caused in part by a party indemnified hereunder. Such obligation shall not be construed to negate, abridge, or reduce other rights or obligations of indemnity which would otherwise exist as to a party or person described in this Subparagraph 10.1.4.

### 10.2 SAFETY OF PERSONS AND PROPERTY

**10.2.1** The Contractor shall take reasonable precautions for safety of, and shall provide reasonable protection to prevent damage, injury or loss to:

.1 employees on the Work and other persons who may be affected thereby;

.2 the Work and materials and equipment to be incorporated therein, whether in storage on or off the site, under care, custody or control of the Contractor or the Contractor's Subcontractors or Sub-subcontractors; and

.3 other property at the site or adjacent thereto, such as trees, shrubs, lawns, walks, pavements, roadways, structures and utilities not designated for removal, relocation or replacement in the course of construction.

**10.2.2** The Contractor shall give notices and comply with applicable laws, ordinances, rules, regulations and lawful orders of public authorities bearing on safety of persons or property or their protection from damage, injury or loss.

**10.2.3** The Contractor shall erect and maintain, as required by existing conditions and performance of the Contract, reasonable safeguards for safety and protection, including posting danger signs and other warnings against hazards, promulgating safety regulations and notifying owners and users of adjacent sites and utilities.

**10.2.4** When use or storage of explosives or other hazardous materials or equipment or unusual methods are necessary for execution of the Work, the Contractor shall exercise utmost care and carry on such activities under supervision of properly qualified personnel.

**10.2.5** The Contractor shall promptly remedy damage and loss (other than damage or loss insured under property insurance required by the Contract Documents) to property referred to in Clauses 10.2.1.2 and 10.2.1.3 caused in whole or in part by the Contractor, a Subcontractor, a Sub-subcontractor, or anyone directly or indirectly employed by any of them, or by anyone for whose acts they may be liable and for which the Contractor is responsible under Clauses 10.2.1.2 and 10.2.1.3, except damage or loss attributable to acts or omissions of the Owner or Architect or anyone directly or indirectly employed by either of them, or by anyone for whose acts either of them may be liable, and not attributable to the fault or negligence of the Contractor. The foregoing obligations of the Contractor are in addition to the Contractor's obligations under Paragraph 3.18.

**10.2.6** The Contractor shall designate a responsible member of the Contractor's organization at the site whose duty shall be the prevention of accidents. This person shall be the Contractor's superintendent unless otherwise designated by the Contractor in writing to the Owner and Architect.

**10.2.7** The Contractor shall not load or permit any part of the construction or site to be loaded so as to endanger its safety.

### 10.3 EMERGENCIES

**10.3.1** In an emergency affecting safety of persons or property, the Contractor shall act, at the Contractor's discretion, to prevent threatened damage, injury or loss. Additional compensation or extension of time claimed by the Contractor on account of an emergency shall be determined as provided in Paragraph 4.3 and Article 7.

## ARTICLE 11

## INSURANCE AND BONDS

### 11.1 CONTRACTOR'S LIABILITY INSURANCE

**11.1.1** The Contractor shall purchase from and maintain in a company or companies lawfully authorized to do business in the jurisdiction in which the Project is located such insurance as will protect the Contractor from claims set forth below which may arise out of or result from the Contractor's operations under the Contract and for which the Contractor may be legally liable, whether such operations be by the Contractor or by a Subcontractor or by anyone directly or indirectly employed by any of them, or by anyone for whose acts any of them may be liable:

.1 claims under workers' or workmen's compensation, disability benefit and other similar employee benefit acts which are applicable to the Work to be performed;

.2 claims for damages because of bodily injury, occupational sickness or disease, or death of the Contractor's employees;

.3 claims for damages because of bodily injury, sickness or disease, or death of any person other than the Contractor's employees;

.4 claims for damages insured by usual personal injury liability coverage which are sustained (1) by a person as a result of an offense directly or indirectly related to employment of such person by the Contractor, or (2) by another person;

.5 claims for damages, other than to the Work itself, because of injury to or destruction of tangible property, including loss of use resulting therefrom;

.6 claims for damages because of bodily injury, death of a person or property damage arising out of ownership, maintenance or use of a motor vehicle; and

.7 claims involving contractual liability insurance applicable to the Contractor's obligations under Paragraph 3.18.

**11.1.2** The insurance required by Subparagraph 11.1.1 shall be written for not less than limits of liability specified in the Contract Documents or required by law, whichever coverage is greater. Coverages, whether written on an occurrence or claims-made basis, shall be maintained without interruption from date of commencement of the Work until date of final payment and termination of any coverage required to be maintained after final payment.

**11.1.3** Certificates of Insurance acceptable to the Owner shall be filed with the Owner prior to commencement of the Work. These Certificates and the insurance policies required by this Paragraph 11.1 shall contain a provision that coverages afforded under the policies will not be cancelled or allowed to expire until at least 30 days' prior written notice has been given to the Owner. If any of the foregoing insurance coverages are required to remain in force after final payment and are reasonably available, an additional certificate evidencing continuation of such coverage shall be submitted with the final Application for Payment as required by Subparagraph 9.10.2. Information concerning reduction of coverage shall be furnished by the Contractor with reasonable promptness in accordance with the Contractor's information and belief.

**11.2    OWNER'S LIABILITY INSURANCE**

**11.2.1** The Owner shall be responsible for purchasing and maintaining the Owner's usual liability insurance. Optionally, the Owner may purchase and maintain other insurance for self-protection against claims which may arise from operations under the Contract. The Contractor shall not be responsible for purchasing and maintaining this Optional Owner's liability insurance unless specifically required by the Contract Documents.

**11.3    PROPERTY INSURANCE**

**11.3.1** Unless otherwise provided, the Owner shall purchase and maintain, in a company or companies lawfully authorized to do business in the jurisdiction in which the Project is located, property insurance in the amount of the initial Contract Sum as well as subsequent modifications thereto for the entire Work at the site on a replacement cost basis without voluntary deductibles. Such property insurance shall be maintained, unless otherwise provided in the Contract Documents or otherwise agreed in writing by all persons and entities who are beneficiaries of such insurance, until final payment has been made as provided in Paragraph 9.10 or until no person or entity

other than the Owner has an insurable interest in the property required by this Paragraph 11.3 to be covered, whichever is earlier. This insurance shall include interests of the Owner, the Contractor, Subcontractors and Sub-subcontractors in the Work.

**11.3.1.1** Property insurance shall be on an all-risk policy form and shall insure against the perils of fire and extended coverage and physical loss or damage including, without duplication of coverage, theft, vandalism, malicious mischief, collapse, falsework, temporary buildings and debris removal including demolition occasioned by enforcement of any applicable legal requirements, and shall cover reasonable compensation for Architect's services and expenses required as a result of such insured loss. Coverage for other perils shall not be required unless otherwise provided in the Contract Documents.

**11.3.1.2** If the Owner does not intend to purchase such property insurance required by the Contract and with all of the coverages in the amount described above, the Owner shall so inform the Contractor in writing prior to commencement of the Work. The Contractor may then effect insurance which will protect the interests of the Contractor, Subcontractors and Sub-subcontractors in the Work, and by appropriate Change Order the cost thereof shall be charged to the Owner. If the Contractor is damaged by the failure or neglect of the Owner to purchase or maintain insurance as described above, without so notifying the Contractor, then the Owner shall bear all reasonable costs properly attributable thereto.

**11.3.1.3** If the property insurance requires minimum deductibles and such deductibles are identified in the Contract Documents, the Contractor shall pay costs not covered because of such deductibles. If the Owner or insurer increases the required minimum deductibles above the amounts so identified or if the Owner elects to purchase this insurance with voluntary deductible amounts, the Owner shall be responsible for payment of the additional costs not covered because of such increased or voluntary deductibles. If deductibles are not identified in the Contract Documents, the Owner shall pay costs not covered because of deductibles.

**11.3.1.4** Unless otherwise provided in the Contract Documents, this property insurance shall cover portions of the Work stored off the site after written approval of the Owner at the value established in the approval, and also portions of the Work in transit.

**11.3.2 Boiler and Machinery Insurance.** The Owner shall purchase and maintain boiler and machinery insurance required by the Contract Documents or by law, which shall specifically cover such insured objects during installation and until final acceptance by the Owner; this insurance shall include interests of the Owner, Contractor, Subcontractors and Sub-subcontractors in the Work, and the Owner and Contractor shall be named insureds.

**11.3.3 Loss of Use Insurance.** The Owner, at the Owner's option, may purchase and maintain such insurance as will insure the Owner against loss of use of the Owner's property due to fire or other hazards, however caused. The Owner waives all rights of action against the Contractor for loss of use of the Owner's property, including consequential losses due to fire or other hazards however caused.

**11.3.4** If the Contractor requests in writing that insurance for risks other than those described herein or for other special hazards be included in the property insurance policy, the Owner shall, if possible, include such insurance, and the cost thereof shall be charged to the Contractor by appropriate Change Order.

**AIA DOCUMENT A201** • GENERAL CONDITIONS OF THE CONTRACT FOR CONSTRUCTION • FOURTEENTH EDITION
AIA® • ©1987 THE AMERICAN INSTITUTE OF ARCHITECTS, 1735 NEW YORK AVENUE, N.W., WASHINGTON, D.C. 20006

**11.3.5** If during the Project construction period the Owner insures properties, real or personal or both, adjoining or adjacent to the site by property insurance under policies separate from those insuring the Project, or if after final payment property insurance is to be provided on the completed Project through a policy or policies other than those insuring the Project during the construction period, the Owner shall waive all rights in accordance with the terms of Subparagraph 11.3.7 for damages caused by fire or other perils covered by this separate property insurance. All separate policies shall provide this waiver of subrogation by endorsement or otherwise.

**11.3.6** Before an exposure to loss may occur, the Owner shall file with the Contractor a copy of each policy that includes insurance coverages required by this Paragraph 11.3. Each policy shall contain all generally applicable conditions, definitions, exclusions and endorsements related to this Project. Each policy shall contain a provision that the policy will not be cancelled or allowed to expire until at least 30 days' prior written notice has been given to the Contractor.

**11.3.7 Waivers of Subrogation.** The Owner and Contractor waive all rights against (1) each other and any of their subcontractors, sub-subcontractors, agents and employees, each of the other, and (2) the Architect, Architect's consultants, separate contractors described in Article 6, if any, and any of their subcontractors, sub-subcontractors, agents and employees, for damages caused by fire or other perils to the extent covered by property insurance obtained pursuant to this Paragraph 11.3 or other property insurance applicable to the Work, except such rights as they have to proceeds of such insurance held by the Owner as fiduciary. The Owner or Contractor, as appropriate, shall require of the Architect, Architect's consultants, separate contractors described in Article 6, if any, and the subcontractors, sub-subcontractors, agents and employees of any of them, by appropriate agreements, written where legally required for validity, similar waivers each in favor of other parties enumerated herein. The policies shall provide such waivers of subrogation by endorsement or otherwise. A waiver of subrogation shall be effective as to a person or entity even though that person or entity would otherwise have a duty of indemnification, contractual or otherwise, did not pay the insurance premium directly or indirectly, and whether or not the person or entity had an insurable interest in the property damaged.

**11.3.8** A loss insured under Owner's property insurance shall be adjusted by the Owner as fiduciary and made payable to the Owner as fiduciary for the insureds, as their interests may appear, subject to requirements of any applicable mortgagee clause and of Subparagraph 11.3.10. The Contractor shall pay Subcontractors their just shares of insurance proceeds received by the Contractor, and by appropriate agreements, written where legally required for validity, shall require Subcontractors to make payments to their Sub-subcontractors in similar manner.

**11.3.9** If required in writing by a party in interest, the Owner as fiduciary shall, upon occurrence of an insured loss, give bond for proper performance of the Owner's duties. The cost of required bonds shall be charged against proceeds received as fiduciary. The Owner shall deposit in a separate account proceeds so received, which the Owner shall distribute in accordance with such agreement as the parties in interest may reach, or in accordance with an arbitration award in which case the procedure shall be as provided in Paragraph 4.5. If after such loss no other special agreement is made, replacement of damaged property shall be covered by appropriate Change Order

**11.3.10** The Owner as fiduciary shall have power to adjust and settle a loss with insurers unless one of the parties in interest shall object in writing within five days after occurrence of loss to the Owner's exercise of this power; if such objection be made, arbitrators shall be chosen as provided in Paragraph 4.5. The Owner as fiduciary shall, in that case, make settlement with insurers in accordance with directions of such arbitrators. If distribution of insurance proceeds by arbitration is required, the arbitrators will direct such distribution.

**11.3.11** Partial occupancy or use in accordance with Paragraph 9.9 shall not commence until the insurance company or companies providing property insurance have consented to such partial occupancy or use by endorsement or otherwise. The Owner and the insurance company or companies and shall without mutual written consent, take no action with respect to partial occupancy or use that would cause cancellation, lapse or reduction of insurance.

**11.4 PERFORMANCE BOND AND PAYMENT BOND**

**11.4.1** The Owner shall have the right to require the Contractor to furnish bonds covering faithful performance of the Contract and payment of obligations arising thereunder as stipulated in bidding requirements or specifically required in the Contract Documents on the date of execution of the Contract.

**11.4.2** Upon the request of any person or entity appearing to be a potential beneficiary of bonds covering payment of obligations arising under the Contract, the Contractor shall promptly furnish a copy of the bonds or shall permit a copy to be made.

# ARTICLE 12

## UNCOVERING AND CORRECTION OF WORK

### 12.1 UNCOVERING OF WORK

**12.1.1** If a portion of the Work is covered contrary to the Architect's request or to requirements specifically expressed in the Contract Documents, it must, if required in writing by the Architect, be uncovered for the Architect's observation and be replaced at the Contractor's expense without change in the Contract Time.

**12.1.2** If a portion of the Work has been covered which the Architect has not specifically requested to observe prior to its being covered, the Architect may request to see such Work and it shall be uncovered by the Contractor. If such Work is in accordance with the Contract Documents, costs of uncovering and replacement shall, by appropriate Change Order, be charged to the Owner. If such Work is not in accordance with the Contract Documents, the Contractor shall pay such costs unless the condition was caused by the Owner or a separate contractor in which event the Owner shall be responsible for payment of such costs.

### 12.2 CORRECTION OF WORK

**12.2.1** The Contractor shall promptly correct Work rejected by the Architect or failing to conform to the requirements of the Contract Documents, whether observed before or after Substantial Completion and whether or not fabricated, installed or completed. The Contractor shall bear costs of correcting such rejected Work, including additional testing and inspections and compensation for the Architect's services and expenses made necessary thereby.

**12.2.2** If, within one year after the date of Substantial Completion of the Work or designated portion thereof, or after the date for commencement of warranties established under Sub-paragraph 9.9.1, or by terms of an applicable special warranty required by the Contract Documents, any of the Work is found to be not in accordance with the requirements of the Contract Documents, the Contractor shall correct it promptly after receipt of written notice from the Owner to do so unless the Owner has previously given the Contractor a written acceptance of such condition. This period of one year shall be extended with respect to portions of the Work first performed after Substantial Completion by the period of time between Substantial Completion and the actual performance of the Work. This obligation under this Subparagraph 12.2.2 shall survive acceptance of the Work under the Contract and termination of the Contract. The Owner shall give such notice promptly after discovery of the condition.

**12.2.3** The Contractor shall remove from the site portions of the Work which are not in accordance with the requirements of the Contract Documents and are neither corrected by the Contractor nor accepted by the Owner.

**12.2.4** If the Contractor fails to correct nonconforming Work within a reasonable time, the Owner may correct it in accordance with Paragraph 2.4. If the Contractor does not proceed with correction of such nonconforming Work within a reasonable time fixed by written notice from the Architect, the Owner may remove it and store the salvable materials or equipment at the Contractor's expense. If the Contractor does not pay costs of such removal and storage within ten days after written notice, the Owner may upon ten additional days' written notice sell such materials and equipment at auction or at private sale and shall account for the proceeds thereof, after deducting costs and damages that should have been borne by the Contractor, including compensation for the Architect's services and expenses made necessary thereby. If such proceeds of sale do not cover costs which the Contractor should have borne, the Contract Sum shall be reduced by the deficiency. If payments then or thereafter due the Contractor are not sufficient to cover such amount, the Contractor shall pay the difference to the Owner.

**12.2.5** The Contractor shall bear the cost of correcting destroyed or damaged construction, whether completed or partially completed, of the Owner or separate contractors caused by the Contractor's correction or removal of Work which is not in accordance with the requirements of the Contract Documents.

**12.2.6** Nothing contained in this Paragraph 12.2 shall be construed to establish a period of limitation with respect to other obligations which the Contractor might have under the Contract Documents. Establishment of the time period of one year as described in Subparagraph 12.2.2 relates only to the specific obligation of the Contractor to correct the Work, and has no relationship to the time within which the obligation to comply with the Contract Documents may be sought to be enforced, nor to the time within which proceedings may be commenced to establish the Contractor's liability with respect to the Contractor's obligations other than specifically to correct the Work.

**12.3 ACCEPTANCE OF NONCONFORMING WORK**

**12.3.1** If the Owner prefers to accept Work which is not in accordance with the requirements of the Contract Documents, the Owner may do so instead of requiring its removal and correction, in which case the Contract Sum will be reduced as appropriate and equitable. Such adjustment shall be effected whether or not final payment has been made.

## ARTICLE 13

## MISCELLANEOUS PROVISIONS

**13.1 GOVERNING LAW**

**13.1.1** The Contract shall be governed by the law of the place where the Project is located.

**13.2 SUCCESSORS AND ASSIGNS**

**13.2.1** The Owner and Contractor respectively bind themselves, their partners, successors, assigns and legal representatives to the other party hereto and to partners, successors, assigns and legal representatives of such other party in respect to covenants, agreements and obligations contained in the Contract Documents. Neither party to the Contract shall assign the Contract as a whole without written consent of the other. If either party attempts to make such an assignment without such consent, that party shall nevertheless remain legally responsible for all obligations under the Contract.

**13.3 WRITTEN NOTICE**

**13.3.1** Written notice shall be deemed to have been duly served if delivered in person to the individual or a member of the firm or entity or to an officer of the corporation for which it was intended, or if delivered at or sent by registered or certified mail to the last business address known to the party giving notice.

**13.4 RIGHTS AND REMEDIES**

**13.4.1** Duties and obligations imposed by the Contract Documents and rights and remedies available thereunder shall be in addition to and not a limitation of duties, obligations, rights and remedies otherwise imposed or available by law.

**13.4.2** No action or failure to act by the Owner, Architect or Contractor shall constitute a waiver of a right or duty afforded them under the Contract, nor shall such action or failure to act constitute approval of or acquiescence in a breach thereunder, except as may be specifically agreed in writing.

**13.5 TESTS AND INSPECTIONS**

**13.5.1** Tests, inspections and approvals of portions of the Work required by the Contract Documents or by laws, ordinances, rules, regulations or orders of public authorities having jurisdiction shall be made at an appropriate time. Unless otherwise provided, the Contractor shall make arrangements for such tests, inspections and approvals with an independent testing laboratory or entity acceptable to the Owner, or with the appropriate public authority, and shall bear all related costs of tests, inspections and approvals. The Contractor shall give the Architect timely notice of when and where tests and inspections are to be made so the Architect may observe such procedures. The Owner shall bear costs of tests, inspections or approvals which do not become requirements until after bids are received or negotiations concluded.

**13.5.2** If the Architect, Owner or public authorities having jurisdiction determine that portions of the Work require additional testing, inspection or approval not included under Subparagraph 13.5.1, the Architect will, upon written authorization from the Owner, instruct the Contractor to make arrangements for such additional testing, inspection or approval by an entity acceptable to the Owner, and the Contractor shall give timely notice to the Architect of when and where tests and inspections are to be made so the Architect may observe such procedures.

**AIA DOCUMENT A201** • GENERAL CONDITIONS OF THE CONTRACT FOR CONSTRUCTION • FOURTEENTH EDITION
AIA® • ©1987 THE AMERICAN INSTITUTE OF ARCHITECTS, 1735 NEW YORK AVENUE, N.W., WASHINGTON, D.C. 20006

The Owner shall bear such costs except as provided in Sub-paragraph 13.5.3.

**13.5.3** If such procedures for testing, inspection or approval under Subparagraphs 13.5.1 and 13.5.2 reveal failure of the portions of the Work to comply with requirements established by the Contract Documents, the Contractor shall bear all costs made necessary by such failure including those of repeated procedures and compensation for the Architect's services and expenses.

**13.5.4** Required certificates of testing, inspection or approval shall, unless otherwise required by the Contract Documents, be secured by the Contractor and promptly delivered to the Architect.

**13.5.5** If the Architect is to observe tests, inspections or approvals required by the Contract Documents, the Architect will do so promptly and, where practicable, at the normal place of testing.

**13.5.6** Tests or inspections conducted pursuant to the Contract Documents shall be made promptly to avoid unreasonable delay in the Work.

**13.6 INTEREST**

**13.6.1** Payments due and unpaid under the Contract Documents shall bear interest from the date payment is due at such rate as the parties may agree upon in writing or, in the absence thereof, at the legal rate prevailing from time to time at the place where the Project is located.

**13.7 COMMENCEMENT OF STATUTORY LIMITATION PERIOD**

**13.7.1** As between the Owner and Contractor:

.1 **Before Substantial Completion.** As to acts or failures to act occurring prior to the relevant date of Substantial Completion, any applicable statute of limitations shall commence to run and any alleged cause of action shall be deemed to have accrued in any and all events not later than such date of Substantial Completion;

.2 **Between Substantial Completion and Final Certificate for Payment.** As to acts or failures to act occurring subsequent to the relevant date of Substantial Completion and prior to issuance of the final Certificate for Payment, any applicable statute of limitations shall commence to run and any alleged cause of action shall be deemed to have accrued in any and all events not later than the date of issuance of the final Certificate for Payment; and

.3 **After Final Certificate for Payment.** As to acts or failures to act occurring after the relevant date of issuance of the final Certificate for Payment, any applicable statute of limitations shall commence to run and any alleged cause of action shall be deemed to have accrued in any and all events not later than the date of any act or failure to act by the Contractor pursuant to any warranty provided under Paragraph 3.5, the date of any correction of the Work or failure to correct the Work by the Contractor under Paragraph 12.2, or the date of actual commission of any other act or failure to perform any duty or obligation by the Contractor or Owner, whichever occurs last.

## ARTICLE 14

## TERMINATION OR SUSPENSION OF THE CONTRACT

**14.1 TERMINATION BY THE CONTRACTOR**

**14.1.1** The Contractor may terminate the Contract if the Work is stopped for a period of 30 days through no act or fault of the Contractor or a Subcontractor, Sub-subcontractor or their agents or employees or any other persons performing portions of the Work under contract with the Contractor, for any of the following reasons:

.1 issuance of an order of a court or other public authority having jurisdiction;

.2 an act of government, such as a declaration of national emergency, making material unavailable;

.3 because the Architect has not issued a Certificate for Payment and has not notified the Contractor of the reason for withholding certification as provided in Subparagraph 9.4.1, or because the Owner has not made payment on a Certificate for Payment within the time stated in the Contract Documents;

.4 if repeated suspensions, delays or interruptions by the Owner as described in Paragraph 14.3 constitute in the aggregate more than 100 percent of the total number of days scheduled for completion, or 120 days in any 365-day period, whichever is less; or

.5 the Owner has failed to furnish to the Contractor promptly, upon the Contractor's request, reasonable evidence as required by Subparagraph 2.2.1.

**14.1.2** If one of the above reasons exists, the Contractor may, upon seven additional days' written notice to the Owner and Architect, terminate the Contract and recover from the Owner payment for Work executed and for proven loss with respect to materials, equipment, tools, and construction equipment and machinery, including reasonable overhead, profit and damages.

**14.1.3** If the Work is stopped for a period of 60 days through no act or fault of the Contractor or a Subcontractor or their agents or employees or any other persons performing portions of the Work under contract with the Contractor because the Owner has persistently failed to fulfill the Owner's obligations under the Contract Documents with respect to matters important to the progress of the Work, the Contractor may, upon seven additional days' written notice to the Owner and the Architect, terminate the Contract and recover from the Owner as provided in Subparagraph 14.1.2.

**14.2 TERMINATION BY THE OWNER FOR CAUSE**

**14.2.1** The Owner may terminate the Contract if the Contractor:

.1 persistently or repeatedly refuses or fails to supply enough properly skilled workers or proper materials;

.2 fails to make payment to Subcontractors for materials or labor in accordance with the respective agreements between the Contractor and the Subcontractors;

.3 persistently disregards laws, ordinances, or rules, regulations or orders of a public authority having jurisdiction; or

.4 otherwise is guilty of substantial breach of a provision of the Contract Documents.

**14.2.2** When any of the above reasons exist, the Owner, upon certification by the Architect that sufficient cause exists to justify such action, may without prejudice to any other rights or remedies of the Owner and after giving the Contractor and the Contractor's surety, if any, seven days' written notice, terminate employment of the Contractor and may, subject to any prior rights of the surety:

.1 take possession of the site and of all materials, equipment, tools, and construction equipment and machinery thereon owned by the Contractor;

.2 accept assignment of subcontracts pursuant to Paragraph 5.4; and

.3 finish the Work by whatever reasonable method the Owner may deem expedient.

**14.2.3** When the Owner terminates the Contract for one of the reasons stated in Subparagraph 14.2.1, the Contractor shall not be entitled to receive further payment until the Work is finished.

**14.2.4** If the unpaid balance of the Contract Sum exceeds costs of finishing the Work, including compensation for the Architect's services and expenses made necessary thereby, such excess shall be paid to the Contractor. If such costs exceed the unpaid balance, the Contractor shall pay the difference to the Owner. The amount to be paid to the Contractor or Owner, as the case may be, shall be certified by the Architect, upon application, and this obligation for payment shall survive termination of the Contract.

**14.3    SUSPENSION BY THE OWNER FOR CONVENIENCE**

**14.3.1** The Owner may, without cause, order the Contractor in writing to suspend, delay or interrupt the Work in whole or in part for such period of time as the Owner may determine.

**14.3.2** An adjustment shall be made for increases in the cost of performance of the Contract, including profit on the increased cost of performance, caused by suspension, delay or interruption. No adjustment shall be made to the extent:

.1 that performance is, was or would have been so suspended, delayed or interrupted by another cause for which the Contractor is responsible; or

.2 that an equitable adjustment is made or denied under another provision of this Contract.

**14.3.3** Adjustments made in the cost of performance may have a mutually agreed fixed or percentage fee.

# APPENDIX
# B

## THE AMERICAN INSTITUTE OF ARCHITECTS DOCUMENT A101

T H E     A M E R I C A N     I N S T I T U T E     O F     A R C H I T E C T S

*AIA Document A101*

# Standard Form of Agreement Between Owner and Contractor
*where the basis of payment is a*
## STIPULATED SUM
### 1987 EDITION

*THIS DOCUMENT HAS IMPORTANT LEGAL CONSEQUENCES; CONSULTATION WITH AN ATTORNEY IS ENCOURAGED WITH RESPECT TO ITS COMPLETION OR MODIFICATION.*
*The 1987 Edition of AIA Document A201, General Conditions of the Contract for Construction, is adopted in this document by reference. Do not use with other general conditions unless this document is modified.*
This document has been approved and endorsed by The Associated General Contractors of America.

## AGREEMENT

made as of the                              day of                              in the year of
Nineteen Hundred and

**BETWEEN** the Owner:
*(Name and address)*

and the Contractor:
*(Name and address)*

The Project is:
*(Name and location)*

The Architect is:
*(Name and address)*

The Owner and Contractor agree as set forth below.

## ARTICLE 1
### THE CONTRACT DOCUMENTS

The Contract Documents consist of this Agreement, Conditions of the Contract (General, Supplementary and other Conditions), Drawings, Specifications, Addenda issued prior to execution of this Agreement, other documents listed in this Agreement and Modifications issued after execution of this Agreement; these form the Contract, and are as fully a part of the Contract as if attached to this Agreement or repeated herein. The Contract represents the entire and integrated agreement between the parties hereto and supersedes prior negotiations, representations or agreements, either written or oral. An enumeration of the Contract Documents, other than Modifications, appears in Article 9.

## ARTICLE 2
### THE WORK OF THIS CONTRACT

The Contractor shall execute the entire Work described in the Contract Documents, except to the extent specifically indicated in the Contract Documents to be the responsibility of others, or as follows:

## ARTICLE 3
### DATE OF COMMENCEMENT AND SUBSTANTIAL COMPLETION

**3.1**  The date of commencement is the date from which the Contract Time of Paragraph 3.2 is measured, and shall be the date of this Agreement, as first written above, unless a different date is stated below or provision is made for the date to be fixed in a notice to proceed issued by the Owner.

*(Insert the date of commencement, if it differs from the date of this Agreement or, if applicable, state that the date will be fixed in a notice to proceed.)*

Unless the date of commencement is established by a notice to proceed issued by the Owner, the Contractor shall notify the Owner in writing not less than five days before commencing the Work to permit the timely filing of mortgages, mechanic's liens and other security interests.

**3.2**  The Contractor shall achieve Substantial Completion of the entire Work not later than

*(Insert the calendar date or number of calendar days after the date of commencement. Also insert any requirements for earlier Substantial Completion of certain portions of the Work, if not stated elsewhere in the Contract Documents.)*

subject to adjustments of this Contract Time as provided in the Contract Documents.

*(Insert provisions, if any, for liquidated damages relating to failure to complete on time.)*

## ARTICLE 4
## CONTRACT SUM

**4.1** The Owner shall pay the Contractor in current funds for the Contractor's performance of the Contract the Contract Sum of
Dollars
($                                                                        ), subject to additions and deductions as provided in the Con-
tract Documents.

**4.2** The Contract Sum is based upon the following alternates, if any, which are described in the Contract Documents and are
hereby accepted by the Owner:

*(State the numbers or other identification of accepted alternates. If decisions on other alternates are to be made by the Owner subsequent to the execution of this Agreement, attach a schedule of such other alternates showing the amount for each and the date until which that amount is valid.)*

**4.3** Unit prices, if any, are as follows:

## ARTICLE 5
## PROGRESS PAYMENTS

**5.1** Based upon Applications for Payment submitted to the Architect by the Contractor and Certificates for Payment issued by the Architect, the Owner shall make progress payments on account of the Contract Sum to the Contractor as provided below and elsewhere in the Contract Documents.

**5.2** The period covered by each Application for Payment shall be one calendar month ending on the last day of the month, or as follows:

**5.3** Provided an Application for Payment is received by the Architect not later than the
          day of a month, the Owner shall make payment to the Contractor not later than the         day of the         month. If an Application for Payment is received by the Architect after the application date fixed above, payment shall be made by the Owner not later than         days after the Architect receives the Application for Payment.

**5.4** Each Application for Payment shall be based upon the Schedule of Values submitted by the Contractor in accordance with the Contract Documents. The Schedule of Values shall allocate the entire Contract Sum among the various portions of the Work and be prepared in such form and supported by such data to substantiate its accuracy as the Architect may require. This Schedule, unless objected to by the Architect, shall be used as a basis for reviewing the Contractor's Applications for Payment.

**5.5** Applications for Payment shall indicate the percentage of completion of each portion of the Work as of the end of the period covered by the Application for Payment.

**5.6** Subject to the provisions of the Contract Documents, the amount of each progress payment shall be computed as follows:

**5.6.1** Take that portion of the Contract Sum properly allocable to completed Work as determined by multiplying the percentage completion of each portion of the Work by the share of the total Contract Sum allocated to that portion of the Work in the Schedule of Values, less retainage of         percent (     %). Pending final determination of cost to the Owner of changes in the Work, amounts not in dispute may be included as provided in Subparagraph 7.3.7 of the General Conditions even though the Contract Sum has not yet been adjusted by Change Order;

**5.6.2** Add that portion of the Contract Sum properly allocable to materials and equipment delivered and suitably stored at the site for subsequent incorporation in the completed construction (or, if approved in advance by the Owner, suitably stored off the site at a location agreed upon in writing), less retainage of         percent (     %);

**5.6.3** Subtract the aggregate of previous payments made by the Owner; and

**5.6.4** Subtract amounts, if any, for which the Architect has withheld or nullified a Certificate for Payment as provided in Paragraph 9.5 of the General Conditions.

**5.7** The progress payment amount determined in accordance with Paragraph 5.6 shall be further modified under the following circumstances:

**5.7.1** Add, upon Substantial Completion of the Work, a sum sufficient to increase the total payments to         percent (     %) of the Contract Sum, less such amounts as the Architect shall determine for incomplete Work and unsettled claims; and

**5.7.2** Add, if final completion of the Work is thereafter materially delayed through no fault of the Contractor, any additional amounts payable in accordance with Subparagraph 9.10.3 of the General Conditions.

**5.8** Reduction or limitation of retainage, if any, shall be as follows:

*(If it is intended, prior to Substantial Completion of the entire Work, to reduce or limit the retainage resulting from the percentages inserted in Subparagraphs 5.6.1 and 5.6.2 above, and this is not explained elsewhere in the Contract Documents, insert here provisions for such reduction or limitation.)*

## ARTICLE 6
### FINAL PAYMENT

Final payment, constituting the entire unpaid balance of the Contract Sum, shall be made by the Owner to the Contractor when (1) the Contract has been fully performed by the Contractor except for the Contractor's responsibility to correct nonconforming Work as provided in Subparagraph 12.2.2 of the General Conditions and to satisfy other requirements, if any, which necessarily survive final payment; and (2) a final Certificate for Payment has been issued by the Architect; such final payment shall be made by the Owner not more than 30 days after the issuance of the Architect's final Certificate for Payment, or as follows:

## ARTICLE 7
### MISCELLANEOUS PROVISIONS

**7.1** Where reference is made in this Agreement to a provision of the General Conditions or another Contract Document, the reference refers to that provision as amended or supplemented by other provisions of the Contract Documents.

**7.2** Payments due and unpaid under the Contract shall bear interest from the date payment is due at the rate stated below, or in the absence thereof, at the legal rate prevailing from time to time at the place where the Project is located.

*(Insert rate of interest agreed upon, if any.)*

*(Usury laws and requirements under the Federal Truth in Lending Act, similar state and local consumer credit laws and other regulations at the Owner's and Contractor's principal places of business, the location of the Project and elsewhere may affect the validity of this provision. Legal advice should be obtained with respect to deletions or modifications, and also regarding requirements such as written disclosures or waivers.)*

**7.3** Other provisions:

## ARTICLE 8
### TERMINATION OR SUSPENSION

**8.1** The Contract may be terminated by the Owner or the Contractor as provided in Article 14 of the General Conditions.

**8.2** The Work may be suspended by the Owner as provided in Article 14 of the General Conditions.

AIA DOCUMENT A101 • OWNER-CONTRACTOR AGREEMENT • TWELFTH EDITION • AIA® • ©1987
THE AMERICAN INSTITUTE OF ARCHITECTS, 1735 NEW YORK AVENUE, N.W., WASHINGTON, D.C 20006    **A101-1987   5**

## ARTICLE 9
## ENUMERATION OF CONTRACT DOCUMENTS

**9.1** The Contract Documents, except for Modifications issued after execution of this Agreement, are enumerated as follows:

**9.1.1** The Agreement is this executed Standard Form of Agreement Between Owner and Contractor, AIA Document A101, 1987 Edition.

**9.1.2** The General Conditions are the General Conditions of the Contract for Construction, AIA Document A201, 1987 Edition.

**9.1.3** The Supplementary and other Conditions of the Contract are those contained in the Project Manual dated
and are as follows:

| Document | Title | Pages |
|----------|-------|-------|
|          |       |       |

**9.1.4** The Specifications are those contained in the Project Manual dated as in Subparagraph 9.1.3, and are as follows:

*(Either list the Specifications here or refer to an exhibit attached to this Agreement.)*

| Section | Title | Pages |
|---------|-------|-------|
|         |       |       |

**9.1.5** The Drawings are as follows, and are dated                     unless a different date is shown below:

*(Either list the Drawings here or refer to an exhibit attached to this Agreement.)*

**Number**                                    **Title**                                    **Date**

**9.1.6** The Addenda, if any, are as follows:

**Number**                    **Date**                                    **Pages**

SAMPLE

Portions of Addenda relating to bidding requirements are not part of the Contract Documents unless the bidding requirements are also enumerated in this Article 9.

**9.1.7** Other documents, if any, forming part of the Contract Documents are as follows:

*(List here any additional documents which are intended to form part of the Contract Documents. The General Conditions provide that bidding requirements such as advertisement or invitation to bid, Instructions to Bidders, sample forms and the Contractor's bid are not part of the Contract Documents unless enumerated in this Agreement. They should be listed here only if intended to be part of the Contract Documents.)*

SAMPLE

This Agreement is entered into as of the day and year first written above and is executed in at least three original copies of which one is to be delivered to the Contractor, one to the Architect for use in the administration of the Contract, and the remainder to the Owner.

OWNER                                           CONTRACTOR

_____                _____
*(Signature)*                                   *(Signature)*

_____                _____
*(Printed name and title)*                      *(Printed name and title)*

# BIBLIOGRAPHY

Acker, Arnold. In *How To Do Practical Construction Cost Estimates*. Howell, J. N., ed. Churchill, 1984.

Adrian, James. *Construction Estimating*. Prentice-Hall, 1982.

Ahuja, Hira N. *Successful Construction Cost Control*. Wiley-Interscience, 1980.

Allen, R. I. G., and W. F. Gossling. *Estimating and Projecting Input-Output Coefficients*. Input-Output, 1975.

Andrews, Lisa, ed. *Building Cost Manual 1988*. Craftsman, 1987.

Avery, Craig, ed. *Concrete Construction and Estimating*. Craftsman, 1980.

Beeston, D. T. *Statistical Methods for Building Price Data*. Routledge, Chapman & Hall, 1983.

Berger & Associates Cost Consultants. *Berger Building and Design Cost File, 1984: Mechanical. Electrical Trades, Vol. 2*. 1984.

Berger, S., et al. *Berger Building Cost File 1987*. Craftsman, 1987.

Berger, Seymour, and Jules B. Godel. *Estimating and Project Management for Small Construction Firms*. Van Nostrand Reinhold, 1977.

Bourgeois, G. Patrick, et al. In *Walker's Quantity Surveying and Basic Construction*. F. R. Walker, 1981.

Branca, Anthony J. *Cost Effective Design-Build Construction*. R. S. Means, 1987.

Brandon, Pete S., et al. *Computer Programs for Building Cost Appraisal*. Sheridan, 1985.

Brief, Richard P. *Estimating the Economic Rate of Return from Accounting Data*. Garland, 1986.

Collier, Keith. *Estimating Construction Costs: A Conceptual Approach*. Prentice-Hall, 1983.

Collier, Keith. *Fundamentals of Construction Estimating and Cost Accounting with Computer Applications*. 2nd ed. Prentice-Hall, 1987.

*Construction Cost Control*. Rev. ed. Am. Soc. of Civil Engineers, 1985.

Cook, Paul J. In *Bidding for the General Contractor*. Gardener, Michael, ed. Routledge, Chapman & Hall, 1985.

Cook, Paul J. *Estimating for the General Contractor*. R. S. Means, 1982.

Cooper, George Henderson. *Building Construction Estimating*. 3rd ed. McGraw-Hill, 1971.

Crespin, Vick S., et al. In *Walker's Manual for Construction Cost Estimating*. F. R. Walker, 1981.

Dagostino, Frank R. *Estimating in Building Construction*. 2nd ed. Prentice-Hall, 1978.

Davis, et al., eds. *Spon's International Construction Costs Handbook*. Routledge, Chapman & Hall, 1988.

Diamont, Leo. *Construction Estimating for General Contractors*. (Practical Construction Guides Ser.) Wiley, 1988.

Edwards, Harry J. *Estimating Controls Systems for HVAC*. McGraw-Hill, 1986.

*Estimating for the General Contractor*. R. S. Means, 1982.

Ferry, Douglas J., and Peter S. Brandon. *Cost Planning of Building*. Beekman, 1980.

Foster, Norman. *Construction Estimates from Take off to Bid*. 2nd ed. (Modern Structure Ser.) Prentice-Hall, 1973.

*Fundamentals of Construction Estimating & Cost Accounting with Computer Applications*. 2nd ed. Prentice-Hall, 1987.

Gladstone, J., et al. *Mechanical Estimating for Building Construction*. 5th ed. McGraw-Hill, 1987.

Godambe, V. P., ed. *Estimating Functions*. Oxford University Press, 1991.

Goodacre, P. *Worked Examples in Quantity Surveying Measurement*. Routledge, Chapman & Hall, 1982.

Hardie, Glenn M. *Construction Estimating Techniques*. Prentice-Hall, 1987.

Helton, Joseph. *Simplified Estimating for Builders and Engineers*. Prentice-Hall, 1985.

Hornung, William J. *Estimating Building Construction*. Prentice-Hall, 1986.

Horsley, F. William. *Means Scheduling Manual*. 2nd ed. R. S. Means, 1984.

Jackson, W. P. *Cost Records for Construction Estimating*. Craftsman, 1984.

Jackson, W. P. *Estimating Home Building Costs*. Craftsman, 1981.

Kempen, Jay V. *Construction Cost Estimating*. Prentice-Hall, 1983.

Killingsworth, Roger. In *Cost Control in Building Design*. Mahoney, William, ed. R. S. Means, 1988.

Lewis, Jack R. *Basic Construction Estimating*. Prentice-Hall, 1983.

Lisa, Andrews, ed. *National Construction Estimator, 1988*. Craftsman, 1987.

Massey, Howard C. *Estimating Plumbing Costs*. Craftsman, 1982.

Masters, Stanley H., and Irwin Garfinkel. *Estimating the Labor Supply Effects of Income-Maintenance Alternatives*. Academic Press, 1977.

Matthews, Lawrence M. *Estimating Manufacturing Costs: A Practical Guide for Manager and Estimators*. McGraw-Hill, 1983.

Mueller, Frederick W. *Integrated Cost and Schedule Control for Construction Projects*. Van Nostrand Reinhold, 1986.

Neil, James M. *Construction Cost Estimating for Project Control*. Prentice-Hall, 1982.

Park, William R. *Construction Bidding for Profit*. (Practical Construction Guides Ser.) Prentice-Hall, 1979.

Parker, A. D., and D. S. Barrie. *Planning and Estimating Heavy Construction*. McGraw-Hill, 1984.

Peurifoy, Robert L. *Estimating Construction Costs*. McGraw-Hill, 1975.

R. S. Means Company, Inc. *Building Construction Cost Data, 1988*. 46th ed. (Professional Cost Guides.) R. S. Means, 1988.

Sarviel, E. *Construction Estimating Reference Data*. Craftsman, 1981.

Spence-Geddes, M. *Estimating for Building & Civil Engineering Works*. 8th ed. Chrystel-Smith, G. and P. Jolly, eds. Butterworth, 1986.

Spradlin, William H., Jr. *Walker's Building Estimator's Reference Book*. 22nd ed. F. R. Walker, 1986.

Spradlin, William H., Jr. *Walker's Pocket Estimator*. 22nd ed. F. R. Walker, 1986.

Steinberg, Joseph, and Martin Stempel. *Estimating for the Building Trades*. 2nd ed. American Technical Society, 1973.

Stewart, R. *Proposal and Bid Preparation for Construction*. Wiley, 1988.

Taylor, Robert. *Builder's Estimating Databook*. TABS, 1988.

Thomas, Paul I. *Handbook of Tables and Formulas for Home Construction Estimating*. Prentice-Hall, 1979.

Thomas, Paul I. *How to Estimate Building Losses and Construction Costs*. 4th ed. Prentice-Hall, 1983.

Tyler, Edward J. *Estimating Electrical Construction*. Craftsman, 1983.

Tysoe, B. A. *Construction Cost and Price Indices: Description and Use*. Routledge, Chapman & Hall, 1981.

Vance, Mary. *Building Estimates and Costs: A Bibliography*. (Architecture Ser.: Bibliography A 1327.) Vance, 1985.

Walker, Frank R., ed. *Building Estimator's Reference Book with Pocket Estimator*. Rev. ed. National Association of Home Builders, 1986.

Ward, Sol A., and Litchfield Thorndike. *Cost Control in Design and Construction*. McGraw-Hill, 1980.

Wass, Alonzo. *Building Construction Estimating*. 2nd ed. Prentice-Hall, 1970.

Willis, A. J., and C. J. Willis. *Practice and Procedure for the Quantity Surveyor*. 7th ed. Beekman, 1976.

Willis, Arthur, and Christopher Willis. *Elements of Quantity Surveying*. 7th ed. Sheridan, 1978.

Willis, Christopher J., et al. *More Advanced Quantity Surveying*. Sheridan, 1984.

# INDEX

Addenda, 15, 81
Advertisement for Bids, 7
Alternates, 113

Bid:
  assessment, 85
  bond, 15
  delivery, 82
  finalizing, 82
  form, 13
  opening, 83
Bidding:
  decision, 58
  documents, 6
  strategy, 58
Bonding:
  costs, 62
  requirements, 62
Bonds:
  bid, 15
  labor and material, 18
  performance, 18

Carpentry:
  pricing, finish and rough: equipment
    and tools, 248
    labor, 248
    materials, 246
  reminder list, 249
  takeoff, finish carpentry, 242
    exterior, 242
    fasteners, 245
    interior, 245
  takeoff, rough carpentry, 234
    ceiling framing, 235
    decking, 236
    fasteners, 241
    floor framing, 235
    roof framing, 239
    sheathing, 236
    subflooring, 236
    wall framing, 237
Computers, 35
  databases, 40
  disks, 39
  software, 39
  spreadsheets, 36

Concrete, precast:
  pricing, 173
  reminder list, 173
  takeoff, 170
Concrete, ready-mix:
  finishing, curing, and protecting,
    169
    pricing, 170
    takeoff, 169
  pricing, 165
    equipment, 166
    labor, 165
    material, 165
  reminder list, 173
  takeoff, 163
Construction:
  companies: organization, 19
    qualifications, 20
  method, 59
  types, 3
Contingencies, 113
Contract types:
  construction management, 5
  cost plus fee, 5
  design-build, 5
  risk by type, 5
  stipulated sum, 4
  unit price, 5
Conveying systems:
  pricing, 269
  reminder list, 271
  takeoff, 269
Cost:
  direct cost, 87
  indirect cost, 87

Earthwork:
  backfilling, 136
  borrow, 138
  building excavation takeoff, 131
    building wall and footing, 135
  equipment production and costs, 100
  excess, 138
  filling and compacting, 140
  grading, 139
  pricing, 141
  reminder list, 142
  rock excavation, 140
  site takeoff, 121
    area average end method, 122

    grid method, 124
  trenching, 139
  underslab requirements, 139
Electrical work:
  pricing, 287
  reminder list, 282
  takeoff, 283
Equipment:
  cost factors, 97
  job overhead tools, 104
  small, 103
Estimates, types of:
  change order, 27, 299
  conceptual, 21
  detailed, 25, 45
  elemental, 23
  factor, 23
  feasibility, 20
  functional unit price, 22
  parametric, 23
  progress, 27, 299
  projected cost, 299
  subcontractor systm, 26, 76, 105
  unit cost per cubic foot, 23
  unit cost per square foot, 22
Estimating:
  carpentry, 231
  computer software, 39
  concrete: formwork, 148
    precast, 170
    ready-mix, 163
  conveying systems, 269
  cost books, 31
  cost to perform, 32
  earthwork, 119
  ethics, 32
  finishes, 264
  formats, 77
  furnishings, 269
  information sources, 29
  masonry, 177
  metals, 205
  reinforcing steel, 156
  risks, 27
  special construction, 269
  special equipment, 269
  specialties, 269
  thermal and moisture protection,
    256
  windows and doors, 262
Estimator qualifications, 2

Finishes:
  pricing, 269
  reminder list, 264
  takeoff, 264
    carpeting, 266
    drywall, 265
    lath and plaster, 265
    painting, 266
    terrazzo, 266
    tile, 266
    wall coverings, 266
Form of agreement, 18
Formwork, concrete:
  pricing, 150
    equipment, 156
    labor, 155
  reminder list, 173
  takeoff, 148
    job-built forms, 150
    material, 150
    prebuilt forms, 150
Furnishings:
  pricing, 269
  reminder list, 270
  takeoff, 269

General conditions, 7

Instructions to bidders, 7
Insurance, 18
Invitation to bid, 7

Labor:
  productivity, 94
  quantity takeoff considerations,
    93
  wage rates, 93
  (*See also specific items of takeoff*)

Masonry:
  bond patterns, 178
  pricing: labor, 193
    material, 198
    tools and equipment, 198
  reminder list, 202
  subcontractors, 199

  takeoff: accessories, 185
    control joint, 189
    deformed bar reinforcing, 188
    flashing, 189
    horizontal reinforcing, 185
    lintels, sills, and copings, 190
    ties, anchors, and inserts, 185
   brick and block, 179
    coursing method, 183
    square foot method, 182
   cleaning, 193
   grout, 188
   insulation, 191
   mortar, 191
   sample panels, 191
  wall types, 178
Material:
  allowances, 92
  buyer and supplier, 91
  delivery, 89
  governmental regulations, 92
  handling, 91
  owner supplied, 93
  pricing checklist, 93
  quantity discounts, 89
  storage, 91
  taxes, 92
  terms of payment, 91
Material quantity takeoff, 64
  measuring calculations, 68
    deductions, 70
    dimensions, 72
    number conversions, 71
    perimeter, 69
    preliminary, 68
    rounding off numbers, 75
  order of takeoff, 66
  units of measure, 67
  waste allowance, 75
Mechanical equipment:
  pricing, 287
  reminder list, 276
  takeoff, 276

Negotiations, 83

Overhead costs:
  general, 108
  job, 111

Prebid meeting, 58
Pricing, 87
  equipment, 97
  form (sheet), 77
  labor, 93
  material, 88
  subcontractors, 105
  (*See also specific items of takeoff*)
Pricing studies, 76
Profit, 113
Project:
  investigation: external facts, 57
    internal facts, 55
  manual, 7
Proposal form, 15


Recapitulation sheet, 77
Reinforcing steel:
  pricing, 163
    equipment, 163
    labor, 163
    material, 163
  reminder list, 173
  takeoff, 156


Solicitation of prices, 59
Special conditions, 11
Special construction:
  pricing, 269
  reminder list, 271
  takeoff, 269
Special equipment:
  pricing, 269
  reminder list, 270
  takeoff, 269
Specialties:
  pricing, 269
  reminder list, 269
  specification takeoff, 62
  takeoff, 269
Structural steel:
  pricing, 222
    equipment, 225
    labor, 223
    material, 222
  reminder list, 227

takeoff, 206
  connections, 211
  decking, 217
  framing members, 206
  light-gauge metal, 217
  plates and rods, 208
  steel joists, 217
Subcontractor:
  bid analysis, 106
  capability, 106
  pricing, 105
  receipt of bids, 106
  system estimate, 105
Summary form (sheet), 77
Supplementary general conditions, 11


Thermal and moisture protection:
  pricing, 269
  reminder list, 256
  takeoff, 257
    built-up, single-ply, and sheet
      roofing, 260
    flashing, 261
    insulation, 257
    roof shingles and tiles, 258
    roof trim, 261
    sealants and caulking, 261
Tools, 104
Transfer of estimate, 86, 289
  accounting, 291
  project management, 292
    change order estimate, 299
    progress estimate, 299
    projected cost estimate, 299
    schedule development, 292
    schedule of values development,
      293
  purchasing, 289


Waste allowance, 75
Windows and doors:
  pricing, 269
  reminder list, 262
  takeoff, 262
Worksheet, 77
Working drawings, 6